THE

# MOTIVATE

SERIES

Macmillan Texts for Industrial, Vocational and Technical Education

# Practical Plumbing

*C. J. Smith and B. Curry*

MACMILLAN

First published 1998 by
MACMILLAN EDUCATION LTD
London and Oxford
*Companies and representatives throughout the world*

www.macmillan-africa.com

ISBN 0–333–61657–X

| 11 | 10 | 9 | 8 | 7 | 6 | 5 | 4 | 3 | 2 |
|----|----|----|----|----|----|----|----|----|----|
| 09 | 08 | 07 | 06 | 05 | 04 | 03 | 02 | 01 | 00 |

This book is printed on paper suitable for recycling and
made from fully managed and sustained forest sources.

Printed in Hong Kong

A catalogue record for this book is available from the
British Library.

**Acknowledgements**
The authors and publishers wish to acknowledge, with thanks, the
following photographic sources:

Copper Development Association fig 1
Mary Evans Picture Library fig 4

The poster designs in fig 1.18 are reproduced by permission of The
Royal Society for the Prevention of Accidents

The cover photograph is courtesy of Jerry Mason
Illustrations by 1-11 Line Art

The publishers have made every effort to trace the copyright holders,
but if they have inadvertently overlooked any, they will be pleased to
make the necessary arrangements at the first opportunity.

**Dedication**
To Sue, Lucy, Jonathan, Katy and Anne for their patience, understanding
and support.

# Contents

iv

# Preface

Plumbing, along with other related services and construction work, is governed by rules and regulations. These are designed to ensure the health and safety of the occupants of private and public buildings, and also the general public. As far as plumbing is concerned, such regulations are also there to ensure the efficient and effective operation of systems, and to prevent contamination and undue wastage of that most valuable of natural resources.... water.

With a book such as *Practical Plumbing* that has been written with a wide readership covering many countries in mind, specific reference to any individual country's legislation and regulations would have been impractical given the range of legislation, and possible differences in them, across the various countries.

There is some consistency, however. Many countries, recognising the high standards and long tradition associated with British plumbing and building legislation have based their own legislation on the British model. The authors therefore have written this work using British codes of practice, regulations and standards as their main guiding principles. So without giving instructions to follow any specific regulation or code of practice, all the work in these pages is based on the highest standards and good practice based on many years of research and application.

There may be occasional differences in regulations or practices in some countries or regions from the ones this work is based on. In these cases, you must *always* follow your own national or regional regulations. If in doubt, seek advice from the local water authority or the building control officer at your local government offices.

The authors have used metric S.I. units throughout the book, although a conversion from the British imperial system of measurement to the metric system is given in the Appendix, Table A3.

The authors acknowledge the invaluable background information gained from a wide range of relevant trade literature, statutory instruments and standards.

Although the title of this book is *Practical Plumbing*, it would be impossible to undertake any plumbing work without having first gained some understanding of the underlying principles involved. For this reason, all the necessary theory associated with the plumbing topics covered in the book is also given. In addition, a comprehensive section covering the mathematics required for plumbing calculations is included as an appendix.

# Introduction

Plumbing is one of the most important services to be found in any modern society. For people in society to lead a healthy life, one of the most basic requirements is to live in clean and sanitary conditions. This means having access to a piped supply of clean water, and accommodation that includes appliances or fittings for washing, cleaning and the collection and disposal of waste matter. Plumbers therefore, as the craftsmen or women who install and maintain such systems, are seen as important figures in society.

Modern plumbing can seem, and often is, complicated, and the modern plumber needs to be well trained to cope with all the different things that he or she has to do. This book is designed to provide help, support and guidance to both teachers and students of plumbing to make their training easier. The book is full of detailed but easy to follow information with hundreds of illustrations and tips to aid understanding.

## Aims of the book

The main aim of the book is to provide you with all the necessary background information and knowledge you need to apply with confidence the plumbing skills that you develop as part of a structured course at a vocational training centre, school or college. It will also be of interest to other tradesmen or laymen in helping them to understand their own plumbing systems.

The book has been designed to follow closely the content of typical plumbing courses and syllabuses that are available throughout the world. It is impossible in a book such as this to cover everything, but it contains all that the plumbing trainee or apprentice and the teacher or trainer of plumbing needs to suit most applications. This will enable it to be used as a classroom or workshop reference book and also as an aid to examination revision.

## Brief history of plumbing

The history of plumbing dates back several thousand years. The use of two of the oldest traditional plumbing materials, lead and copper, can be traced back to the ancient Egyptians. They used lead oxide as a decorative glaze on pottery, but more importantly, the earliest example of part of a plumbing system using copper pipe, found in the Nile delta in Egypt, dates from around 2750 BC (Figure 1).

The ancient Greeks are known to have mined lead, as did the Romans. The Romans mined and smelted lead on a commercial scale, initially using it for weights and coins before seeing its potential for use in sanitary installations. Both the Greeks and the Romans developed quite sophisticated plumbing systems for their day.

*Figure 1* Ancient Egyptian copper water pipe from the Nile delta c. 2730 BC

Examples of the early use of terracotta or clayware for sanitary appliances and pipes can be seen at the Palace of Knossos in Greece (Figure 2). The palace appears to have had a complex system of clay drainage pipes, with separate branches serving different parts of the building. It was probably the Romans, however, who had the most influence on the development of plumbing. The word 'plumber' itself is taken from the Latin word for lead, *plumbum*. Plumbers were originally seen as workers of lead. There are still examples to be seen of lead pipes laid by the Romans in use today in the City of Bath, England.

As the great civilisations died away, so too did much of the knowledge and developments associated with plumbing and living in sanitary conditions.

Towards the end of the eighteenth century, renewed interest in providing sanitary conditions, at least as far as the privileged classes in Europe were concerned, led to the development of early 'modern' appliances, including water closets (Figure 3). It soon became a status symbol amongst the upper classes to have fully equipped bathrooms with

running water. This saw the establishment of the plumber as the specialist in installing bathroom appliances and pipework (Figure 4).

For the masses of people, however, bathrooms and running water was but a dream. As industrialisation took a grip in Europe and North America in particular, the migration of workers into the cities where factories were

*Figure 2*  Early clay drain pipes from the palace at Knossos, Greece c. 2000 BC

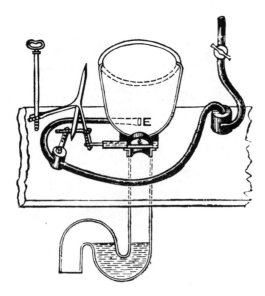

*Figure 3*  Early water closet, England c. 1775

*Figure 4*  A 'modern' eighteenth century plumber c. 1790

established led to a rapid expansion of these areas. Cheap housing was built for the workers but they soon became overcrowded and little attention was paid to sanitation. In many cities, the streets were nothing more than open sewers and soon illness and disease took its toll.

As governments began to realise the effects that rapid industrialisation was having on people, especially in relation to health and sanitation, steps were taken to overcome the problems. By the end of the nineteenth century and the early twentieth century, most of the open sewers had been replaced by large underground piped sewers. A series of regulations and laws were passed concerning building and the provision of sanitary accommodation, making sanitary conditions within the reach of most people. Large but well-planned social housing projects were also established and the rapid development in design of low-cost but effective sanitary appliances ensured plumbers were in great demand.

As a result of continued design and research throughout the twentieth century, the plumber now has a vast range of appliances, materials and pipework systems at his or her disposal. With international communications and commerce now being what they are, it is possible to export the technology, expertise, training and manufacturing capability to enable all parts of the world to benefit from living with clean and efficient sanitary accommodation.

As a plumber, you will be central in helping the people in your area to benefit from these developments.

# The role of the plumber

The importance of the role of the plumber in society cannot be underestimated. In some societies, plumbers are considered to be just as important as doctors because of the work the plumber does in contributing towards providing sanitary living conditions. Some people, however, give little thought to the work of the plumber, unless there is a problem with their toilet or water supply... then the plumber is the most important person around! It is only when such problems occur that the majority of people realise how important it is to have the basic requirements of a water supply and decent sanitation.

However, plumbing is not just about water supply and sanitation. Plumbers install pipework and equipment for gas supplies for cooking and heating; they also fix sheet metal weatherings to roofs and install rainwater collection and disposal systems and are involved in a range of other things. Unlike many other tradesmen or women, for example carpenters and joiners who work mainly with wood, or bricklayers who work with bricks or blocks, plumbers work with and need to be familiar with dozens of different materials. By using this book as part of a planned training course, it will not only introduce you to and help you to understand the many different materials and components used by the plumber, but it will also help you to develop the practical skills needed to install and maintain them.

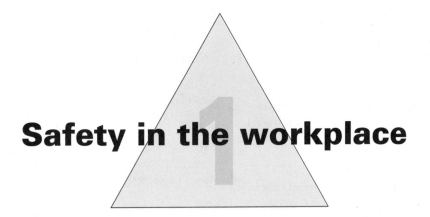

# Safety in the workplace

## Introduction

The health and safety of people working in the plumbing industry is of major concern to us all. It is widely known that the construction industry as a whole, of which plumbing is a part, accounts for many of the accident statistics recorded. What is not always appreciated is the huge cost, both to the individuals who are unfortunate enough to have an accident and to the industry as a whole, in terms of lost manpower. Days off work due to accidents and injuries can cost industry many millions of dollars every year. More importantly, the cost in suffering to individual workers and their families in terms of injuries and possible loss in wages can be difficult to overcome. However, with a little common sense and by observing a few rules, many accidents can be avoided.

In many countries, laws have been introduced to enforce safe practices. These laws require both employers and employees to observe strict health and safety procedures in the workplace. Such laws have helped to reduce the number of serious accidents. However, accidents can and do still happen, mainly because workers do not think sensibly about what they are doing, or take short cuts, or rush to complete a job.

In countries with few or no official health and safety laws, it is essential that individual workers take on the responsibility of carrying out their work safely, so as not to endanger themselves or others. Using common sense and being aware of potential hazards and taking suitable precautions to avoid or prevent them from happening are much more important than the existence of regulations. Sometimes you may need to tell your employer about a particular hazard or problem so that the hazard can be removed, or suitable equipment can be provided to enable you to work safely. This chapter covers both general safety hazards and specific hazards associated with common plumbing activities, and suggests ways of dealing with them.

## Protective clothing

Wherever possible, and regardless of the actual job being done, you must wear some form of special work clothing, overalls or boiler suit (Figure 1.1), either instead of everyday clothes or over the top of them. Work clothes prevent your

*Figure 1.1* Overalls to protect everyday clothes

1

everyday clothing from becoming contaminated by oils, grease, fluxes or general dust and dirt. They also cover loose clothing, ties etc., which could get caught in machines. At the end of a working day, you can leave the overalls or boiler suit at the workplace, which helps to reduce the amount of dirt and dust being brought into the home.

> ⚠ Always tie long hair back, and fasten or remove loose-fitting clothes. Remove jewellery, including long necklaces and dangling earrings, if there is any danger of getting it caught in machinery.

Other forms of protective clothing have been developed, and have been shown to provide excellent protection against a range of possible hazards. Some of them are worn for general purposes, others when more specific activities are being carried out.

## Safety helmet or hard hat

You should always wear a safety helmet or hard hat when working on large building sites (Figure 1.2). Sometimes this is a legal requirement; if so a safety notice at the site entrance will tell you. Safety helmets are usually made of toughened plastic or steel. They give some protection against injury caused by objects falling from scaffolding, for example, and against injury caused by walking into projections on buildings and scaffolds.

## Safety goggles

Always wear clear safety goggles where operations are being carried out that create a lot of airborne dust or grit, or where there is a chance of flying debris getting into your eyes (Figure 1.3), for example when cutting masonry, when drilling or cutting holes in bricks or blocks, where small pieces of metal or swarf are thrown from machines, or where molten solder splashes.

*Figure 1.3*  Clear safety goggles

## Welding goggles

These must have dark or shaded lenses to protect the eyes from the intense bright light and sparks created by arc welding or gas welding (Figure 1.4).

*Figure 1.2*  Safety helmet or hard hat

*Figure 1.4*  Tinted welding goggles

## Gloves

Heavy-duty gloves can give protection against a range of things. There are various types of gloves. Rubber or plastic gloves give protection against skin irritation when handling materials like cement, oils or grease, or they can give general protection when handling dirty or contaminated materials. Heavy-duty canvas gloves are used when handling materials with sharp edges, like glass or sheet metals, and can also be used when handling hot materials (Figure 1.5).

*Figure 1.6* Safety boots

*Figure 1.5* Heavy-duty gloves

▲ Use of a hand barrier-cream, rubbed in before you start any job involving handling dirty, greasy or oily materials, will give added protection and will make it easier to clean your hands at the end of the job.

▲ When working in trenches or cuttings or wherever water is present, wear some form of rubber footwear to help prevent water-borne contaminants or micro-organisms, worms etc., from coming into contact with your skin.

## Face mask

The simplest form of mask is one that covers the mouth and nose (Figure 1.7). This will give moderate protection against general dust inhalation. Where there is a high concentration of dust or fumes, wear some kind of respirator. In some situations, for example when welding in a confined space, some form of fume extraction system must be installed.

## Safety footwear

Many injuries result from not wearing appropriate footwear or in some cases from not wearing any footwear. If a job involves moving or using heavy equipment or handling heavy materials, wear some form of boots to protect your feet in case something falls on them. Boots with steel toe caps will provide even more protection. Boots also give some protection against standing on sharp objects (Figure 1.6). Boots with steel inner soles give even better protection, especially if you are working in an area where there is likely to be a lot of metal turnings or swarf, such as a machine shop, or where there could be discarded timber with protruding nails, as on a building site.

*Figure 1.7* Face mask

## Ear protectors

Plumbers do not often carry out work that involves or brings them into contact with loud and constant noise, but sometimes, particularly in a workshop, some form of ear protection is necessary. On these occasions, wear either cotton ear plugs or full ear protectors (Figure 1.8).

*Figure 1.8*  Full ear protectors

## Keeping the working area tidy

Whether you are working on a building site, in a private house or flat, or in a workshop, it is essential to keep the working area tidy. This will ensure that jobs are carried out safely and more efficiently. Many accidents can be avoided if you take care to replace tools and materials when you are not using them; do not allow 'obstacles' and hazards to build up by leaving tools and materials lying around.

### Working in houses or flats

The main problem associated with working in private houses or flats is that the work area is usually small and confined. In these situations it is more important than ever to prevent tools and materials from cluttering up the work area. Accidents here are usually caused by tripping over tools, materials or trailing cables. Avoid cables for power tools trailing excessively around the working area. Kneeling on or putting hands on small fittings, screws etc. can also cause painful

injury. When tools are not in use, return them to the toolbox or bag. The same applies to fittings, fixings and materials in general. Only keep at hand those materials that are immediately needed, return materials and fittings including material off-cuts and scrap to a materials box or bag. Make sure the lids are put back on tins of flux, jointing materials or adhesives immediately after use to reduce the possibility of spillage.

> When applying fluxes, jointing pastes or adhesives, always use a brush and avoid skin contact. Always use adhesives in a well-ventilated area.

Soldering in confined spaces, whether in a house, flat or on a building site, brings with it possible fire hazards. Always protect the surroundings near the soldering area by using some kind of flameproof mat or material to prevent stray flames and sparks from setting combustible materials alight. Have available a suitable small fire extinguisher, bucket of water or bucket of sand (see section on fire prevention).

## Safety in the workshop

The same general principles regarding tidiness apply in workshops. In a well-organised workshop, standard procedures should ensure that the workshop is kept tidy at all times. All too often, however, correct procedures are not followed: the result is usually that the workshop becomes cluttered with tools, materials and scrap, making access to machines and workbenches difficult and dangerous (Figure 1.9).

> Keep workbenches and machines clear of unnecessary tools and materials, and free of scraps and offcuts. Remove all combustible materials such as timber, paper and cardboard packaging, because they can be a fire hazard if left around a workshop. Sweep floors and workbenches regularly to remove shavings, metal offcuts and swarf, and general rubbish. If they are allowed to remain, apart from posing a fire hazard, they could cause workers to trip and fall into machines, bang their heads or stand on sharp objects (see section on fire prevention).
>
> Check benches regularly to make sure that there are no protruding nails, screws or splinters that could cause injury. Workbenches should be solid, secure and level. All bench equipment, such as vices, should be fixed securely. Never leave long pipes protruding from pipe vices as they could cause injury.

*Figure 1.9* Untidy and cluttered workshops contain many hazards

Machinery and other equipment in workshops must be installed in accordance with the manufacturer's instructions. Most machines for workshop use must be level and securely fixed to the floor to prevent them falling over when in use. Check the manufacturer's literature. Only qualified or proficient and trained personnel should operate machinery.

---

All machines and equipment with moving parts should be fitted with appropriate protective safety guards, with all operating and safety procedures displayed alongside the machines.

All fixed electrically powered machinery should have a safety 'panic button' shut-off switch clearly visible and painted in a distinctive colour.

---

Workbenches, machines and other fixed equipment must be positioned so that there is sufficient space between them for workers to operate safely and efficiently.

Although materials need to be nearby, they are best stored separately in a secure storeroom. They should be stored in a manner that is both safe and does not damage the material. For example, store pipes horizontally at a suitable height for access, on strong, evenly spaced pipe racks. Sheet materials may be stored horizontally or vertically, depending on the type and size of the material, but should always be suitably supported.

---

Store bottled gases apart from other materials, preferably in a separate, fireproof building or shed. Store full bottles and empty bottles separately and upright.

In workshops where welding, brazing or soldering take place, there should be suitable ventilation to remove the fumes. This is best achieved by bench-level or overhead ducted mechanical extraction. Where this is not possible there must be sufficient natural ventilation through openings (doors and windows) to prevent a build-up of fumes.

---

## Hand tools

All hand tools used in workshops and on site must be kept and maintained in good working order. They must also be used correctly, that is for the purpose for which they were designed. Poor maintenance and incorrect use of tools are common sources of injury. Here are some general guidelines:

1. Keep all blades and cutting surfaces sharp and, if possible, covered when not in use. A blunt hacksaw may stick or get jammed. The continued force of the cutting action can then cause it to jump off the material and cut into the user's hand or fingers (Figure 1.10).

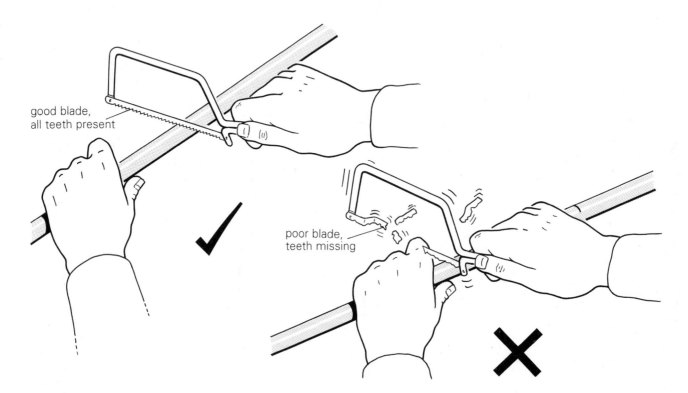

good blade, all teeth present

poor blade, teeth missing

*Figure 1.10*   Using good and bad hacksaw blades

2. The striking surface of all steel chisels used for cutting masonry should be kept free of excessive splay or 'mushrooming', which creates a hazard not only because of the sharp edges but also because the steel could splinter upon striking and cause an eye injury (Figure 1.11).

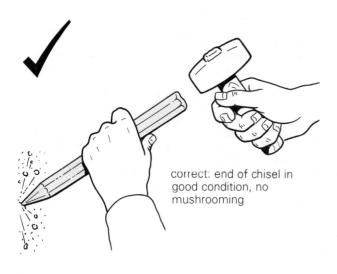

correct: end of chisel in good condition, no mushrooming

incorrect: burrs on chisel forming a mushroom head, which can chip off and cause injury

*Figure 1.11* Good and poor maintenance of steel chisels

3. Never use files and similar tools without handles. The pointed end of the file that fits into the handle, the tang, could stick into the hand or wrist if there is no handle fixed (Figure 1.12).
4. Wedge the heads of all hammers securely to prevent them from flying off during use and causing injury (Figure 1.13).

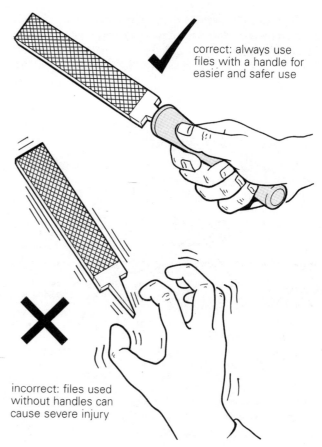

correct: always use files with a handle for easier and safer use

incorrect: files used without handles can cause severe injury

*Figure 1.12* Correct and incorrect use of a file

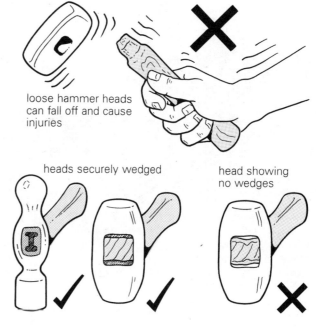

loose hammer heads can fall off and cause injuries

heads securely wedged

head showing no wedges

*Figure 1.13* A selection of hammers with and without wedges and the results of using a hammer without wedges

5.  Only use the correct size and type of screwdriver when fixing screws. Otherwise the screwdriver could slip and cause an injury (Figure 1.14).

6.  Ensure that all cables for portable electric power tools are securely fixed to the terminals and that the cables are not frayed or damaged. Make all extension connections with approved plug and socket connectors. Never use the cable to lift or lower power equipment as this may pull the wire from the terminals (Figure 1.15). Avoid trailing cables; position them away from sources of potential damage and keep them well away from water. If possible, use low-voltage equipment (110 volts) with a transformer, or re-chargeable battery-operated equipment. Otherwise use double-insulated equipment, designed and manufactured to ensure that under no circumstances can the outer casing become live.

All double insulated equipment should be stamped with the international symbol of a 'square within a square' (Figure 1.16). If in doubt, see your electrical equipment supplier.

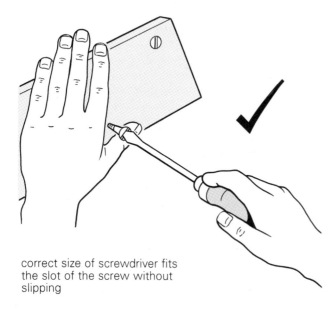

correct size of screwdriver fits the slot of the screw without slipping

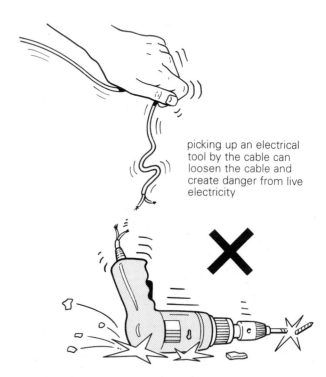

picking up an electrical tool by the cable can loosen the cable and create danger from live electricity

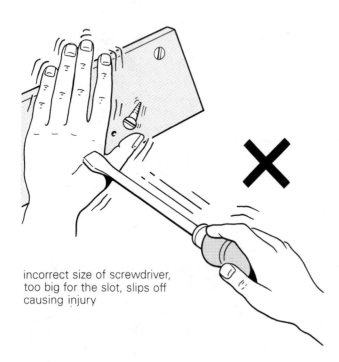

incorrect size of screwdriver, too big for the slot, slips off causing injury

*Figure 1.15*  The possible result of picking up equipment by the cable

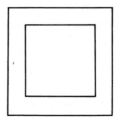

*Figure 1.14*  Using correct and incorrect sizes of screwdriver

*Figure 1.16*  The international symbol for double-insulated electrical equipment

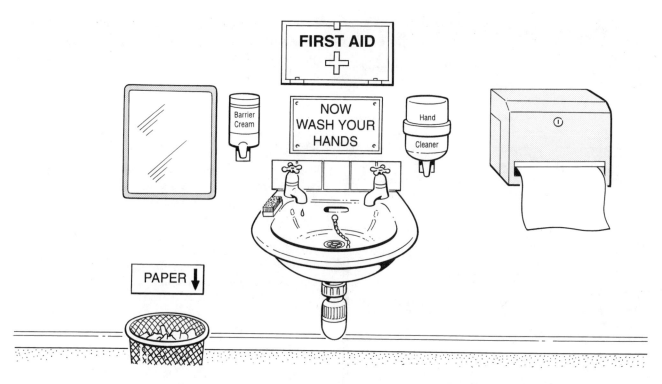

*Figure 1.17*  Workshop washing facilities with a first aid box in a prominent position

## General cleanliness

Workshops should always have hand-washing facilities to wash off grease, dirt etc. at the end of the day. A suitable industrial-type hand cleanser will make it easier to remove oil and grease from your hands. Barrier cream should be available for use before starting work (Figure 1.17). Protective clothing should also be available when needed.

To draw attention to various hazards and health and safety procedures in workshops and on building sites, display appropriate safety notices and posters in prominent positions (Figure 1.18).

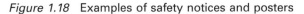

*Figure 1.18*  Examples of safety notices and posters

# Safety on building sites

On building sites, it is difficult for an individual to control the general layout from the point of view of tidiness and therefore safety. This should be the overall responsibility of the site manager. Individual workers should, however, be able to identify potential hazards and bring these to the attention of the site manager. As pointed out above, it is also the responsibility of individual employees to help to maintain a safe working environment. Some potential hazards can be dealt with quickly and easily by individuals, but because of the range and number of activities, and the number of people working on building sites, extra care needs to be taken.

> Because of the particular dangers associated with working on building sites, it is usual for safety notices to be displayed around the site to inform of any specific hazards or whether any special precautions need to be taken regarding wearing protective clothing. The design and colours of the signs themselves are more or less universally recognised and accepted around the world (Figure 1.19).

Most accidents on building sites result from people falling from ladders, working platforms or scaffolds, or buildings themselves. Falling objects, tools or materials from buildings or scaffolds account for many others. If suitable precautions are taken, the potential for accidents and injury can be greatly reduced.

## Ladders

These are used for access to work or working platforms at medium to high level off the ground. Before use, check them to make sure they are in good order. All the rungs must be securely fixed to the stiles. The stiles should not be split, warped or splayed at the bottom. All fittings on extension ladders should be in sound condition. Where extension ladders are fitted with ropes or cords, they must be in good condition and without frays.

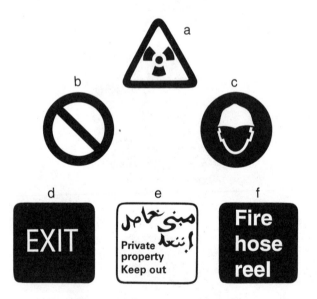

a   Warning (risk of danger), black writing, yellow background
b   Prohibition (don't do), red writing on white background or vice-versa
c   Mandatory (must do), white writing, blue background
d   Emergency (the safe way), white writing, green background
e   General (information), black on white background
f   Fire fighting (emergency), white on red background

*Figure 1.19*  Examples of safety signs and how to recognise them

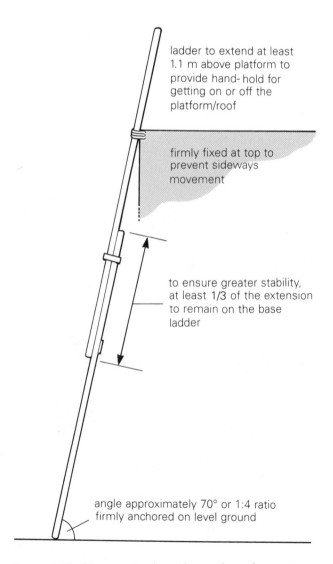

ladder to extend at least 1.1 m above platform to provide hand-hold for getting on or off the platform/roof

firmly fixed at top to prevent sideways movement

to ensure greater stability, at least 1/3 of the extension to remain on the base ladder

angle approximately 70° or 1:4 ratio firmly anchored on level ground

*Figure 1.20*  Diagram to show the angle and correct use of an extension ladder

**Safety on ladders**

- Never extend ladders above two-thirds the extension length, otherwise they may become unstable (Figure 1.20).
- If a ladder cannot be repaired properly.... scrap it! Ladders should never be painted, because the paint may hide defects.
- Always erect timber ladders so that the safety ties are underneath the rungs. Aluminium ladders should be erected with the tread side of the rungs uppermost. The foot of the ladder should be level and securely anchored if it is on soil or grass (Figure 1.21).
- Never reach too far off a ladder to save time. Come down off the ladder and reposition it.
- Always wipe mud and clay off your shoes or boots before climbing a ladder to prevent slipping.

The correct working angle for a ladder is approximately 70° from the ground, or 'one rung out for every four rungs up', and there should always be enough space around the rungs to get a good foothold (Figure 1.20). If anchoring the ladder is difficult, for example where the ladder is standing on concrete, someone should hold the ladder at the bottom to prevent sideways movement. The ladder should always be anchored at the top to prevent sideways movement also. When used as access to a working platform or scaffold, or access to get on a roof, the ladder should always extend above the working platform, scaffold or roof by at least 1.1 metres to provide a hand grip when getting off or on (Figure 1.20).

If a working platform is not available and work is to be carried out while standing on the ladder, do not try and carry too many tools and materials.

Store ladders flat and off the ground on strong supports to prevent undue strain pulling the rungs out of the stiles. Storing ladders off the ground also helps to prevent damage to the wood caused by dampness and rot (Figure 1.22).

Working on pitched roofs will require the use of 'cat-ladders', or crawlers. Fragile roof coverings of all kinds, for example asbestos, whether flat or pitched, will require the use of 'cat-ladders' or 'duck-boards'. These help to prevent damage to the roof, which could cause accidents, by distributing the load over a wider area (Figure 1.23).

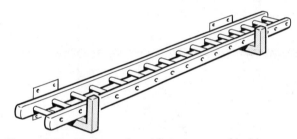

*Figure 1.22*   Horizontal and flat storage of ladders

tread uppermost

the space beneath a ladder must be free from obstructions to enable a good foothold on the rungs

tie wire beneath the rung

*Figure 1.21*   Diagram to show the correct way of erecting ladders and how to secure them at the bottom

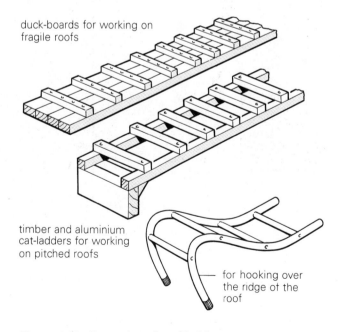

duck-boards for working on fragile roofs

timber and aluminium cat-ladders for working on pitched roofs

for hooking over the ridge of the roof

*Figure 1.23*   Examples of roof ladders

## Working platforms and scaffolds

The simplest working platform for low-level work or access to low-level platforms is a stepladder. These can be either wooden, aluminium or steel. Always make sure that they are fully open before use, and that the stays or cords are in good condition.

There are many types of scaffold and working platform and the plumber should have a basic understanding of some of the simpler low-rise platforms and 'easy-fit' mobile scaffolds available. The erection of large-scale tubular steel or timber scaffolding is outside the scope of this book because it is a specialist job best left to experts. However, because plumbers sometimes do use these scaffolds, it is worth briefly reviewing some of the key safety features and practices associated with their use. Before you use a scaffold, spend a few minutes checking for faults.

The scaffold should look and feel secure. If made of timber, all members should be free from splits and rot. All connectors should be tight and secure. The uprights or standards should all be bedded on a sound and level base/sole board. Diagonal braces should connect front to back uprights, and diagonals should also connect across all the front uprights. This helps to prevent distortion of the scaffold frame. The scaffold should be secured or tied to the building. All working platforms should be wide enough to work off and free from overlaps or 'traps'. A kickboard to prevent tools and materials from falling off should be fixed along the edges of platforms and a handrail fixed at a suitable height around all platforms (Figure 1.24).

Aluminium mobile tower scaffolds are easy to erect and use (Figure 1.25). They consist of interlocking tubes, which can be built up to the desired height. They have wheels, which must be locked when in use, and diagonal struts for extra stability.

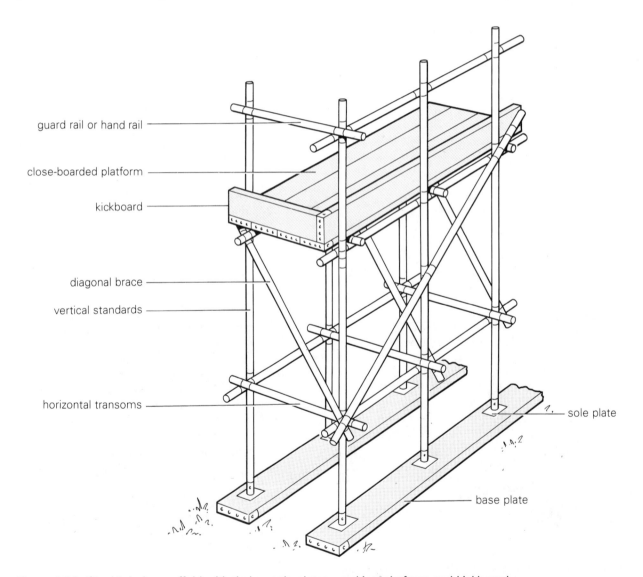

guard rail or hand rail
close-boarded platform
kickboard
diagonal brace
vertical standards
horizontal transoms
sole plate
base plate

*Figure 1.24* Steel tubular scaffold with timber sole plates, working platform and kickboard

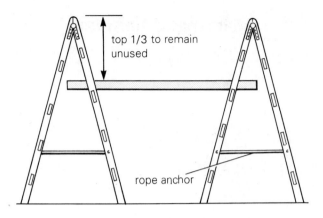

top 1/3 to remain unused

rope anchor

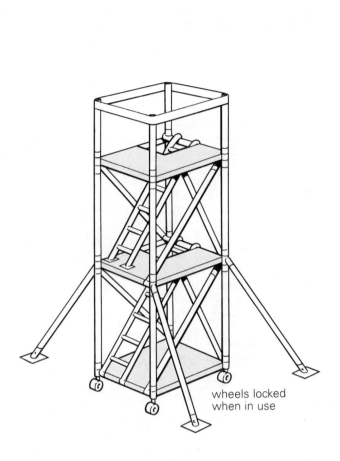

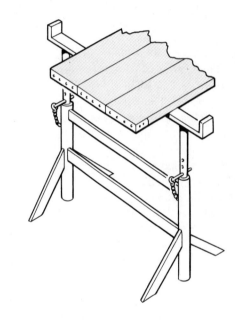

wheels locked when in use

*Figure 1.25* Mobile tower scaffold

*Figure 1.26* Working platforms and trestles

Never move a tower scaffold with a person still on it. These scaffolds have many uses in plumbing where previously a ladder would have been used, although their height is limited. As with other scaffolds, they should only be used on firm and level ground.

Trestles are useful for supporting working platforms at lower levels. Only use them for light work of short duration. The working platform itself can be supported on timber 'A' frame trestles or steel 'H' frame trestles (Figure 1.26). The 'A' frames should always be fully extended, and the boards forming the platform positioned no more than two-thirds of the way up the frames. The boards should be fully supported on the trestle with no long overhangs. When using standard boards or planks the distance between supports should be no more than 1.5 metres. If purpose-made thicker staging platforms are used, the distance between supports can be increased to approximately 3 metres. The adjustable 'H' frame trestles, because they are made of steel and therefore heavier, have the advantage of being more secure and stable, although their height is limited. As with scaffolds, the trestles must only be used on firm and level ground. 'A' frames are normally used indoors, while 'H' frames can be used either indoors or outdoors.

**Safety on platforms and scaffolds**
- Never place or use stepladders on top of working platforms or scaffolds to gain extra height. They must be placed on firm and level ground.
- Whenever working on or near a scaffold wear a safety helmet or hard hat.
- Never use mobile tower scaffolds near overhead electric power cables.
- Never overload a working platform or scaffold with tools or materials because they may cause it to become unstable.
- Timber scaffold members have a limited life. Never use timber that has obviously seen a lot of wear and tear, as shown by excessive nail holes and splinters.
- Never use trestles if a person could fall more than 4.5 metres.

# Lifting and handling

An essential part of any worker's job, including the plumber's, is to handle, lift, move and fix materials and components. Some protective measures have already been covered in relation to protecting the hands against injury from handling hot, oily or sharp materials. However, protective gloves will not give much protection in preventing your fingers from being crushed. Take great care when lifting, carrying and putting down heavy objects.

Apart from crush injuries, the biggest cause of injury associated with handling and lifting is back injury. This usually results from trying to lift too heavy a load.

Even with a relatively light load, incorrect lifting and carrying can result in severe back injury. The backbone is made up of a series of vertebrae or small bones separated by intervertebral discs, which are like spongy disc 'bearings' (Figure 1.27). If these discs are put under excessive strain due to bending, there is a possibility that they will become damaged and displaced. This condition, sometimes known as a 'slipped disc', can be extremely painful.

The correct method of lifting to avoid back problems is to lift using the legs and body weight as both an 'anchor' and a 'lever'. The knees should be bent to get into a crouched position with the back straight, but not necessarily vertical. The legs should be supporting the body weight. In this position, the applied load (object to be lifted) should transmit through the arms to the body and in turn to the legs. The back should not be put under any undue strain at any point in the operation. Once the object is lifted, stand up straight, keeping the back straight at all times (Figure 1.28).

Back straight at all times

Figure 1.28  Correct posture for lifting using legs and body as an anchor and lever, and keeping backbone straight

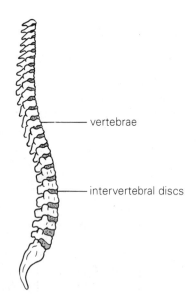

Figure 1.27  Diagram of backbone composed of small bones or vertebrae separated by spongy bearings called intervertebral discs

— vertebrae

— intervertebral discs

**Lifting check-list**
- Before lifting, check that there are no obstacles in your pathway.
- Try not to lift with your fingers under the load. If unavoidable, it is safer to lever the edges up and place wedges or spacers underneath so that you can get a better grip. Also, position wedges or spacers where the load is to be put down to avoid trapping your fingers (Figure 1.29).
- Never overestimate your strength. When in doubt, get assistance, or consider using mechanical equipment.
- Never stack materials too high as they may become unstable.
- Always make sure you can see where you are going when carrying materials and equipment.
- When carrying long objects like pipes and ladders, be careful when going round corners. Angle the projecting ladder or pipe away from the corner until you can see that there is nobody in the way.

Use wedges; leave a gap to prevent
trapping fingers

*Figure 1.29*  The use of wedges or spacers when lifting
loads or putting them down

## Fire prevention

Many of the jobs that plumbers carry out involve the use of
blowlamps. Whenever such things are used there is always a
possible risk of fire. Provided the equipment is used
correctly and care is taken to remove or protect all
combustible material near the working area, the use of
blowlamps will carry minimum fire risk. In the event of a
fire, however, the plumber must have a basic knowledge of
how to deal with it.

There are three key things that are needed to create a fire:
- combustible material or fuel;
- oxygen or air;
- an ignition source.

The removal of any one of these things will cause the fire
to go out.

Most fires spread very quickly, so it is important
to be able to act quickly if you discover a fire.
When working inside a building or workshop, part of
the overall safety procedure is to know where the
nearest exit or escape route is in case of a fire.

You can deal with some small fires quickly and effectively
by using the appropriate fire extinguisher, but it is essential to
recognise the various types available and what types of fire
they are designed for (Figure 1.30 and Table 1.1). Fire
extinguishers work on the principle of smothering the
flames and cutting off the oxygen supply to the fire or
making the fuel or burning material temporarily
incombustible by soaking it in water.

*Table 1.1* Fire extinguishers

| Type of fire | Type of extinguisher | Usual colour of container |
|---|---|---|
| Burning wood, paper fabrics and similar materials | Water | Red |
| Burning liquid fires | Foam | Yellow or cream |
| Burning liquid and electric fires | Powder | Blue |
| Burning liquid and electric fires | Carbon dioxide ($CO_2$) | Black |
| Burning liquid and electric fires | Halon | Green |

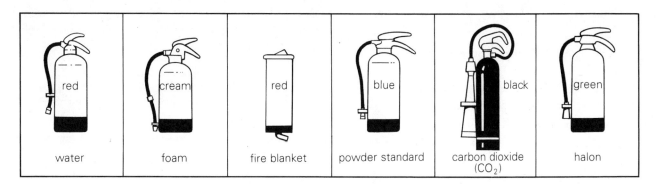

*Figure 1.30*  Types of fire extinguisher

**Fire extinguishers**
- When using a fire extinguisher to fight a small fire, get in a position where you can make a quick and safe retreat if necessary.
- Crouch down to keep clear of smoke and heat while you are fighting the fire, and make sure that the fire is completely extinguished before you leave the scene.
- Never use water on burning liquid, electrical or flammable metal fires.
- Dry sand specially stored in red buckets can be used to smother flames in most types of fire if other extinguishers are not available.
- Fire blankets, which are normally stored in red containers, can be used to smother small fires involving burning fat or grease.

Whatever the type of fire, carry out the following procedures:

1. Identify the shortest and safest route out of the building or away from the fire.
2. Raise the alarm by setting off the fire bell and if anyone else is present tell them to report the outbreak and then return to give assistance.
3. If inside a building or workshop, get everyone out quickly and safely.
4. Close all doors and windows, if it is safe to do so, to help shut off the oxygen supply to the fire.
5. If electrical appliances are involved, try to shut off the electrical supply.
6. If anyone's clothes are on fire, wrap them in a blanket or carpet and lay them on the floor to prevent the flames from reaching their head.
7. If it is safe to do so, try to contain the fire using a fire extinguisher, as directed above, until help arrives.

Do *not* continue to fight a fire if:

1. You consider it is dangerous to do so.
2. Your escape route could be cut off by smoke or flames.
3. Gas cylinders are near the fire.
4. The fire looks as though it is getting out of control.

## CHECK YOUR UNDERSTANDING

- It is the duty of everyone in the workplace to adopt a responsible attitude where safety is concerned.
- The existence of health and safety laws does not guarantee that accidents will not happen: care and common sense in all activities are essential.
- Before starting work, if possible rub barrier cream on your hands, and *always* wash your hands before eating and at the end of the working day.

- Before carrying out a job, assess whether there is any safety risk and act accordingly by wearing appropriate protective clothing and doing the job according to good practice.
- Always ensure that the working area is kept tidy; this will help to prevent accidents.
- Ensure that all workshop areas are kept free from excess materials and scrap. Fixed machinery and equipment should be surrounded by clear areas to enable safe operation.
- Workbenches should be regularly swept and tidied up to prevent a build-up of scrap and unused tools and materials, which could cause a hazard.
- All fixed equipment and machines in workshops should be regularly maintained, equipped with protective guards where necessary, and have operating instructions and safety procedures clearly displayed.
- Suitable ventilation should be provided in all areas where welding, soldering or the use of adhesives and solvents takes place.
- Hand tools should be maintained in good condition and should be used in a responsible way.
- Never use tools that have blunt blades, missing handles, loose or broken parts, or have not been maintained properly.
- Only use tools for the job they were intended for.
- Where available, always use low-voltage (110 volts) or battery-operated portable power tools on site.
- Always handle power tools with the greatest of care. Never use them in damp or wet conditions. Check all cables to make sure that they are in good condition.
- Observe all safety notices and signs.
- Always check that ladders, scaffolds and working platforms are in good condition before using them and *never* reach too far off working platforms or ladders. If necessary move the platform or ladder.
- Be careful when handling and lifting goods and equipment manually. Use appropriate protective footwear and gloves and maintain good posture when lifting; keep your back straight at all times. If the load is too heavy, do not attempt to lift it; seek assistance.
- Become familiar with the various types of fire extinguisher available and the types of fire they are suitable for. Have an evacuation plan ready in the event of a fire in a workshop.
- In the event of a fire, always raise the alarm and, if possible, send someone to seek assistance. Only fight a fire if it is small and you feel it is safe to do so.

## REVISION EXERCISES AND QUESTIONS

Answer questions 1 to 5 by selecting one of the four options given.

1   Before using ladders it is essential to:
    i)    make sure you have all tools ready for the job
    ii)   check that they are in good condition
    iii)  make sure that they are painted the right colour

iv) notify the senior manager of the site or workshop
2 Ladders should always be erected with the tie-wires:
   i) removed
   ii) underneath the rungs
   iii) above the rungs
   iv) loose
3 Never overload a scaffold or working platform with tools or materials or it will:
   i) become unstable and dangerous
   ii) cut off access to the work
   iii) need a hoist or lift fixing to it
   iv) require inspecting by the site manager
4 When using a blowlamp, always make sure that:
   i) the fire brigade are notified
   ii) the building is evacuated
   iii) the surroundings are protected
   iv) you wear a safety helmet
5 Only use a fire extinguisher to fight a fire if:
   i) it is a burning liquid fire
   ii) the fire looks like getting out of control
   iii) there is no alarm bell to warn people
   iv) you consider it safe to do so
6 Why should long hair and loose clothing be tied back when working?
7 In terms of general working practices, what can a plumber do to help prevent accidents when working in private houses or flats or in a workshop?

8 Why is it necessary to keep the back straight when lifting materials or equipment off the floor?
9 Figure 1.31 shows details of an untidy and potentially hazardous workshop. Identify and list as many hazards as you can, suggesting ways of removing the hazards. You should be able to identify at least 15 things that could create an accident.
10 Table 1.2 lists several activities that a plumber may be involved in. Complete the table by identifying possible hazards associated with each activity and precautions or protection that could be taken to help reduce the possibility of an accident occurring.

*Table 1.2* Plumbing activities

| Operation | Possible hazard | Recommended precaution |
|---|---|---|
| Chiselling | | |
| Grinding | | |
| Handling hot, greasy or rough materials | | |
| Working on or near scaffolds | | |
| General site work | | |
| Working in areas with high dust concentrations | | |
| Working with molten metals and welding | | |
| Working in damp conditions | | |

# First aid

## Introduction

In Chapter 1 we were concerned with how to make sure that the workplace was as safe as possible. Although there may be rules and regulations relating to safety, the most important and effective strategy is for all workers to act in a responsible way where safety is concerned. Even when great care is taken and all safety procedures are followed, accidents still sometimes happen. In this situation, if an injury occurs, you must be in a position to know what to do, who to contact and how to attend to the injured person until help arrives.

This chapter will deal with all the main procedures to follow in the event of an accident. It covers the general reporting and notification procedures as well as dealing with the more practical and immediate steps to be taken in relation to some of the more common injuries resulting from accidents in the workplace.

Although this chapter gives details of basic first aid procedures that you can follow, wherever possible you must try to get someone properly trained in first aid to give temporary treatment to the casualty until the doctor or ambulance arrives.

Short training courses in first aid are available in most countries. Make enquiries with local health and safety organisations, hospitals or with the local St John Ambulance Association.

---

**What is first aid?**
- First aid is the immediate treatment given to an injured or ill person before professional help and treatment can be given. As the name suggests it is the *first* help to be given.
- First aid is *not* a substitute for professional help. It is temporary help given whilst waiting for professional help to arrive.

---

## Safety and first aid policy

It is usual these days, often by law, for all employers to have a safety policy that outlines such things as roles and responsibilities and procedures to follow in the event of an emergency. You should find out if such a policy document exists and ask to have a look at it so that you can familiarise yourself with it. In many cases employers reproduce the most important things from the document and produce a health and safety guide booklet for all employees. If you are self-employed, you need to find out what regulations, if any, cover your responsibilities regarding safety. At the very least, study this chapter carefully so that you can develop your own procedures to follow in the event of an emergency. You may work on your own but you will often be working near other people and your work may affect other people.

If your work is carried out in one place, for example in a workshop, a safety policy covering practices and procedures is more likely to be in force and understood by employees than if your work is carried out on temporary sites, such as private premises or building sites. Even in these cases, in particular on building sites, some form of safety policy should be in force. Information and instructions on most of the areas covered in this chapter should be found in a health and safety policy document or handbook.

### Health and safety laws and regulations

Details of any national and/or local regulations in force on health and safety matters should be read and understood, particularly relating to individual roles and responsibilities. Key points should be contained in company policy documents and employee handbooks.

# Safety officers and first-aiders

If you work within a large organisation employing many people there should be a safety officer who has responsibilities for co-ordinating safety policy. First-aiders who have been trained in basic first aid should be found in both large and small organisations.

> The names, telephone numbers and locations where first-aiders can be found should be clearly displayed near telephones, on notice boards and in safety handbooks. These should be kept up-to-date at all times.

## Emergency services

Telephone numbers and addresses of all the emergency services should be clearly displayed near telephones, on notice boards and in handbooks. These include doctors, hospitals, ambulance services, the fire brigade and the police.

## Reporting safety or health hazards

It is the responsibility of all workers to report potential safety or health hazards. This is best done in writing, stating the nature and location of the hazard and the date it was seen. This should then be passed on to someone in authority in the company or to the company safety officer if there is one. Typical hazards include:

- faulty, damaged or badly maintained tools and equipment including electrical equipment;
- untidy work areas;
- obstructions in passageways and other access routes;
- poor lighting in the workplace and passageways;
- no safety guards on machinery;
- slippery floor surfaces;
- poor ventilation where dust or fumes are present;
- no protective clothing;
- badly stored materials, including substances hazardous to health (gas cylinders, acids, solvents etc.);
- unsupported excavations and trenches.

## Reporting accidents and emergencies

All accidents and incidents involving injuries should be reported. The main reason for this is to identify the cause of the accident so that steps can be taken to make sure that it does not happen again. There is usually an accident report form or book for this purpose.

The procedure to follow, including who to inform, depends on the nature and severity of the accident/ occurrence. Types of incident are usually classified as:

- fatal accident;
- major injury;
- other injury;
- dangerous occurrence;
- fire or explosion (other than a dangerous occurrence).

Guidance on what is considered to be a 'major' injury etc., together with advice on how to fill in these reports and who to contact, should be found in the company policy document or handbook. The main information needed includes the name of the injured person or persons, the nature of the injury and a description of the cause of the injury if known.

All accidents, no matter how small, must be reported and copies of the reports should be kept for inspection by health and safety officers. An example of a typical accident report form is shown in Figure 2.1.

## First aid box

These should be highly visible, usually coloured green, and clearly marked with a white cross. They should be fixed where easily accessible. In workshops they are often fitted close to wash basins (Figure 2.2). On building sites they can be positioned in the site offices or workers canteen or shelter. If you work on your own you should carry one in your vehicle. The contents of a first aid box will vary according to where it is fitted, the number of workers employed and the type of work carried out in that place. A typical first aid box contains the following:

- various sizes of bandages;
- various sizes of sterile dressings;
- sterile eye pads with bandage;
- triangular bandage;
- various sizes of gauze;
- safety pins;
- moist antiseptic cleansing wipes;
- cotton wool;
- disposable plastic gloves.

 First aid boxes should not contain any medicines or pills

First aid boxes should be kept in a clean and tidy condition and anything used should be replaced immediately. An up-to-date list of contents should also be kept inside.

| **PART A** – To be Completed by the Supervisor | |
|---|---|

1. Department: _ _ _ _ _ _ _ _ _ _ _ _ _ _ _ _ _ _ _   Establishment Name: _ _ _ _ _ _ _ _ _ _ _ _ _ _ _

   Address: _ _ _ _ _ _ _ _ _ _ _ _ _ _ _ _ _ _ _ _ _ _ _ _ _ _ _ _ _ _ _ _ _ _ _ _ _ _ _ _ _ _ _ _ _ _

   Place where incident occurred: _ _ _ _ _ _ _ _ _ _ _ _ _ _ _ _ _ _ _ _ _ _ _ _ _ _ _ _ _ _ _ _ _ _ _

   _ _ _ _ _ _ _ _ _ _ _ _ _ _ _ _ _ _ _ _ _ _ _ _ _ _ _ _ _ _ _ _ _ _ _ _ _ _ _ _ _ _ _ _ _ _ _ _ _ _ _

2. INJURED PERSON

   Forename(s): _ _ _ _ _ _ _ _ _ _ _ _ _ _ _   Surname: _ _ _ _ _ _   Age: _ _ _ _ _ _   Sex: _ _ _ _ _

   Address: _ _ _ _ _ _ _ _ _ _ _ _ _ _ _ _ _ _ _ _ _ _ _ _ _ _ _ _ _ _ _ _ _ _ _ _ _ _ _ _ _ _ _ _ _ _

   Date of Birth: _ _ _ _ _ _ _ _ _ _ _ _ _ _ _ _   Single/Married/Widowed: _ _ _ _ _ _ _ _ _ _ _ _ _ _ _

3. Occupation: _ _ _ _ _ _ _ _ _ _ _ _ _ _ _ _ _ _ _   Place of Employment: _ _ _ _ _ _ _ _ _ _ _ _ _ _ _
   (*State if Public, Visitor, etc*)

   Was work engaged in at time of accident            Normal Hours of     From: _ _ _ _ _ _ _ _ _ _ _ _ _ _
   a recognised part of duties?                       Employment on
                                                      day of accident     To: _ _ _ _ _ _ _ _ _ _ _ _ _ _ _

                                                      Payroll No: _ _ _ _ _ _ _ _ _ _ _ _ _ _ _ _ _ _ _ _

4. Date of Accident: _ _ _ _ _ _ _ _ _ _ _ _ _ _ _   Time: _ _ _ _ _ _ _ _ _ _ _ _ _ _ _ _ _ _ _ _ _ _ _

   Accident/Dangerous Occurrence          _ _ _ _ _ _ _ _ _ _ _ _ _ _ _ _ _ _ _ _ _ _ _ _ _ _ _ _ _ _ _ _
   Description of Circumstances:
   (*including machinery, equipment, etc*) _ _ _ _ _ _ _ _ _ _ _ _ _ _ _ _ _ _ _ _ _ _ _ _ _ _ _ _ _ _ _ _

                                          _ _ _ _ _ _ _ _ _ _ _ _ _ _ _ _ _ _ _ _ _ _ _ _ _ _ _ _ _ _ _ _

   Nature of Injury: Please state fatal   _ _ _ _ _ _ _ _ _ _ _ _ _ _ _ _ _ _ _ _ _ _ _ _ _ _ _ _ _ _ _ _
   or major injury (*also left or right*
   *if not clear from above*)             _ _ _ _ _ _ _ _ _ _ _ _ _ _ _ _ _ _ _ _ _ _ _ _ _ _ _ _ _ _ _ _

   To what cause is the Accident          _ _ _ _ _ _ _ _ _ _ _ _ _ _ _ _ _ _ _ _ _ _ _ _ _ _ _ _ _ _ _ _
   attributed?
                                          _ _ _ _ _ _ _ _ _ _ _ _ _ _ _ _ _ _ _ _ _ _ _ _ _ _ _ _ _ _ _ _

5. First aid treatment given (*state if admitted to Hospital – including name of Hospital and date of admittance*)

   _ _ _ _ _ _ _ _ _ _ _ _ _ _ _ _ _ _ _ _ _ _ _ _ _ _ _ _ _ _ _ _ _ _ _ _ _ _ _ _ _ _ _ _ _ _ _ _ _ _ _

   _ _ _ _ _ _ _ _ _ _ _ _ _ _ _ _ _ _ _ _ _ _ _ _ _ _ _ _ _ _ _ _ _ _ _ _ _ _ _ _ _ _ _ _ _ _ _ _ _ _ _

   Signature of first aider: _ _ _ _ _ _ _ _ _ _ _ _ _ _ _ _ _ _ _ _ _ _ _ _ _ _ _ _ _ _ _ _ _ _ _ _ _ _ _

6. To whom was accident reported? _ _ _ _ _ _ _ _ _ _ _ _ _ _   Date: _ _ _ _ _ _ _ _ _ _ _ _ _ _ _ _ _

   Name and Address if any Witnesses: _ _ _ _ _ _ _ _ _ _ _ _ _ _ _ _ _ _ _ _ _ _ _ _ _ _ _ _ _ _ _ _ _

   _ _ _ _ _ _ _ _ _ _ _ _ _ _ _ _ _ _ _ _ _ _ _ _ _ _ _ _ _ _ _ _ _ _ _ _ _ _ _ _ _ _ _ _ _ _ _ _ _ _ _

   _ _ _ _ _ _ _ _ _ _ _ _ _ _ _ _ _ _ _ _ _ _ _ _ _ _ _ _ _ _ _ _ _ _ _ _ _ _ _ _ _ _ _ _ _ _ _ _ _ _ _

7. Was accident due to negligence, insobriety, wilful misconduct, disobedience of orders or defect of property? If so give particulars
   (*to be completed by the person's supervisor*):

   _ _ _ _ _ _ _ _ _ _ _ _ _ _ _ _ _ _ _ _ _ _ _ _ _ _ _ _ _ _ _ _ _ _ _ _ _ _ _ _ _ _ _ _ _ _ _ _ _ _ _

   _ _ _ _ _ _ _ _ _ _ _ _ _ _ _ _ _ _ _ _ _ _ _ _ _ _ _ _ _ _ _ _ _ _ _ _ _ _ _ _ _ _ _ _ _ _ _ _ _ _ _

8. Date of Completion: _ _ _ _ _ _ _ _ _ _ _ _ _ _ _ _ _ _ _ _ _ _ _ _ _ _ _ _ _ _ _ _ _ _ _ _ _ _ _ _

   Date copy passed to Head of School/Unit: _ _ _ _ _ _ _ _ _ _ _ _ _ _ _ _ _ _ _ _ _ _ _ _ _ _ _ _ _ _

   Date copy passed to Safety Advisor: _ _ _ _ _ _ _ _ _ _ _ _ _ _ _ _ _ _ _ _ _ _ _ _ _ _ _ _ _ _ _ _ _

   Signature of person making report: _ _ _ _ _ _ _ _ _ _ _ _ _ _ _ _ _ _ _ _ _ _ _ _ _ _ _ _ _ _ _ _ _

   Designated Post: _ _ _ _ _ _ _ _ _ _ _ _ _ _ _ _ _ _ _ _ _ _ _ _ _ _ _ _ _ _ _ _ _ _ _ _ _ _ _ _ _ _

*Figure 2.1* Part of a typical accident report form

*Figure 2.2* A typical first aid box sited near washbasins

## Practical first aid treatment

Before carrying out any first aid it is important to take care that *you* do not become a casualty yourself when giving first aid. Make sure that the source of the accident/injury has been removed or, if appropriate, that the casualty has been moved to a safe area.

Use protective clothing and equipment if necessary and always send for assistance.

> The general procedure to follow with accidents or injuries is:
> 1. assess the situation and make the area safe if necessary;
> 2. diagnose the condition;
> 3. give appropriate first aid;
> 4. make the casualty comfortable;
> 5. call for an ambulance or doctor if needed.

### Burns and scalds

If possible, immerse in cold water or place under running cold water to cool the burn or scald until the pain subsides, then apply a sterilised dressing.

When treating burns:

- Never apply adhesive or sticky type dressings, plasters or cotton wool to burns.
- Burn creams and lotions should also be avoided – they can create problems during later treatment.
- If the burns appear serious, call a doctor or ambulance immediately.

Try to remove clothing from around the burn area but *do not* try to remove clothing that is stuck to the burn – leave that to the doctor. If it is a large burn area, cover it with a clean loose cloth or towel.

Burns that are caused by chemicals should be flushed and cooled with water making sure that the water runs off the burn area. Avoid contaminating yourself with the chemical.

### Eye injuries

Wherever possible, eye wash apparatus should be used. This consists of a plastic bottle filled with clean water, with a tube attached to direct the water into the eye. By 'irrigating' the eye using a constant flow of water, most loose foreign bodies will be removed from the eye.

If the eye is still sore or if the foreign body is not removed, place an eye pad over the eye and call the doctor or ambulance. If chemicals are splashed into a person's eye, give constant eye irrigation for about 15 minutes and call for the doctor or ambulance.

Eye injuries caused by welding flash or heat burns must be covered with an eye patch before calling for the doctor or ambulance.

### Minor wounds and scratches

The skin around the wound or scratch should be washed, but avoid washing the actual wound because it may result in infection. Put a sterilised dressing on the wound as soon as possible.

### Insect and snake bites

If these result in poisoning, in severe cases it may result in drowsiness, unconsciousness, vomiting or convulsions. If possible ask the casualty what happened. Try to identify the type of insect or snake involved.

> If possible, and *only* if safe to do so, try to trap the insect or snake by throwing a box or bowl over it so that it can be identified. This may help the doctor to treat the casualty more effectively.

Put the casualty in the recovery position and call the doctor or ambulance immediately. Do not give the casualty any food or drink. Keep talking to the casualty to reassure him or her.

If the casualty falls unconscious, keep the airways open and check that the tongue does not block the back of the throat.

Check breathing and pulse. If the casualty stops breathing or there is no pulse, carry out emergency resuscitation (see mouth to mouth resuscitation below).

## Bleeding

Squeeze the sides of the wound together and apply direct pressure for several minutes then apply a sterilised dressing. If the wound is on an arm or leg and the limb is not broken, after dressing, raise the limb and support it to help reduce the flow of blood. Call for the doctor or ambulance.

---

**When dealing with a casualty who is bleeding:**

● If *you* have any exposed cuts or abrasions you must cover them with a waterproof dressing, washing your hands both before and after applying the dressing, before treating the casualty.

● Wherever possible avoid contact with the casualty's blood. Use sterilised disposable plastic gloves if available.

● If the bleeding is slight and the casualty is capable, let the casualty apply the dressing him/herself under your direction.

● Always wash your hands before applying dressings to wounds.

---

## Broken bones or suspected fractures

Unless the casualty continues to be in danger, do *not* move him/her until the fractured part is strapped so that it cannot move. Arms can be strapped to the body using bandages, with cotton wool pads or dressings acting as a cushion. A broken leg can be strapped to the good leg in the same way (Figure 2.3).

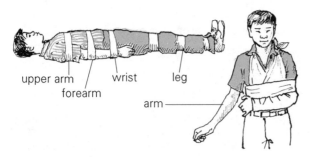

*Figure 2.3* Diagram to show position of bandage straps to prevent movement of limbs

If you suspect a spinal injury, do *not* move the casualty unless immediate danger is present. In all cases call the doctor or ambulance.

## Choking

The visible signs of choking are serious fits of coughing, being unable to speak and violent attempts to breathe.

Try to remove any obvious obstructions from the mouth then encourage the casualty to cough. If the obstruction is not removed, bend the casualty over until the head is approximately lower than the lungs and give a short sharp slap on the casualty's back, between the shoulder blades. Repeat several times; this should free it. If this does not work, an alternative method known as 'abdominal thrust' can be used.

**Abdominal thrust: procedure (Figure 2.4)**

1. Stand behind the casualty and put one arm round the front of the abdomen so that your fist is positioned between the navel and the breastbone.
2. Hold the fist with your other hand from the other side.
3. Pull upwards and inwards in a quick thrusting action.
4. Repeat several times; keep checking until the obstruction is removed by coughing it up or it is visible in the mouth from where it can be removed.
5. If this does not work, try back-slapping again, followed by the abdominal thrust again.

*Figure 2.4* Abdominal thrust technique

If still unsuccessful and the casualty loses consciousness, carry out mouth to mouth resuscitation.

## Gassing

Check to see that the atmosphere is clear; if not, try to turn off or stop the source of the gas. If this is not immediately possible and you can see the casualty and are confident that you can carry or drag him/her out into the open, take several deep breaths then quickly go in and remove the casualty. If available, wear breathing apparatus. Carry the casualty into the fresh air and check to see if he/she is breathing; if not, start mouth to mouth resuscitation (see below and Figure 2.5). Call the doctor or ambulance immediately.

## Mouth to mouth resuscitation

One of the priorities in first aid is to check whether the casualty is breathing. A casualty can stop breathing as a result of many things, including gassing, electric shock, drowning and choking.

To check for breathing, lie the casualty on his/her back and put your ear over his/her mouth to listen for signs of breathing. At the same time watch his/her chest for movement.

The main aim is to get the casualty breathing before lack of oxygen damages the brain and other organs.

If the casualty has suffered an electric shock, turn off the supply if possible or move the casualty away from the source of the electricity with something non-conductive, such as a wooden pole. Do not attempt to touch the casualty until it is safe to do so.

**Mouth to mouth resuscitation: procedure (Figure 2.5)**

1. Place the casualty on his/her back.
2. Make sure the mouth is clear; remove any obstructions.
3. Tilt the casualty's head backwards so that the nostrils face upwards; this should lift the tongue clear of the airway.
4. Kneel beside the casualty, pinch the nostrils together with one hand and open the mouth with the other hand.
5. Take a deep breath, seal his/her mouth with your own and blow deeply and steadily into the casualty's lungs until you see his/her chest rise.
6. Remove your mouth and let the chest fall. *Watch to see that it rises again and that the casualty has started breathing.*
7. If the casualty does not start breathing continue to inflate the lungs at a rate of once every four seconds until breathing starts.
8. At this stage you must check for a pulse. If there is none it indicates that the heart has stopped beating. In this case, external chest compression may be needed (see below).

9. When the casualty is breathing unaided place him/her in the recovery position, face down with the head turned to one side supported by one hand, with the other flat on the floor, and with one leg bent and the other straight (Figure 2.6).
10. Call the doctor or ambulance immediately.

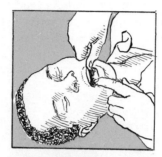

1. Place casualty on his/her back and check for mouth obstructions

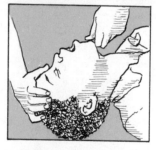

2. Loosen neckwear and tilt casualty's head backwards so that nostrils face upwards

3. Kneel beside casualty, pinch nostrils together with one hand, open the mouth with the other, take a deep breath then seal your mouth over the casualty's and breathe deeply and steadily into the casualty's lungs until you see his/her chest rise. Repeat until casualty's chest rises on its own

*Figure 2.5* Procedure for mouth-to-mouth resuscitation

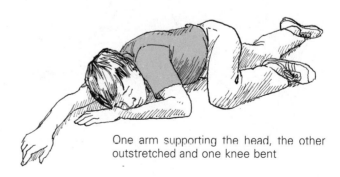

One arm supporting the head, the other outstretched and one knee bent

*Figure 2.6* Casualty recovery position

## Checking for a pulse: heart failure and external chest compression

The best way to check for a heart beat is to check for a pulse at the neck. This is called the carotid pulse.

### Checking for a pulse: procedure (Figure 2.7)

Gently place your fingertips on the neck of the casualty near the voice-box and slowly move them down into the hollow between the voice-box and the connecting muscle. You should be able to detect a pulse easily if the heart is beating.

If no pulse is felt and the heart is not beating, external chest compression is needed. If possible send someone to call for the doctor or ambulance immediately.

### External chest massage: procedure (Figure 2.8)

1. Lay the casualty on his/her back on a firm solid surface (e.g. the floor).
2. Cover one hand with the heel of the other one, lock your fingers together and with your arms straight, place the heel of your hand on the chest, keeping your fingers off the chest.
3. Press down on the chest about 3 to 5 cm (1 to 2 inches) then move back to release the pressure in a firm but smooth action.

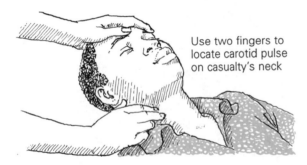

Use two fingers to locate carotid pulse on casualty's neck

*Figure 2.7*   Checking for a pulse

4. Repeat the process *fifteen* times, counting 'one and two and three' between each compression. This is just over once a second, or 80 times per minute.
5. Immediately after this, mouth to mouth resuscitation should be given. Two good inflations of the chest, then the pulse checked. If there are two first-aiders, one can do the mouth to mouth resuscitation while the other does the external chest compression.
6. If still no pulse, repeat chest compression then mouth to mouth resuscitation for *three* minutes, then check for a pulse again.
7. Continue alternate chest compression and mouth to mouth resuscitation until a normal pulse is felt.
8. When a pulse is felt, contvinue mouth to mouth resuscitation until normal breathing starts.
9. Put casualty in the recovery position and cover with a blanket until the doctor or ambulance arrives.
10. Watch the casualty closely.

## Treatment for general shock and after care

Casualties should never be treated standing up, even when apparently stable. Always sit them down or lie them down. Sometimes there may be no obvious outward signs of injury; the person may be suffering from shock. If so, lie them down in the recovery position and make them comfortable, covering them with a blanket to keep them warm.

Call the doctor or ambulance; do not give the patient any liquids or food. Talk to the patient and reassure him/her until help arrives.

After all emergencies and accidents, and after you have given the casualty initial emergency first aid *and the doctor or ambulance has been called*, you or someone else must stay with the casualty, talking to and reassuring them. You must also keep watching the casualty for signs of deterioration of their condition or a relapse.

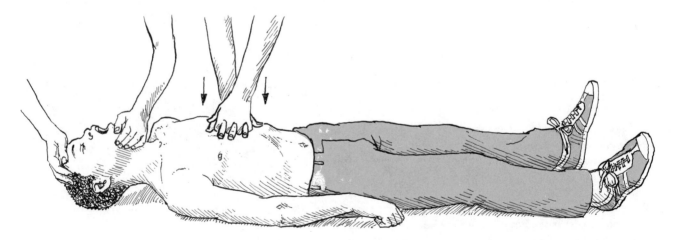

*Figure 2.8*   Technique for external chest massage

Ask the casualty for the name, address and telephone number of family or friends who can be contacted. It is important that you try to contact them. When you do make contact, explain briefly in simple, clear terms and in a controlled tone of voice the nature of the injury and that things are under control. As when talking to the casualty, this must be done in a reassuring way to help prevent panic.

> ● The most important thing with first aid is to preserve life. If you can carry out some of the above procedures in a confident manner, without endangering your own life, you should attempt to do so until professional help arrives.

## CHECK YOUR UNDERSTANDING

● First aid is *not* a substitute for professional treatment. It is the immediate treatment given to an injured or ill person *before* professional help arrives.

● All organisations should have, and operate, a safety policy covering all health and safety issues. Both employers and employees should know the main procedures to follow in the event of an accident or emergency.

● The names, locations or addresses, and telephone numbers of all people trained in first aid and all emergency services should be clearly displayed in all workshops, site cabins or other central places close to where work is being carried out.

● If an accident or emergency occurs, wherever possible, get somebody to call for help while you or somebody else gives first aid. If you are on your own, give immediate emergency first aid then call for help.

● All accidents should be reported by completing an accident report form and informing your superior or employer.

● First aid boxes should be available at or near all places of work. They should be clearly visible and fully stocked.

● Before giving any first aid treatment make sure that the area is clear of any danger and is safe to work in. Avoid becoming a casualty yourself.

● Burns and scalds should be cooled under running water before applying a dry sterilised dressing or, if a large area is involved, covering with a towel. Never try to remove clothing that is stuck to burns.

● To stop bleeding, put a dry sterilised dressing over the wound or cut and apply direct pressure. Avoid coming into contact with the casualty's blood. Any open cuts that you have should be covered with a waterproof dressing. Wash your hands before treating and if possible use a pair of disposable plastic gloves. If the casualty is conscious and capable, get him/her to wash and dress the cut him/herself under your direction.

● If the casualty has or is suspected of having a broken bone, do not move him/her unless there is danger in leaving him/her in that position. In such cases, try to strap the broken limb or area to prevent it moving.

● If the casualty is not breathing, carry out emergency mouth to mouth resuscitation until breathing is established.

● If the patient appears to have heart failure, check for a pulse, and if there is none, carry out emergency external chest compression.

## REVISION EXERCISES AND QUESTIONS

Answer questions 1 to 5 by selecting one of the four options given.

1  What kind of treatment is first aid?
   i)   permanent treatment
   ii)   temporary treatment
   iii)   professional treatment
   iv)   private treatment

2  All organisations should have a health and safety:
   i)   policy document
   ii)   treatment room
   iii)   nurse
   iv)   officer

3  The names, locations and contact numbers of all trained first-aiders should be:
   i)   inside the first aid box
   ii)   clearly displayed near telephones
   iii)   memorised by all workers
   iv)   written in the accident book

4  If an accident or emergency occurs, the very first thing to do is to:
   i)   give first aid no matter what the circumstances are
   ii)   remove all tight clothing
   iii)   assess the situation and make the area safe
   iv)   send for the first aid box

5  The 'recovery position' means that the casualty should be:
   i)   lying on his/her back with both knees raised
   ii)   sat upright on a hard chair in the open air covered with a blanket
   iii)   sat upright in bed covered in blankets to keep warm
   iv)   lying on his/her side, one hand supporting the head, one knee bent

6  If you discover a safety hazard, what should you do?

7  Describe how you should treat a minor burn to the hand.

8  What should you do if someone gets bitten by an insect or snake?

9  List the steps to be taken when treating a wound to stop it bleeding, highlighting precautions that can be taken to minimise contact with the casualty's blood.

10  In simple, brief words or sentences, list the steps to be taken when giving mouth to mouth resuscitation.

# Hand and machine tools

## Introduction

There is a saying known the world over by all craftsmen and women, particularly plumbers: 'a good workman never blames his tools.' All too often, however, tools are blamed for jobs that go wrong or for mistakes that are made. This is usually because the wrong tool has been used for a job or because the tools have not been maintained properly. This chapter will show you all the common tools used by the plumber, what they are used for and tips on how to get the best out of them. Most plumbing activities involve the following:

- measuring;
- cutting;
- bending;
- jointing;
- fixing and installing.

Furthermore, most of these activities will be related to the installation and maintenance of pipework systems and components. This chapter will therefore concentrate on the common tools used for the above activities in relation to pipework systems. A section at the end of the chapter deals with tools used for sheet metal work but detailed application of these tools is dealt with in the chapter on sheet weathering.

## Measuring tools

Tools used for measuring include flexible steel tapes and rigid steel rules. Most are marked off in both metric and British imperial units.

### Tapes, rules and squares

The most popular used by the plumber is the flexible steel tape measure (Figure 3.1). You can get these in various lengths from 1 to 30 metres (1 foot to 100 feet) but the 3 metre (10 feet) tape is the most popular. They consist of a flexible, coiled steel tape marked off in millimetres, centimetres and metres and also feet and inches, housed in a small steel or plastic case. The end of the tape has a lip or hook on it to hold it firmly on the end of a pipe or other material being measured; when released the tape usually retracts back into the case automatically. Some tapes have a

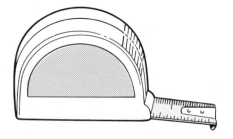

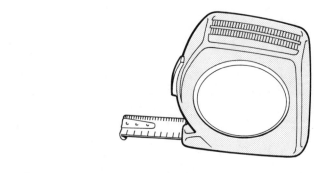

*Figure 3.1* Flexible steel tapes and folding steel rule

locking device to prevent accidental retraction. They are popular because they fit easily into a pocket or clip on to a belt. Always retract the blade when not in use to prevent damage caused by standing on the blade.

The most popular sizes of rigid steel rules are the 300 mm single-piece and the 600 mm two-piece folding rules. These have the advantage of being rigid and self-supporting so they can be placed in position on a piece of material without fear of the blade retracting or of it falling over. The blades are more robust and much less likely to get damaged than tape measures. Folding rules also have the advantage of being able to be used as a **template** when bending pipes to check angles.

Most countries use the **metric** system of measurement. This has the base unit of a metre (m) which is split up into centimetres (cm) and millimetres (mm). There are 10 mm in a cm, 100 cm in a metre, and 1000 mm in a metre. A conversion chart for metric and imperial units is shown in Chapter 4, Table 14.3.

When measuring lengths of pipework to be cut, remember to allow for depth of sockets on fittings. Dimensions on drawings or plans are often given from centre line to centre line. On site you must take account of any fittings used (Figure 3.2 and the Appendix, Figure A27).

When in doubt … 'measure *twice* and *cut* once…'

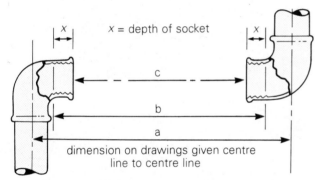

the actual length of pipe needed to fit between the elbows = b *or* c + (2 × x)

*Figure 3.2* **Allowing for socket depth when measuring pipe lengths**

For checking angles on site or in the workshop, large steel squares or wooden set squares are used. Rough workshop drawings and templates can be marked out using wooden protractors and compasses (Figure 3.3).

# Cutting tools

A variety of cutting tools are used by the plumber to cut and bend the various materials used in plumbing installations. Whether cutting, bending, jointing or forming, one item of equipment that is essential is a vice to hold the material.

## Pipe vice

A pipe vice is one of the first essential tools for doing any kind of pipework, whether on site or in the workshop. They are used to hold pipes when cutting, filing, reaming, bending, cutting threads or any of a number of other jobs. Although engineer's vices are sometimes used to grip steel pipework in workshops, the straight jaws of the vice can deform the pipe wall so are not recommended.

Pipe vices are designed to grip the pipe equally around its circumference to prevent deformation of the pipe wall. They are available as free-standing, portable site vices or as fixed bench vices. Both types are available as either a chain vice, with a linked chain that goes round the pipe and grips it against a set of jaws at the base of the vice, or as a yoke vice, with an adjustable yoke jaw at the top which tightens against a fixed jaw at the bottom (Figure 3.4).

## Hacksaws

These are used mainly for cutting pipes of various materials but are also used for cutting steel bars and bolts. There are two main types, the adjustable frame hacksaw, which uses blades of between 250 and 300 mm long, and the smaller 'junior' hacksaw with blades approximately 150 mm long (Figure 3.5). The adjustable hacksaw can be used for cutting

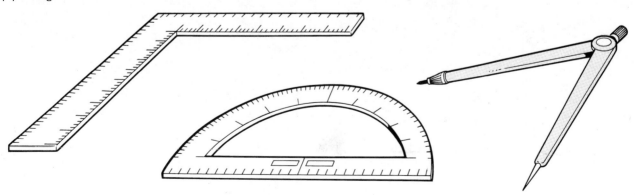

*Figure 3.3* Drawing tools

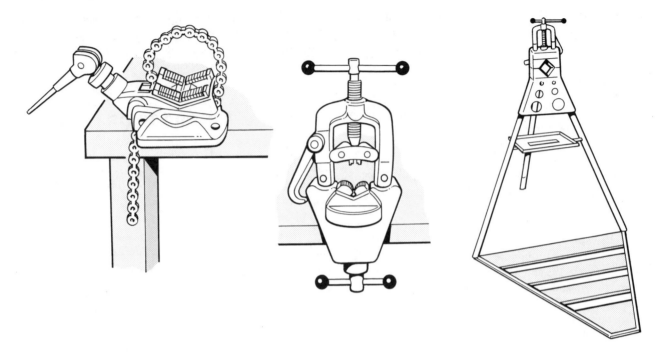

*Figure 3.4*  Pipe vices

steel, copper, plastics and lead but the 'junior' is only suitable for cutting small diameter copper and plastic pipes. A wing-nut on the end of the larger hacksaw allows you to alter the size and increase the tension to make cutting easier.

Although several types of blade are available for the larger hacksaw, for most plumbing work, flexible tungsten blades with between 24 and 32 teeth per 25 mm of blade will be adequate. Blades for the small hacksaws are standard.

**Using a hacksaw**
- Check that the measurement and marking are correct before starting the cut.
- Stand comfortably with the feet slightly spread to provide a sound base. Commence the cut slowly with pressure on the forward stroke only. Make sure the blade is at 90° to the pipe and vertically straight on the pipe, to ensure a straight cut.
- Always make sure the blade is fixed with the teeth facing forwards – to cut on the forward stroke (Figure 3.6).
- Never use blades that are worn or have teeth missing.

When you cut pipes with a hacksaw you will notice that it leaves behind small particles of metal or other material that the pipe is made from. This is called **swarf** and must be removed with a file, otherwise, if it gets trapped inside the pipe, it could damage the system.

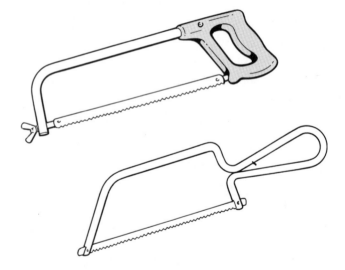

*Figure 3.5*  Adjustable frame hacksaw and junior hacksaw

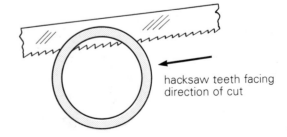

hacksaw teeth facing direction of cut

*Figure 3.6*  Hacksaw cutting a pipe

## Pipe cutters

Like hacksaws, there are also large and small pipe cutters (Figure 3.7). The larger ones can have 1, 3 or multiple cutting wheels and are adjustable to cut a range of pipe sizes. The 1- and 3-wheel cutters are normally used on steel pipes with the multiple-wheel cutters being used on brittle pipes, such as cast-iron and earthenware. Small single-wheel cutters are also available for use on small-bore copper pipe. Pipe cutters have the advantage of producing a straight cut every time, unlike the hacksaw, which, if you are not careful can produce an angled cut, which may cause problems during jointing of the pipe.

The single-wheel cutter has 1 cutting wheel and 2 guide wheels. Place the cutter on the pipe at 90° so that both guide wheels are in contact with the pipe (Figure 3.8). Then turn the adjustable handle to bring the cutting wheel into contact with the pipe. Use the handle to turn the whole tool completely around the pipe through 360°. Continue to do this while slowly increasing the pressure from the cutting wheel until it eventually cuts through the pipe.

The action of the 3-wheel cutter is similar but has the advantage of only needing a 120° maximum turn because of the cutting wheels in 3 different positions. This can be useful when cutting fixed pipework in awkward positions.

If wheels get broken or become blunt they can be replaced. Some small wheel cutters contain a spare wheel stored on the end of the handle.

Multiple-wheel cutters are used on brittle pipes, such as cast-iron, earthenware or clay drains. Each wheel is connected to a separate link which can be added to or removed depending on the size of pipe to be cut. Because of the number of wheels around the pipe, little turning

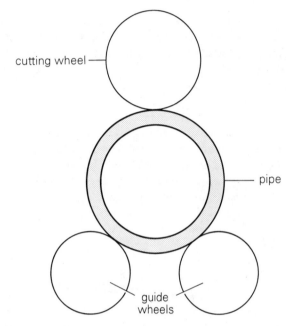

*Figure 3.8* **Single-wheel pipe cutter**

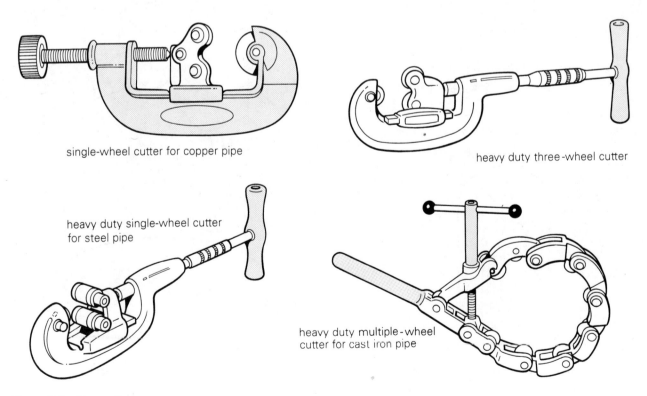

single-wheel cutter for copper pipe

heavy duty three-wheel cutter

heavy duty single-wheel cutter for steel pipe

heavy duty multiple-wheel cutter for cast iron pipe

*Figure 3.7* **Pipe cutters**

movement is needed. The main cutting action is achieved by increasing the pressure of the wheels on the pipe by turning a large 'butterfly' nut on the cutter, which eventually causes the brittle pipe to break along the cutting lines. Some multiple-wheel cutters have a long handle which acts as a lever, reducing the physical effort needed to increase the cutting pressure (Figure 3.9).

At the beginning of a cut, make sure that on the first turn the cut meets all the way round the pipe before increasing the pressure, otherwise spiral 'tracking' may occur where the cutter simply 'threads' its way along the pipe. Increase the pressure gradually to prevent excessive **burrs** being created on the cut end of the pipe.

Although swarf is not produced when using pipe cutters, their action does cause burrs to be created on both the inside and outside of the cut end of pipe. This is the term given to the slightly raised surface of the material both on the outside and inside of the cut end which causes an increase in the outside diameter and a decrease in the inside diameter (Figure 3.10). This will cause problems of jointing on the outside and a reduction of flow on the inside, and therefore must be removed.

## Reamers

These are purpose-made tools used to remove internal burrs from steel or copper pipes. They are usually cone-shaped with several cutting edges which can either be hand-turned or machine-turned (Figure 3.11). Some smaller pipe-cutters have built-in reamers.

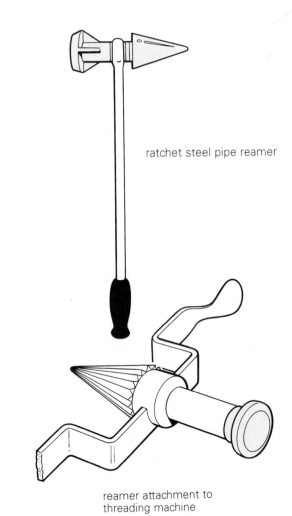

ratchet steel pipe reamer

reamer attachment to threading machine

small reamer for copper pipe attached to pipe cutter

**Figure 3.11**   Pipe reamers

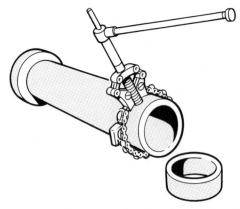

*Figure 3.9*   Multiple-wheel pressure pipe cutter

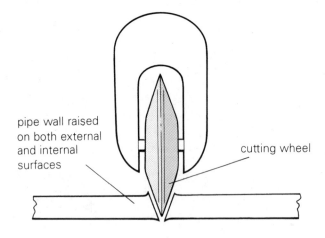

pipe wall raised on both external and internal surfaces

cutting wheel

*Figure 3.10*   Effect of pipe cutters on pipe wall

## Files

Files are used for general shaping of metal and the preparation of pipes before jointing, including the removal of burrs and swarf. Although files come in all shapes and sizes, the ones used most frequently by the plumber are the following:

1. double-cut flat file for general work, including removal of external swarf and burrs;
2. bastard cut half-round file for general work, including removal of internal swarf and burrs;
3. single-cut round file ('rat-tail') for removing internal swarf and burrs;
4. dreadnought half-round for heavy work, including removal of internal and external burrs and swarf;
5. half-round rasp for general work on soft materials, including lead pipe.

These files are shown in Figure 3.12. As a general guide, the smoother single cut files are used for soft materials, such as copper, with the rougher double-cut files being used on steel. The exception to this is the dreadnought for very rough work on steel and the rasp for use with very soft materials, such as lead.

---

**Using a file**
- Before using a file you should always check that the handle is secure and that the teeth are free from metal swarf. If necessary brush the file with a wire brush to clean. As with a hacksaw, files only cut on the forward stroke so make sure you are standing in a comfortable position with your feet slightly spread to form a sound base and apply firm, even pressure on the forward stroke, releasing the pressure on the backward stroke.
- Never use a file without a handle.
- Never run your fingers over the edges of pipes to check the cut.

---

## Hole cutters or hole saws

These are used for cutting holes in plastic soil pipes, and steel or plastic cisterns and tanks, or for cutting holes in sheet metal. Some can also cut out washers from sheet metal. There are several types available (Figure 3.13). Most have a central guide or pilot drill with an outer cutting blade which may be fixed or adjustable. They can be turned by hand or by powered drill – check the manufacturer's instructions. The washer cutter has an outer and an inner cutting blade, as well as the pilot drill, to cut **annular** washers (Figure 3.14).

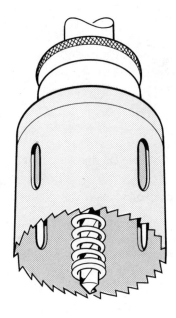

*Figure 3.13*  Hole saw

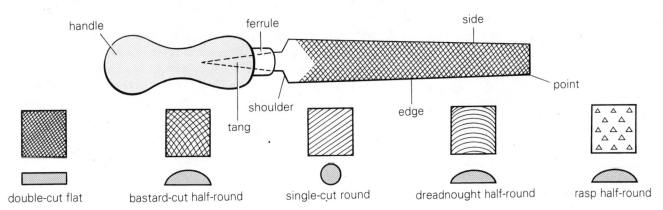

double-cut flat          bastard-cut half-round          single-cut round          dreadnought half-round          rasp half-round

*Figure 3.12*  Common files used by the plumber

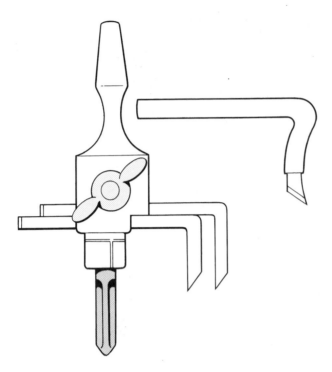

*Figure 3.14*  Washer cutter and tank cutter

## Padsaw or compass saw

In these saws the blade is only fixed at one end, in a wooden or metal handle. They are used for cutting holes in sheet materials and sawing in difficult and restricted positions where a hacksaw will not fit. Blades for cutting a range of materials – metal, wood or plastic – are available (Figure 3.15).

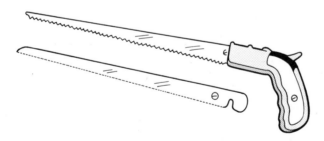

*Figure 3.15*  Padsaw

# Bending tools

Most bends or changes in direction of pipework can be done using special purpose fittings and joints, but this can work out costly on big installations where you need a lot of fittings and some bends cannot be made-up easily using available fittings. In these cases you will have to bend the pipe yourself. The method chosen will be governed by the size and type of pipe used. Some bends on steel, copper and certain types of plastics, for example, can be done by heating. In most situations, however, the easiest way is to use a machine.

## Steel pipe

The easiest and most popular method of bending steel pipe is to use a hydraulic pipe-bender. There are several types available but the simplest is the hydraulic press-bender which can bend pipes from 15 mm diameters up to 100 mm diameters (Figure 3.16). It consists of a hydraulic ram on which different sizes of former can be put to bend the pipe against a frame containing adjustable pins and stops.

### Using a hydraulic press-bender to make a 90° bend

This is used to make a 90° bend from a fixed point, say 800 mm from the end of the pipe to the centre line of a bracket fixed on a wall (Figure 3.17).

1. Mark the pipe 800 mm from the end.
   2. Deduct from this the diameter of the pipe, and make a fresh mark on the pipe, for example if you are using 35 mm diameter pipe, your new mark should be 800 minus 35, or 765 mm from the end. This will now be the centre of the bend, to allow for the 'gain' in pipe length caused by a bend.
3. Lift up the top bar of the frame on the machine and put the stops and pins in the correct position (35 mm) and put sand the 35 mm former on the end of the hydraulic ram. Lower the bar on to the top of the pins.
4. Position the pipe in the machine against the stops and with the centre line of the former in line with your mark on the pipe. Gently pump the ram until it locates against the pipe in the correct position and the pipe is held secure.
   The bleed valve on the hydraulic cylinder must be in the closed position otherwise it will not build up pressure to pump.
5. Pump the machine carefully until the bend is almost at 90°, and check this with a set-square or template. To allow for **spring-back**, you must bend the pipe a few degrees beyond 90°. When the pressure is removed it will spring back to the desired angle.
6. When you are happy that the bend is right, making the allowances mentioned, open the valve on the machine body to release the pressure and slowly pump the handle which will pull back the ram. The former will probably be jammed on the pipe, but do not remove it yet.
7. Check with a set-square that the angle is correct, then remove the former by holding it with one hand and striking the end of the pipe on a piece of wood on the floor; this should loosen it. If it needs bending more, simply return it to the machine and increase the bend. If you have bent it too much, it is possible to open the bend by a couple of degrees by securing one leg of the bend in a

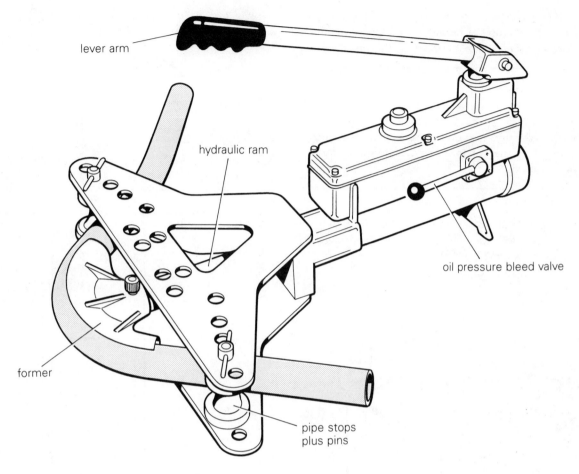

lever arm

hydraulic ram

oil pressure bleed valve

former

pipe stops
plus pins

*Figure 3.16*  Hydraulic press-bender

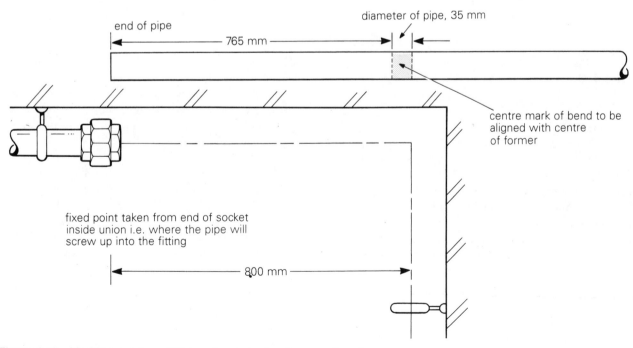

diameter of pipe, 35 mm

end of pipe

765 mm

centre mark of bend to be
aligned with centre
of former

fixed point taken from end of socket
inside union i.e. where the pipe will
screw up into the fitting

800 mm

*Figure 3.17*  Marking out for a 90° bend on a hydraulic press-bender

vice and carefully applying leverage to the other leg to pull
it back slightly. This is *not* recommended if it needs pulling
back much over 5°, since it will deform the pipe wall.

---

**Safety precautions for hydraulic press-benders**
- Always make sure the oil level in the machine is kept
  topped-up. Check the manufacturer's literature.
- Never leave formers or other machine parts on the
  floor where they could become damaged or cause
  safety hazards.

---

Motorised hydraulic benders are also available which are
quicker to use and reduce the physical effort involved in
pumping the lever press.

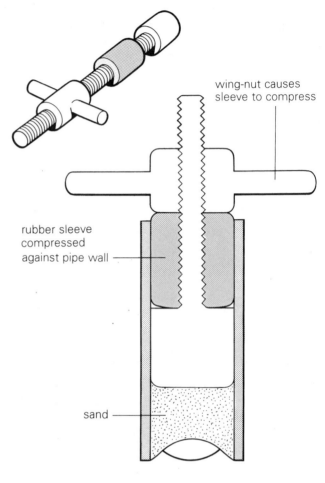

*Figure 3.19* Sand compressor

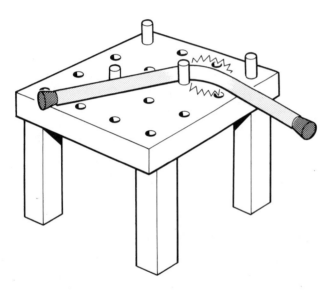

*Figure 3.18* Steel pins and bending table

### Heat bending

Steel pipe can also be bent by loading the pipe with dry sand,
heating it up in a furnace or with a large flame from a
blowlamp or oxy-acetylene torch, then bending it round a
former or between steel pins on a bending table (Figure 3.18).

The sand must be clean and dry with no debris or large
particles in it. A cap or wooden plug must be put over one
end of the pipe and the sand must then be poured carefully
into the pipe in stages, compacting it by tapping the pipe
after each pour. When the pipe is almost full place a rag in
the end, then drive a tapered wooden plug into the end to
compact the sand and hold it in position. Purpose-made
sand compressors, which just fit into the end of the pipe
and are tightened up, are also available for this purpose
(Figure 3.19).

The most important thing to do when heat bending is to
calculate and mark off accurately on the pipe the actual
section of pipe to be heated; this is known as the **heat
length**. If you heat too much pipe the radius will be too
big; if you heat too little the radius will be too small and
the pipe may **kink**.

### Calculating the heat length for a 90° bend

1. Mark off on the pipe the distance from a fixed point, say 500
   mm to the centre of the bend. This is the centre line of the
   projected bent leg of the pipe. This point will also be the end
   of the actual **travel** or length of the bend (Figure 3.20).

   For a 90° bend the actual length or travel of the bend
   will be a quarter of the circumference of a circle made to
   the radius of the given bend. Unless a radius is specified,
   use a radius equal to 4 times the outside diameter of the
   pipe to be bent.

2. If we assume the pipe is 28 mm, the radius will be 4 × 28,
   which is 112 mm. If the travel or length of bend is equal to a

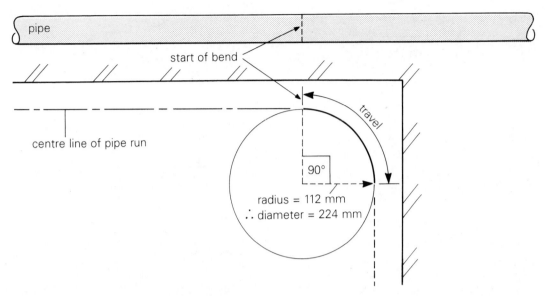

*Figure 3.20* Calculating the heat length for a 90° bend

quarter of the circumference of a circle having a radius of 112 mm the heat length will be:

the circumference of the circle divided by a quarter or $\pi D$. This will be $2 \times 112 \times 3.142$ which is 181 mm to the nearest mm. The heat length then is 181 mm (Figure 3.21).

3. From the centre line of the bend already marked out on the pipe (500 mm), measure *back towards the fixed point* 181 mm, the calculated heat length, and mark off on the pipe. This marks the position of the start of the bend.

4. The section of pipe from the start to the end of the bend must now be clearly marked because this is the *only* section of pipe to be heated.

5. Position the pipe so that the flame from the forge or blowtorch heats up the bend area to a bright red colour. Cool the area outside the marked bend by pouring water on the pipe either side of the bend to prevent it bending there.

5. Position the pipe in the former or on the bending table and carefully lever the pipe between the pins until the desired angle is reached. Use a set-square to check the angle. You may need to re-heat to complete the bend if it cools too quickly.

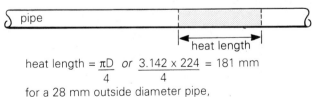

heat length = $\dfrac{\pi D}{4}$ *or* $\dfrac{3.142 \times 224}{4}$ = 181 mm
for a 28 mm outside diameter pipe,
this is marked off from the start of the bend

*Figure 3.21* Marking out the heat length on a pipe

- It is useful to produce a working drawing on the workshop floor or on wooden or steel sheeting as a guide (see Appendix). A piece of steel rod could also be bent round to the desired radius to use as a template to guide you during bending.
- Always wear heavy-duty gloves when handling hot metals.

## Copper pipe

Several machines are available for bending light gauge copper pipe and most of them work on the same principle. One of the most popular for general site and workshop use is the floor-mounted bender (Figure 3.22). This is suitable for all sizes up to and including 35 mm.

**Using a floor-mounted bending machine to make a 90° bend**

1. Mark off on the pipe the centre of the bend (y). This will usually be from a fixed point. You can also use the inside or outside of the bend but make sure you position the pipe correctly against the former (Figure 3.23).

2. Select the correct size of former and place it in the machine using the centre pin to secure it.

3. Place the pipe in the machine so that the fixed point leg of the pipe is held against the pipe stop and the other leg is secure in the former.

4. Select the correct size of guide and place it in position on the pipe and against the former as shown and bring the roller down on to the guide using the bending handle.

5. Adjust the pipe until the centre (y) is square with the centre of the former.

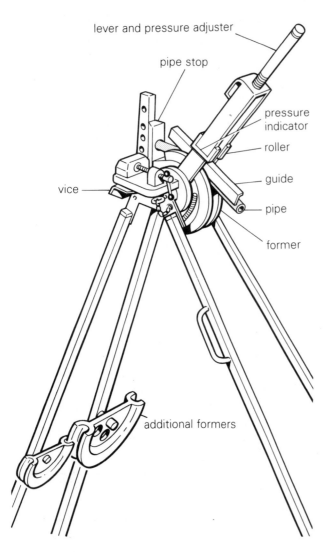

*Figure 3.22* Floor-mounted copper pipe bending
machine

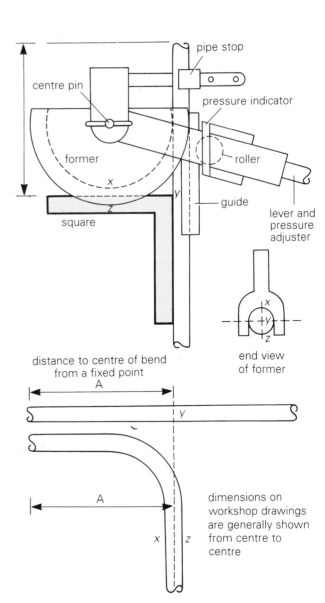

6.  Adjust the roller until the pressure indicator is parallel with
    the pipe.
7.  Bend the pipe using the lever handle, check for square or
    90° using a set-square, then bend a couple of degrees
    tighter to allow for spring-back.
8.  Always make sure the roller guide is parallel and feels tight
    on the guide: too slack and the pipe will **ripple** and **kink**;
    too tight and a **throating** will result on the pipe.

**Using a floor-mounted bending machine to make an offset**

1.  Decide where the offset needs to begin and mark this on
    the pipe. If the offset is from a fixed position and the angles
    are critical then a template will need to be taken but for
    most purposes these things are not critical, only the
    actual distance of the offset is (Figure 3.24).
2.  Following the same general procedure as for the 90° bend,
    bend the pipe to an approximate angle of 45°.

distance to centre of bend
from a fixed point
A

dimensions on
workshop drawings
are generally shown
from centre to
centre

to put a 90° bend on a piece of pipe to a given
dimension A, using a square set up pipe in machine so
that y (centre line of pipe) lines up with centre line
of former

dimensions to inside of bend line up to x,
inside of former

dimensions to outside of bend line up to z,
outside of former

*Figure 3.23* Use of a floor-mounted copper pipe bending
machine

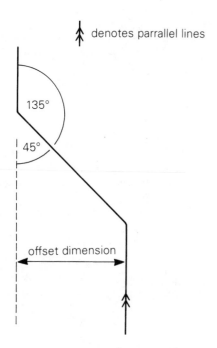

*Figure 3.24* Measuring offset

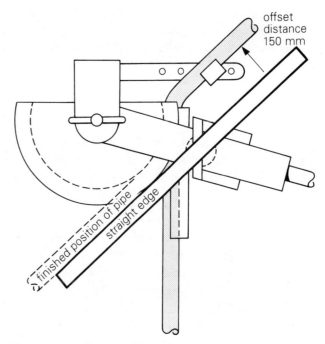

*Figure 3.25* Making offset

3. Pull the handle back, reduce the roller pressure slightly, remove the guide and loosen the pipe from the former, then twist the pipe round and replace the guide and roller to reposition the pipe as shown. You may have to reposition the pipe-stop. This is in effect reversing the pipe ready to bend or pull it back parallel to form the offset (Figure 3.25).

4. Using a straight edge as shown, move the pipe with the straight edge against the former and parallel to the pipe until the offset distance, say 150 mm, can be read in this position. It is easier to measure the return bend using *outside* bend measurements.

5. With the bending handle in position and the roller suitably tightened, sight along the pipe and the handle to check that they are in line, otherwise, when bent, both legs of the offset will be set out of line.

6. Bend the pipe until the return bend brings it back in line and parallel to the first leg of the bend, adding a couple of

degrees to allow for spring-back. Check with a straight edge before removing from the machine.

Smaller hand-held machines or bending 'pliers' are also available with fixed formers, roller and pipe-stop for use with 15 mm and 22 mm pipe (Figure 3.26). There is much less chance of pipes rippling and kinking with these although the actual bending requires more physical effort. Small 'mini-benders' are also available for use with microbore tubes of 8, 10 and 12 mm diameter (Figure 3.27).

## Bending springs

These are for use with small-bore light gauge copper pipes, lead waste pipes and certain types of thermoplastic (Figure 3.28). They are easy to use and can fit into a tool box or bag. Unlike bending machines which support the outside of the pipe during bending to prevent pipe deformation, most

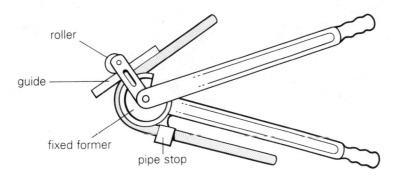

*Figure 3.26* Small hand-held bending pliers

bending springs support the inside of the pipe although external springs are available. Separate sized springs are needed for different sizes of pipe, 15 and 22 mm being the commonest sizes bent using this method.

Simply insert the spring in the pipe to the position where you want to bend, support yourself against a wall and carefully pull the bend using your knee as a former. It is a quick and easy way to make bends and offsets in small-bore copper pipe on small jobs without the fuss of detailed setting out. For more accurate work you can set out the bends using the same procedure as that shown for heat bending.

Copper pipes above 22 mm will need **annealing** before using a spring. The method of marking out the heat length is exactly the same as that shown for steel pipe (Figure 3.20 and 3.21). The only difference is that the pipe will remain soft even when cooled, so it is bent cold.

Some plastic pipes can be bent cold using a spring but generally for plastic pipes, such as PVC, spring bending must be done when hot. Unlike steel and copper pipes, it is hot air rather than a hot flame that must be used, otherwise the plastic will melt or burn. This can be done by directing the flame of a blowlamp through a steel tube (Figure 3.29). Bends in PVC pipes must be held in position until cooled in some form of **jig**, otherwise they will spring back (Figure 3.30). Setting out the heat length is the same as for copper and steel pipes.

Always take great care when removing bending springs. Bend a little tighter than the angle desired then pull back to the desired angle to loosen the spring. If it remains tight, twist gently in the direction the spring is coiled while

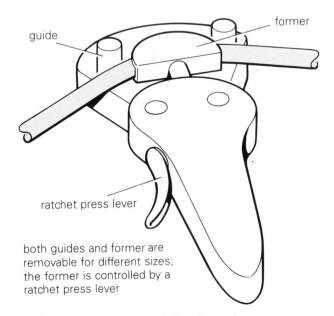

Figure 3.27   Micro-bore minibender

both guides and former are removable for different sizes; the former is controlled by a ratchet press lever

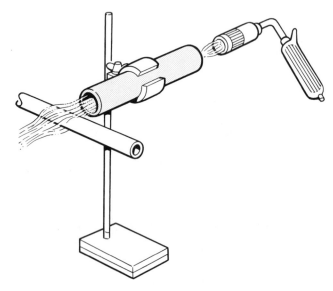

*Figure 3.29*   Forming a hot air jet to heat plastic pipes

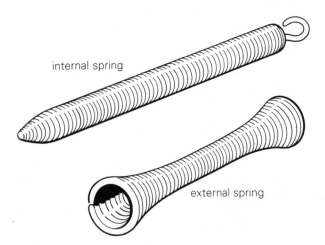

*Figure 3.28*   Bending springs

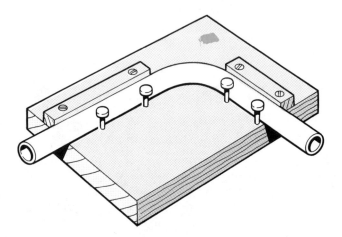

*Figure 3.30*   A simple jig for forming 90° bends

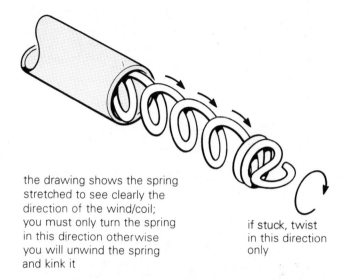

the drawing shows the spring stretched to see clearly the direction of the wind/coil; you must only turn the spring in this direction otherwise you will unwind the spring and kink it

if stuck, twist in this direction only

Figure 3.31   Bending spring showing direction of winding

pulling to prevent unwinding and kinking the spring (Figure 3.31). Both copper and plastic pipes can also be bent by sand loading.

Special bending springs are available for bending thin-walled lead waste pipes. They have different diameters from those used for copper and plastics and should not be used for anything other than lead pipe. The pipes are generally bent cold although sometimes a little gentle heat may be applied.

## Jointing tools

The formation of joints in various materials is an essential part of the installation and maintenance of pipework systems and components.

### Stocks and dies

These are used to form threads on the end of steel pipes prior to jointing. There are several types available but the commonest hand-held tools are the chaser die or non-receder stocks (Figure 3.32) and the drop-head block dies (Figure 3.33). The stock is the main body of the tool including the handle. This contains the dies which actually cut the thread. Chaser die stocks contain a set of four dies which will cut threads within a certain size range. These must be changed for other sizes.

#### Using chaser stocks and dies to cut a thread on steel pipe
1. Make sure the pipe is secure in the pipe-vice, cut the pipe square, and remove swarf and burrs.
2. Loosen the locking handle and rotate the scroll-plate on the stock until the 'change dies' marks line up and insert the correct size of die. The dies are numbered 1 to 4; these

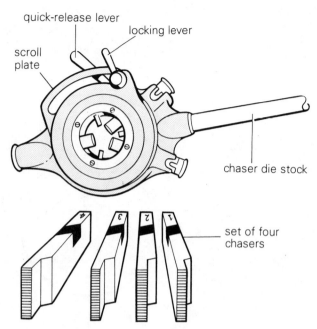

Figure 3.32   Non-receder stocks and dies

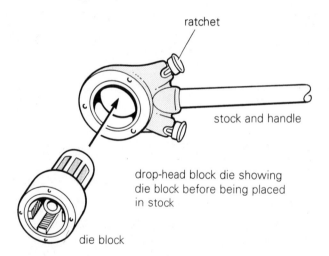

Figure 3.33   Drop-head block dies

must go into the corresponding holes on the stock (Figure 3.34).
3. Making sure the quick-release lever is in the closed position, rotate the scroll-plate until the correct pipe size lines up with the graduations marked on the stock. Close the locking handle and check to make sure that when you open the quick-release lever, the dies move outwards (Figure 3.35).

If you cannot do this, the dies must have been set with the lever in the open position. You will need to re-set the dies with this in the closed position, otherwise, when the thread is cut, you will have to unscrew the dies back along

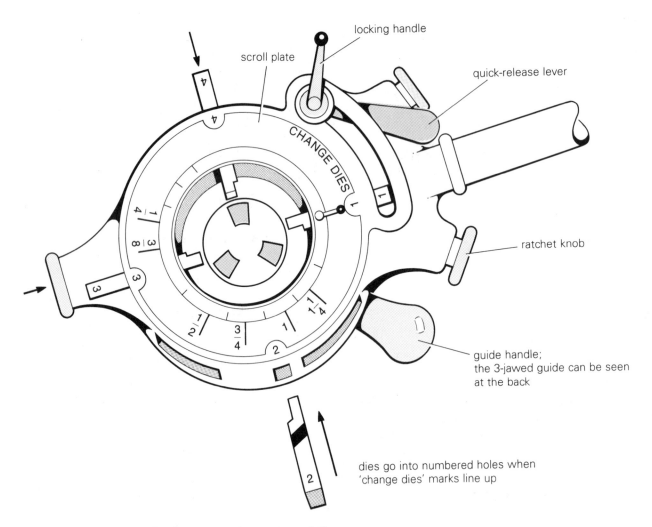

*Figure 3.34*   Changing dies in non-receder stocks and dies

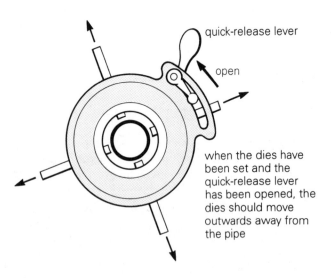

*Figure 3.35*   Quick release lever action

the thread. With the swarf still on the thread it is likely to damage it.

4. Place a **drip tray** on the floor under the end of the pipe to catch oil and swarf, apply some cutting paste or oil to the pipe and place the stocks on the pipe, guide side first, until the dies locate with the end of the pipe. Close the guide handle to centre the stocks on the pipe.

5. Set the **ratchet** so that the dies only rotate on the downward turning action, and apply pressure to the end of the stock on the pipe with one hand, while slowly turning the handle with your other hand. Continue to do this for a few strokes until you can see the thread clearly forming. At this stage you can release the end pressure and concentrate with two hands on the handle.

6. The thread is finished when the end of the dies or chasers are level with the end of the pipe (Figure 3.36).

7. When the thread is completed, turn the handle one last time while at the same time opening the quick-release lever. This action helps to remove the swarf and enables

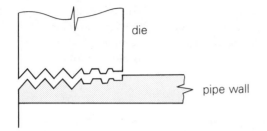

*Figure 3.36*   Die cutting thread

the stocks and dies to be removed by sliding them off over the thread when the guide handle is loosened. Once removed, any remaining swarf can be removed by striking the pipe above the thread hard with a hammer which will cause it to drop off. Never run your finger over the thread to remove swarf.

The dies in drop-head block dies are fixed to cut one specific size only; different blocks are needed for different sizes of pipe. There is no adjustment and no quick-release lever. They must be unscrewed back along the cut thread. They are only really useful for smaller sizes of pipe or for cutting threads on bars, bolts and conduits.

Threads can be formed either on site or in the workshop; the pipes are then screwed into factory made fittings to make the joint. There are various types of thread but the **British Standard Pipe Thread (BSPT)** is widely used. The formed thread is tapered but the thread in the fittings may be

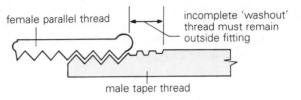

*Figure 3.37*   Parallel thread fitting on to a taper thread

parallel or tapered. Both will give a good joint when they are screwed together (Figure 3.37).

The front of the dies will only cut an incomplete thread to enable the dies to mount the pipe at the start. As the dies move along, the full and complete thread is cut by the rest of the die. Because there will always be an incomplete section at the end of any thread, you must make sure that this **washout** section of thread remains outside the fitting when the joint is made otherwise it may result in a leak. Before screwing the joints on the pipe, jointing tape or hemp and paste are applied to the thread. The method chosen will depend on what the pipeline is to be used for (see Chapter 4, Table 4.3).

## Threading machines

There are various types available but the most popular are the multipurpose machines that also include a pipe cutter, reamer and automatic oiler (Figure 3.38). They have chaser dies that are set in the same way as the hand stocks and dies. Bolt and nipple threading attachments are available.

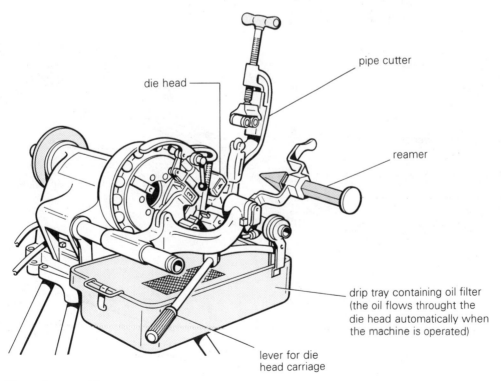

*Figure 3.38*   Threading machine

Unlike hand-operated stocks and dies, the actual pipe itself rotates in the machine and the dies are brought into contact with the pipe using a lever which supports the die-head carriage. Once the thread starts to cut, the pressure is taken off until the thread is fully cut.

Threading machines can cut threads on pipes from 6 mm diameter up to 150 mm diameter. The power is foot operated and they can cut right or left-hand threads. Left-hand threads are normally used on the connecting fittings to combustible gas cylinders and equipment and are identified by notches on the union nuts.

Because the pipe rotates, always position the machine so that the end of the rotating pipe is not causing a hazard.

## Pipe wrenches

These include some of the commonest tools associated with the plumber. They are used for tightening or loosening fittings and pipes. As with many tools used in plumbing they are often referred to by the manufacturer's name.

### Stilson pipe wrench

This is a general purpose pipe wrench with adjustable jaws (Figure 3.39). Stilsons are available in different sizes to suit a range of pipe sizes up to 150 mm. You should only use the size of wrench recommended for the size of pipe (Table 3.1).

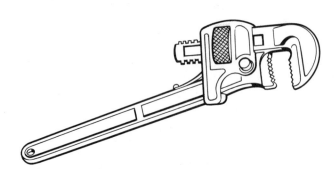

Figure 3.39   Stilson pipe wrench

Table 3.1 Recommended pipe wrench size for size of pipe

| Pipe size | | Wrench size | |
|---|---|---|---|
| (mm) | (inches) | (mm) | (inches) |
| 27 | 3/4 | 200 | 8 |
| 34 | 1 | 250 | 10 |
| 40 | 1 1/4 | 300 | 12 |
| 49 | 1 1/2 | 350 | 14 |
| 60 | 2 | 450 | 18 |
| 76 | 2 1/2 | 600 | 24 |
| 102 | 3 1/2 | 900 | 36 |
| 142 | 5 | 1200 | 48 |

Their main use is for tightening fittings on to pipes at low-level. If used on the pipe itself it may deform the pipe. Care should be taken to keep the teeth free from paste and swarf otherwise they will not grip and the tool will slip off.

Never try to extend the handle for extra leverage as this may damage the fitting or pipe.

### Chain wrench

Chain wrenches or 'chain dogs' as they are often known are used for tightening pipes into fittings (Figure 3.40). Because the chain grips right around the pipe, gripping it against the teeth of the wrench, there is less chance of the pipe becoming deformed. These are suitable for high-level work because they are less likely to slip off. They are available in a range of sizes. Keep teeth clean and regularly check for loose chain links.

### Footprint pipe wrench

This adjustable pipe wrench is available in different sizes but is normally only used on small diameter pipework and fittings (Figure 3.41).

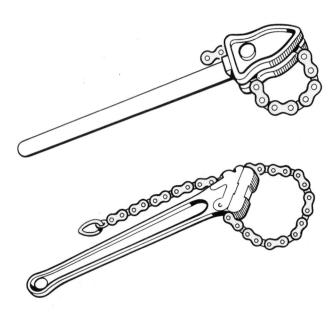

Figure 3.40   Chain wrench or chain dogs

Figure 3.41   Footprint pipe wrench

## Universal pliers

These are also known as gland pliers or water pump pliers. They are more of a general purpose tool for gripping or tightening small diameter fittings. They are adjustable but tend to slip if too much leverage is applied (Figure 3.42).

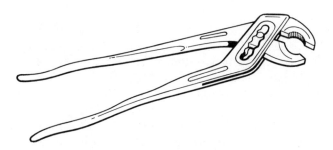

*Figure 3.42* Universal multi-position pipe wrench

## Spanners

These are used for tightening or loosening nuts on pipe fittings and nuts and bolt of all sizes. There are three main types used by the plumber: adjustable spanner; open-ended fixed spanner; ring spanner (Figure 3.43). Adjustable spanners are only adjustable over a small range and are

therefore available in a range of sizes. A large range of fixed spanners are also available. Although available for large diameter pipe sizes, in practice most plumbers only use these spanners for light work which includes the jointing of compression fittings on copper pipe. Ring spanners are used mainly for tightening up nuts and bolts. Because they fit around the whole nut or bolt-head they are less likely to slip off.

## Swaging tools

These are used to open out pipe ends to form sockets or lips on copper or plastic pipes prior to jointing. The simplest type consists of a circular steel bar with a graduated diameter to form sockets for capillary joints on copper pipe or solvent-cemented joints on plastic pipe (Figure 3.44). Other steel swaging tools have a cone-shaped head to form a lip for use with manipulative-type compression fittings on copper or plastic pipes (Figure 3.45). Both of these usually require the pipe to be heated up or annealed. Some tools are available with interchangeable heads that are lever operated to form sockets on light-gauge copper tube for capillary jointing (Figure 3.46).

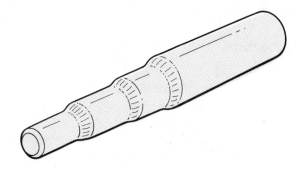

*Figure 3.44* Graduated head swaging tool

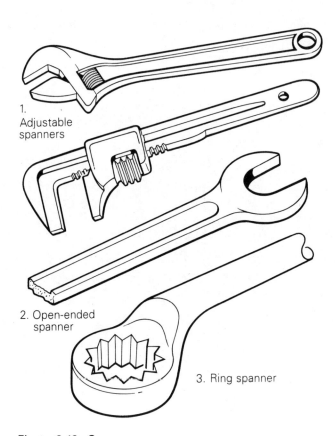

1. Adjustable spanners

2. Open-ended spanner

3. Ring spanner

*Figure 3.43* Spanners

*Figure 3.45* Cone-headed swaging tool

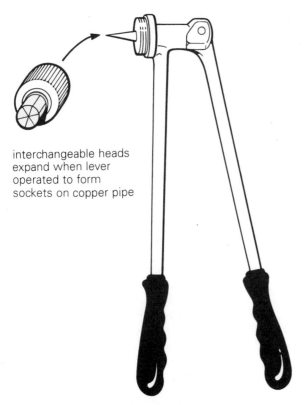

interchangeable heads
expand when lever
operated to form
sockets on copper pipe

*Figure 3.46*  Lever-operated pipe expander

## Caulking tools

These tools are used mainly in the jointing of cast-iron pipes.
They consist of a range of cranked pieces of steel which are
used with a lump hammer to pack jointing yarn into the
sockets of cast-iron pipes (Figure 3.47). They are then used to
compress or **caulk** lead down into the joint which may have
been poured in a molten state and allowed to set, or was
placed in the joint as fine lead 'wool'. To prevent the molten
solder escaping during pouring into horizontal joints, an
asbestos-based rope or 'squirrel's tail' is wrapped around the
joint.

## Blowlamps

The most popular blowlamps are the petrol blowlamp, the
small liquid petroleum gas (LPG) cylinder and torch, and
the medium-sized LPG bottle and torch (Figure 3.48). They
are used as a heat source for a range of plumbing work,
although their main use is for soldering work. Petrol
blowlamps are small and portable but require pre-heating
before use.

Small LPG cylinders, usually containing butane gas, are
portable but are only suitable for jobs requiring a small
flame. The cylinders are not reusable and must be carefully
discarded when empty. A good supply of refills is needed if
you are doing a lot of work. Medium-sized LPG bottles and
torches, containing butane or propane gas, are the most
versatile of all the blowlamps. Interchangeable torch
nozzles can give a range of flame sizes to suit most needs.
The popular size of bottle contains 4.5 kg of LPG which is
many times more than the smaller cylinders contain. They
can also be refilled but only with *the same gas*. Although
butane and propane are similar gases they operate at
different pressures and need to have different pressure
regulators or governors fixed to the outlet valve. All hoses
must be synthetic rubber or reinforced canvas because LPG
will attack natural rubber. Hoses must be kept as short as
possible and should be secured with special hose clips.

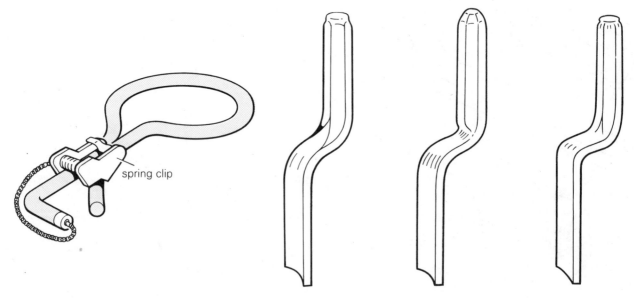

spring clip

*Figure 3.47*  Caulking tools and squirrel-tail jointing sleeve

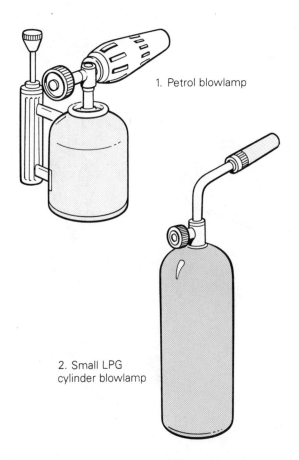

1. Petrol blowlamp

2. Small LPG cylinder blowlamp

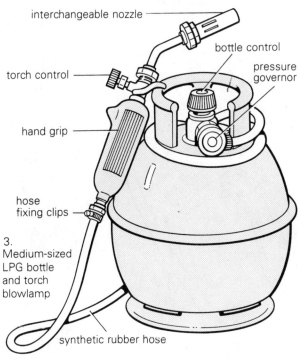

interchangeable nozzle

torch control

hand grip

hose fixing clips

3. Medium-sized LPG bottle and torch blowlamp

bottle control

pressure governor

synthetic rubber hose

*Figure 3.48*  **Blowlamps**

**Care of LPG cylinders**

- Check all hoses and clips regularly for signs of wear.
- All union nuts on LPG equipment have left-handed threads and are identified with a cut notch on the nut (Figure 3.49).
- When soldering or 'sweating' capillary fittings, always make sure that any combustible surroundings are protected from the flames using a non-combustible mat.
- Always have a suitable small fire-extinguisher or a bucket of sand available when using a blowlamp.
- Do not subject LPG cylinders to heat and always keep them upright in use.

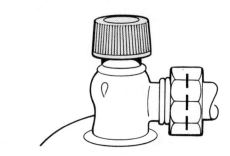

*Figure 3.49*  LPG union nuts

## Lead pipework tools

The use of lead pipe to carry water supplies has dropped over recent years due to the risks associated with lead poisoning, particularly in very acidic or **plumbo-solvent** waters. Lead soil and waste pipes are also used less these days due to the widespread use of plastics which are cheaper and quicker to install. It is still necessary, however, for the plumber to be able to maintain and joint existing services. The tools are shown in Figure 3.50.

**Rasp**  This rough file is used to shape the end of lead pipes prior to jointing.

**Shavehook**  The triangular or heart-shaped blade on this tool is used to 'shave' the surface off lead pipe to clean it prior to jointing.

**Tanpin or turnpin**  This cone-shaped wooden or plastic tool is inserted in the end of the pipe and struck with a hammer or mallet to open out the end of the pipe in order to form a lipped socket to receive the spigot end of a pipe prior to jointing.

**Auger**  Similar to a corkscrew, this tool is used to cut a hole in lead pipe so that a branch joint can be made.

**Bentpin or bending bolt**  This crank-shaped piece of steel is the tool used, with a hammer, to open out the hole made with an auger so that it is large enough to receive a branch pipe.

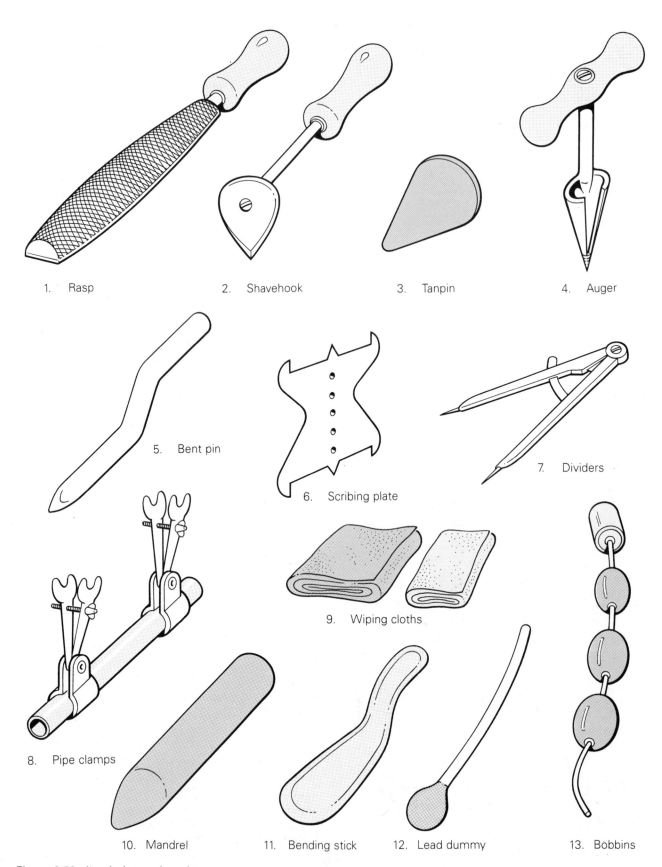

1.  Rasp

2.  Shavehook

3.  Tanpin

4.  Auger

5.  Bent pin

6.  Scribing plate

7.  Dividers

8.  Pipe clamps

9.  Wiping cloths

10.  Mandrel

11.  Bending stick

12.  Lead dummy

13.  Bobbins

*Figure 3.50*  **Lead pipework tools**

**Scribing plate and dividers** These are used when making branch joints to mark out the correct size of joint area to clean.

**Pipeclamps** These hold the pipework in position during jointing. They are adjustable and can hold pipes in a range of positions. Various types are available for use with both copper and lead pipe.

**Wiping cloth** This is a piece of thick cloth used to shape the 'wiped' molten solder joint. They are usually made from cotton and flax folded together with a piece of cardboard or thin sheet metal inside to help form the shape of the finished joint. Before use, they are usually soaked in tallow to provide a non-stick surface. They are available in different sizes to suit joints on different sizes of pipe, with branch joints requiring smaller cloths than straight joints.

**Mandrel** These are only used with thin-walled waste and soil pipes. Because the walls are thin, they often get deformed. Mandrels are solid wooden cylinders that are inserted into the pipe to help remove the dents and bumps. As the mandrel is inserted into the pipe the bumps are dressed out against the mandrel using a flat dresser or bending stick.

**Bending stick** Made of wood or plastic, this tool is used with bobbins or a mandrel when removing dents in thin-walled soil or waste pipes when forming bends.

**Lead dummy** This is simply an oval-shaped lead head on a bent steel rod which is used to help dress out dents and kinks on the inside of large diameter soil pipes during bending. The pipe is bent a little at a time – each time the kinks formed on the inside are knocked out by resting the handle of the dummy on a piece of wood which acts as a **fulcrum**, then with a repeated lever action the head inside the pipe will knock out the kinks.

**Bobbins** These are used to restore the internal shape of large diameter waste and soil pipes during the bending process. After a lead dummy has been used to remove the kinks, the true bore of the pipe can be restored by pulling a set of bobbins through the pipe. A set of bobbins consists of several wooden 'beads' connected together with a strong cord to pull them through the pipe, with a steel one at the rear to provide 'pushing' force. Bobbins are available in a range of sizes to suit the pipe diameter.

# Fixing and fastening tools

The tools used for fixing and installing include many of the general tools used by the plumber. Also included at the end of this section are the tools used for sheet roof work.

## Spirit levels and plumb bobs

These are used for setting out horizontal or vertical pipework runs so that when clips or brackets are fixed they will be horizontally level or vertically plumb. They are also used to level appliances and components during installation. Both large and short 'boat' levels are available, usually consisting of two small sealed clear glass tubes containing spirit set in a wooden or aluminium alloy frame (Figure 3.51). A bubble of air in the tube will fall between two marks on the tube when it is level or plumb, depending on which bubble is read. Very small 'utility' levels are also available.

A **plumb bob** is simply a lead or steel weight tied to a length of strong cord or string used to set out vertical pipe runs. Rub the string with chalk, then fix the string at the high point of the run by wrapping it round a nail, leaving the weighted end

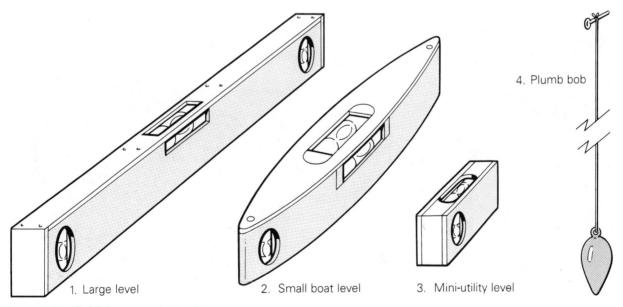

4. Plumb bob

1. Large level     2. Small boat level     3. Mini-utility level

*Figure 3.51* Spirit levels and plumb bobs

hanging free near the bottom of the run. When the string and weight are still, hold the bottom of the string tight against the wall and pull the string above away from the wall so that it flicks back and leaves a perfectly plumb chalk line on the wall to use as your guide.

## Drills

These are used to make holes in metals, plastics, wood and masonry. They consist of the drill bit, which actually makes the hole, and the drill itself which provides the action to turn the drill bit. There are two types of drill bit commonly used by the plumber, the twist drill for metals and plastics and the masonry drill for masonry and brick work (Figure 3.52).

There are many types and sizes of twist drill available, all made of steel with varying amounts of carbon and alloy added, such as tungsten, chromium and vanadium. When operated at high temperatures with an electric drill, some of the higher carbon content twist drill bits will become blunt unless lubricant is added. You need to specify high-speed drills for such jobs.

Masonry drills can be identified by their tungsten carbide tips, which are very hard-wearing but only suitable for drilling brick, stone, ceramic tiles and concrete.

Both twist drills and masonry drills can be fitted in either mains electric, rechargeable battery or hand-powered machines (Figure 3.53).

When drilling holes through wood, a joiner's brace and wood bit, or a special high speed wood bit for use with an electric drill, can be used (Figure 3.54).

> Wherever possible, low-voltage (110 volt) power equipment should be used on-site to cut the risk of accidents. Transformers are available to step-down voltages but advice must be sought from your electrical equipment distributor.

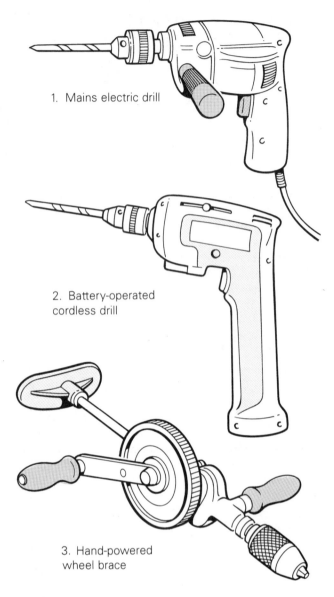

1. Mains electric drill

2. Battery-operated cordless drill

3. Hand-powered wheel brace

*Figure 3.53*  Drills

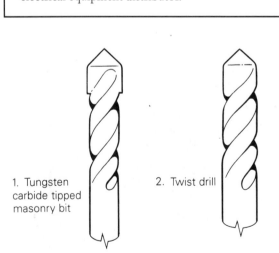

1. Tungsten carbide tipped masonry bit

2. Twist drill

*Figure 3.52*  Drill bits

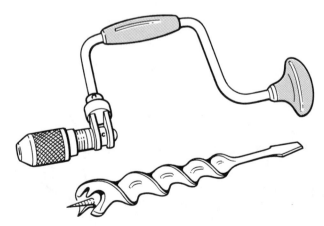

*Figure 3.54*  Joiner's brace and wood bit

## Centre punch

Before drilling any hole, a centre-punch should be used to make an indentation in the material that will prevent the drill from slipping (Figure 3.55).

## Rawl-drill and star drill

These are more like chisels than drills and are only used on masonry (Figure 3.56). They are struck repeatedly with a hammer while constantly turning them. Long channels or 'flutes' in the chisels allow the cut particles of masonry to be released as the operation proceeds. They are available in different sizes; the rawl-drill has interchangeable bits. They are small, convenient and only require hand power. Always wear goggles when using this type of drill.

Figure 3.55   Centre punch

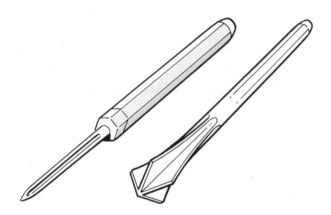

Figure 3.56   Rawl-drill and star drill

## Screwdrivers

There are many types available for either slotted screws or 'Philips' cross-slot screws (Figure 3.57). It is essential to choose the right size of screwdriver to fit the screw. If the screwdriver head is too small for the slot, it may damage the slot making it difficult to screw in or remove. Use of the wrong sized screwdriver may also cause it to slip off the screw causing an accident or damage to the fixing surface.

## Bradawl

This is used in a similar way to the centre-punch but for making guide holes for fixing screws into timber. It is like a very small screwdriver (Figure 3.58).

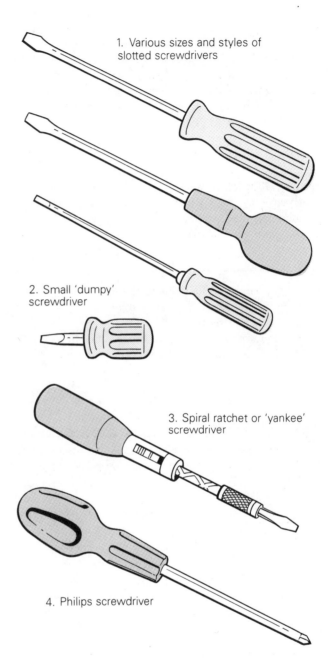

1. Various sizes and styles of slotted screwdrivers

2. Small 'dumpy' screwdriver

3. Spiral ratchet or 'yankee' screwdriver

4. Philips screwdriver

Figure 3.57   Screwdrivers

Figure 3.58   Bradawl

## Ballistic fixing gun

As an alternative to using drills and screwdrivers for fixing pipe supports and clips, you can use ballistic tools such as the Hilti-gun to 'shoot' fixings into a range of materials such as brick, wood and steel. You put threaded steel pins into a chamber which is revealed when the barrel is opened and put a small cartridge, which provides an explosive charge, into the firing chamber. The cartridges are colour coded, each colour representing a different strength depending on the material to which you are fixing. For safety reasons, the gun can only be operated when the flat metal collar surrounding the barrel is pressed against the material and further pressure on a spring enables the trigger to be pulled (Figure 3.59).

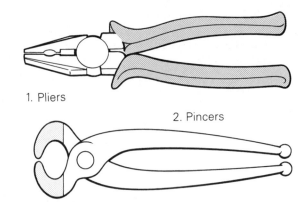

1. Pliers

2. Pincers

*Figure 3.60*   Pliers and pincers

---

**Safety precautions for ballistic tools**
- Before use, expert instruction from the supplier should be given.
- Always wear goggles when using ballistic tools.
- Always use the correct colour-coded cartridge.

---

## Pliers and pincers

These are general purpose gripping tools with a scissor/lever action to grip small objects. Pincers are used to grip and remove nails and tacks (Figure 3.60).

## Chisels

Plumbers need a variety of chisels, and a selection are shown in Figure 3.61. Cold chisels are used for cutting holes through concrete, stone and brickwork. They are available in different sizes, but a 250 mm long, 25 mm diameter chisel is a useful size for most plumbing work. They are made from high

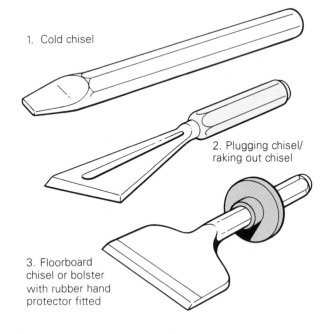

1. Cold chisel

2. Plugging chisel/ raking out chisel

3. Floorboard chisel or bolster with rubber hand protector fitted

*Figure 3.61*   Chisels

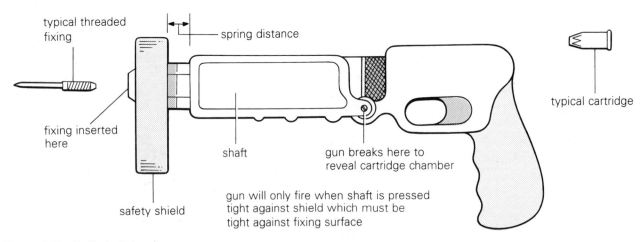

typical threaded fixing

spring distance

fixing inserted here

safety shield

shaft

gun breaks here to reveal cartridge chamber

gun will only fire when shaft is pressed tight against shield which must be tight against fixing surface

typical cartridge

*Figure 3.59*   Ballistic fixing gun

carbon steel with hardened cutting edges capable of cutting cold metal, which gives them their name.

Raking-out or plugging chisels have a wedge-shaped cutting edge used for raking out mortar joints between blockwork and brickwork. Floorboard chisels have a wide, thin blade which is used to cut through the tongues on timber tongue and grooved floorboards so that the boards can be lifted.

Always wear goggles when chiselling masonry and make sure the striking head of the chisel is in good condition with no sharp 'mushroom' edges. Wherever possible, use chisels with rubber hand protectors.

## Hammers

Various types of hammer are available. Some are for specialist use, such as those used for sheet metalwork. The type chosen will depend on its use but the general purpose hammers used by plumbers consist of a steel head mounted on a wooden shaft. They are classified according to the shape and weight of the head. The commonest used by the plumber are the straight-pein, the ball-pein and the lump hammer (Figure 3.62). Claw hammers, often with a steel shaft, are also popular, especially when lifting timber floorboards.

The head should be securely wedged on the shaft of the hammer before use.

## Basin wrench

These are mainly used in the fixing of sanitary appliances, such as baths, basins and sinks. They are specially designed to tighten nuts in awkward places on these appliances. Some are similar to a spanner but with the jaws set at a right-angle to the handle. There are two common types available, one with fixed jaws the other with adjustable jaws (Figure 3.63).

## Taps and tapwrench

These are used for forming **female threads** in holes in steel sheet or bars to receive threaded **bolts** or **set screws**. Holes should be made with a drill one size smaller than the size of the thread needed, then the tap will be able to cut out the thread (Figure 3.64).

Taps are classified according to bolt thread sizes. Taps come in sets of two or three, each one being used in turn to complete the full thread. The tapered tap is used first, followed by the second cut tap (optional) and finally the plug tap. Taps are rotated using an adjustable tap wrench.

Plumbers often use taps to repair existing but damaged threads in appliances and components.

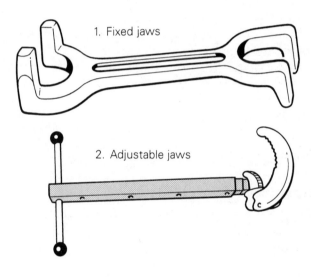

1. Fixed jaws

2. Adjustable jaws

*Figure 3.63*  Basin wrenches

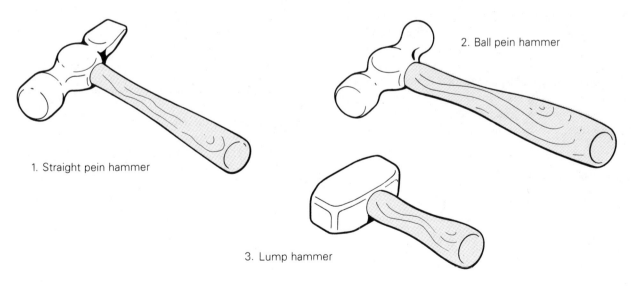

1. Straight pein hammer

2. Ball pein hammer

3. Lump hammer

*Figure 3.62*  Hammers

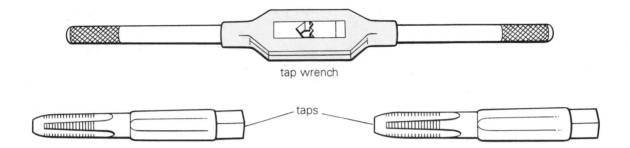

*Figure 3.64*  Taps and tapwrench

## Tap reseating tool

This tool has nothing to do with the taps used for forming female threads. It is used to machine down the seating in screw-down taps when they become worn or when scale deposits build up.

Tap reseating tools can fit a range of tap sizes, and models are available to reseat ball-valve seatings. It is a cheaper alternative to replacing worn taps. They are quick and easy to use. The tap mechanism is unscrewed from the main body, without taking the tap out of the appliance, and the tool is screwed into the tap body. The cutting surface is rotated by a wheel knob at the top of the tool (Figure 3.65).

## Testing pump

This is used to check pressure pipework systems and appliances for leaks. It consists of a steel cistern for holding up to 12 litres of water, a lever-operated pump, flexible rubber pipework and couplings with flow valves, and a pressure gauge (Figure 3.66).

To check for leaks, fill the system or appliance with water then connect to the pump. Fill the pump cistern with water, open the outlet valve (a), close the drain valve (b) and operate the pump until the desired pressure shows on the gauge (up to a maximum of 25 bars on the smaller models), then close the outlet valve.

The system is sound if no pressure drop shows on the gauge for a specified period. A small drop in pressure is acceptable in the first few minutes to account for absorption.

When filling, care must be taken to let all air out of the system.

## Sheet roofing tools

Most sheet roofing work done by the plumber involves the laying, fabrication and fixing of sheet metal. These metals include zinc, aluminum, lead, copper and steel. In addition, non-metallic bitumen-bonded fibre sheet is also sometimes used. The type of sheet used depends on cost, availability and the local environment but the tools used are common to most and are shown in Figure 3.67.

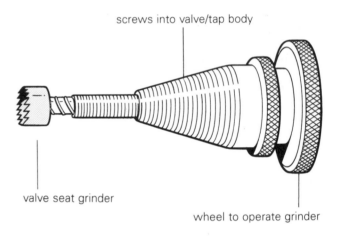

*Figure 3.65*  Tap reseating tool

**Flat dresser**  This tool, made from boxwood or plastic, is used to dress the material down flat on to the fixing surface. It is also used to dress out dents and bumps.

**Bossing stick**  Also made from boxwood or plastic this is used for working or bossing metal into various shapes. For example, working a piece of metal to fit around an external or internal corner.

**Bossing mallet**  This is used for general purpose bossing and working of sheet metal. The oval-shaped head is often used to support metal when using a bossing stick. Bossing mallets generally have a boxwood head and a cane shaft.

**Tinsmith's mallet**  This mallet has a cylindrical head with flat ends, and is used to strike other tools or for general dressing work on copper, aluminum or zinc.

**Engineer's hammer**  Special hammers with chrome or carbon steel heads for work with 'hard' metals.

**Rubber and soft-faced hammers**  Special hammers for use where minimum marking of metal or components is required.

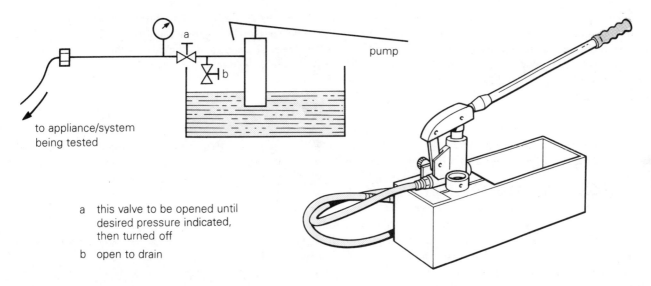

a   this valve to be opened until
    desired pressure indicated,
    then turned off

b   open to drain

*Figure 3.66*   Water pressure testing pump

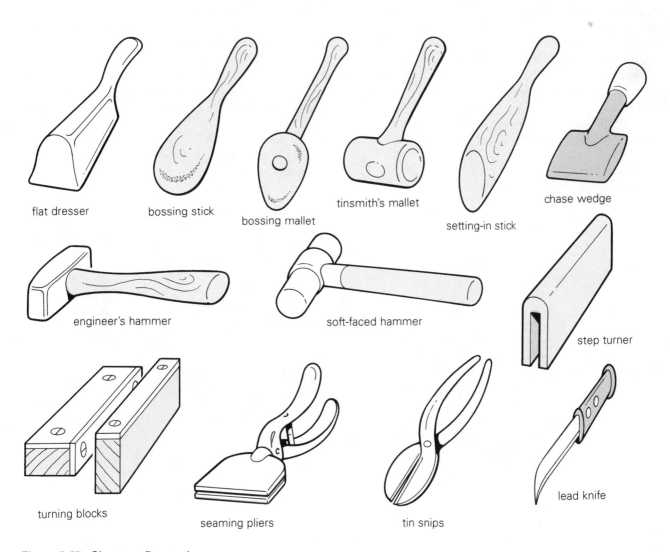

*Figure 3.67*   Sheet roofing tools

**Chase wedge**   This is used to drive or chase in corners, creases and angles in difficult or restricted areas where other tools would be difficult to use. Made from wood with a brass ferrule on the striking end to prevent damage.

**Setting-in stick**   This is used for the same job as the chase wedge but in large open areas where access is easy. It can be used on its own or struck with a mallet.

**Step turner**   A simple tool made of wood with a groove cut into it. The edge of the metal is put into the groove and bent to form a right-angle. Useful for forming the building-in edge on flashings.

**Turning blocks**   There are several types made from wood, wrought iron or steel. The wooden ones have metal edges to prevent wearing and provide an accurate angle. They are simply blocks of various sizes used to dress the edges of metal over when making welts. Some have sloping edges for turning down the ends of standing seams.

**Tinsnips**   There are used for cutting all types of sheet metal. They are available with straight or curved blades.

**Leadknife**   With large sheets of lead it is often easier and quicker to cut with a knife than with tinsnips. Using a straight edge, the knife is first used to score the lead two or three times; the lead is then ripped along the scored line.

Great care must be taken when using a leadknife. Always use a deep straight edge to act as a guide and hold it down securely.

**Seaming pliers**   These are very wide jawed pliers used for turning and closing welts and seams on copper, aluminium, zinc and steel.

**Soldering irons**   These are used as a heat source when soldering seams and welts on sheet metal. They consist of a solid copper head fixed to a steel rod supported by a wooden handle. The bit is heated up by a blowlamp or in a small furnace. The copper bit is then used to melt the solder on to the seam and to run along it to seal the seam (Figure 3.68).

### CHECK YOUR UNDERSTANDING

● A good job is only possible if you choose the correct tool and use it in the way it was designed to be used.

● When measuring, if in doubt ... measure twice ... cut once!

● Vices to hold pipework should support the pipe wall all the way around its circumference, otherwise the pipe wall will deform.

● Hacksaws cut on the forward stroke so their blades must be fixed with the teeth facing forwards.

● After cutting pipes always remove swarf and burrs with a file or reamer.

● When using pipe benders always bend a little more than you want to allow for spring-back.

● When heat or spring bending use a minimum radius of 4 times the outside diameter of the pipe.

● The quick-release lever on chaser stocks and dies must be in the closed position when setting the dies.

● Remove swarf and turnings from freshly cut threads by banging the pipe with a hammer. *Do not run your fingers over the thread.*

● Dies cut male threads on pipes and taps cut female threads inside holes or fittings.

● Never extend the handle on pipe wrenches – it may damage the pipe, fitting and wrench.

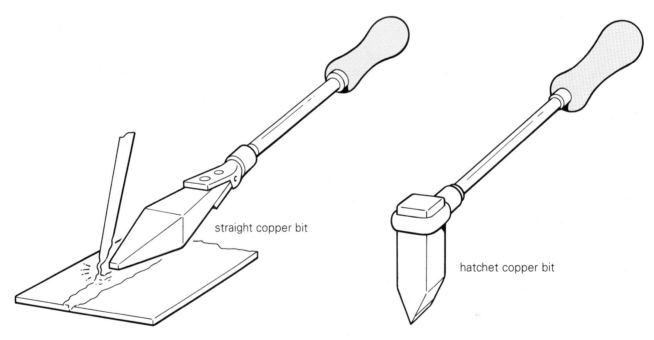

straight copper bit

hatchet copper bit

*Figure 3.68*   Soldering irons

● Only use recommended clips and couplings for assembling LPG torches and hoses. Remember that all threads are left-handed on LPG equipment. After assembly, check for leaks with soapy water.

● Protect your eyes with safety goggles when chiselling brickwork or masonry.

● Use low-voltage power tools wherever possible.

● Always use the correct size of screwdriver for the screw.

## REVISION EXERCISES AND QUESTIONS

Answer questions 1 to 5 by selecting one of the four options given.

1  You are asked to cut a piece of pipe so that it is half a metre long. How many millimetres will this be?
   i)   0.5 mm
   ii)  5 mm
   ii)  50 mm
   iv)  500 mm

2  Why should you apply the pressure gradually when using pipe cutters on steel or copper pipe?
   i)   to prevent excessive burrs
   ii)  to prevent excessive throating
   iii) to prevent excessive swarf
   iv)  to prevent excessive kinking

3  To allow for spring-back when using a bending machine you must:
   i)   bend a couple of degrees more than the angle needed
   ii)  keep the bleed valve closed
   iii) bend a couple of degrees less than the angle needed
   iv)  keep the bleed valve open

4  Why must you set chaser dies with the quick-release lever closed?
   i)   so that the thread is cut quicker

   ii)  so that after threading you can remove the dies without unscrewing
   iii) so that the thread is cut more accurately
   iv)  so that after threading the dies will not need resetting

5  Which of the drills shown is suitable for masonry?

   i)              ii)              iii)              iv)

6  Describe the key points to be observed when using a hacksaw.

7  Why is it necessary to remove the burrs after cutting steel pipes and how would you do this?

8  Describe the step-by-step process of working out the heat length for a 90° bend on a piece of 25 mm diameter steel pipe.

9  Which tool should be used to screw a piece of steel pipe into a fitting at high level? Give reasons for your choice.

10 Name three tools used when forming a hole in lead pipe to receive a branch.

11 Describe how to mark a vertical/perpendicular line on a wall for clip fixing without the aid of a spirit level.

12 Why is it necessary to wear goggles when drilling holes into masonry?

13 Draw the tool used for tightening-up fittings in difficult places when fixing sanitary appliances like baths and basins.

14 What tools are used to form a thread in a hole drilled into a piece of steel and what is this type of thread called?

15 Describe what a setting-in stick is used for and name an alternative tool used for the same job.

# Materials and components

## Introduction

As a plumber you will use many different kinds of material and they will come in a variety of forms. Many will be metals, however, and most of these will be in the form of pipes and fittings, taps and valves. Increasingly, because of their ease of use and relatively low cost, synthetic plastics have also become one of the plumber's favoured materials. Other non-metallic materials, such as ceramics, are also important in plumbing.

This chapter will introduce you to all of the common plumbing materials that you are likely to come across, both metals and non-metals. It also includes a section on taps, valves and other flow-control fittings.

Before looking at the different materials it will be necessary to consider some of the different properties they have in order to understand their use. This is particularly important for metals. Many metals are unsuitable for plumbing in their natural state and must be combined with other elements to form alloys which will give the desired properties.

## Properties of metals

**Brittleness**  Brittle metals are liable to fracture or break when a load is applied. They include high carbon steels, such as cast iron.

**Coefficient of linear expansion**  This is a figure which indicates the amount a material will expand when heated by 1°C. Always make allowances when installing materials with a high coefficient of linear expansion if they are going to be subjected to high temperature changes.

**Colour**  This relates to the visual appearance of a material and is important for identification purposes.

**Creep**  This is where a heavy material will slowly **flow**, usually under its own load, when installed in certain situations. It is similar to plasticity. Lead has this tendency.

**Density**  This is the weight or mass per unit volume measured in kilograms per cubic metre ($kg/m^3$).

**Ductility**  This is the degree to which a metal can be stretched. Most non-ferrous metals have a high ductility, including copper, lead and aluminium.

**Durability**  This describes a metal's ability to withstand corrosion and its ability to remain strong and sound for a long time.

**Elasticity**  This describes the ability of a metal to go back to its original shape after being distorted under a load. It is the opposite of plastic.

**Fatigue**  This is the point when a metal fails or fractures when subjected to variations in the direction of applied pressure. The constant expansion and contraction of metals subject to temperature changes can cause this.

**Hardness**  This is the degree to which a metal can withstand scratching or indentation. High carbon steels, such as cutting tools, are usually very hard.

**Malleability**  This describes the ability of a metal to be worked or rolled into thin sheet without splitting or cracking. It also allows metals to be worked into different shapes without springing back or fracturing. Malleability will increase with many metals if they are heated up or annealed.

**Melting point**  This is the temperature at which a metal changes from a solid into a liquid. It is an important consideration when soldering or welding.

**Plasticity**  This is the opposite of elasticity. If a plastic material is deformed under load it will stay deformed even when the load is removed.

**Specific gravity**  This is a number which denotes the weight of a material in relation to water. Water has a specific gravity of 1, lead has a specific gravity of 11.3; this means lead is 11.3 times heavier than water.

**Tenacity**  This is the property that describes the ability to withstand compression and fracture when opposite pulling forces are applied at each end along the length of a metal.

**Thermal conductivity**  This is the degree to which a material will transmit heat by conduction. Copper has a high thermal conductivity. Materials with poor thermal conductivity often make good insulators.

**Work hardening and annealing**   During bossing, bending or hammering, some metals will eventually become hard and difficult to work. This is because the molecular structure of the material alters during such working. It may be desirable to harden some steels, but often it is undesirable, and to make the metal workable again it must be heated up or annealed. Copper is annealed by heating it up to a 'cherry red' colour, aluminium can be annealed by heating it until the red end of a match drawn across the surface leaves a black mark.

# Iron and steel

Iron and steel are amongst the commonest materials used by the plumber. Various types are available depending upon the properties required.

## Cast iron

Cast iron is iron with a relatively high carbon content that also contains manganese, phosphorus, silicon and sulphur. Grey in colour, it is very durable and hard, but also brittle. Because of its fluidity when molten it can be cast into intricate shapes. It is used for the manufacture of baths, boilers, cisterns, pipes and tanks. Cast-iron pipe for underground water mains is usually spun cast iron, which is stronger than the vertically cast type used for most other pipes.

Cast-iron pipes are used for water mains and both above and below ground drainage. Underground water mains and underground drainage pipes are heavier gauge than above ground drainage pipes, with rainwater pipes being the lightest gauge. Most are available with a bitumen-based coating to protect against corrosion.

Pipes are available in various standard lengths and in diameters from 50 mm up to 600 mm, with either spigot and socket or plain ends. They can be jointed using rigid caulked lead joints, flexible rubber sealing rings in sockets or compression-type mechanical joints, depending on their use (Figure 4.1).

## Malleable iron

Malleable iron contains similar elements to cast iron but in different quantities. Black/grey in colour, the strength and ductility of this metal results from the long and carefully regulated heat treatment it is given. It is used for threaded fittings for steel pipe (Figure 4.4).

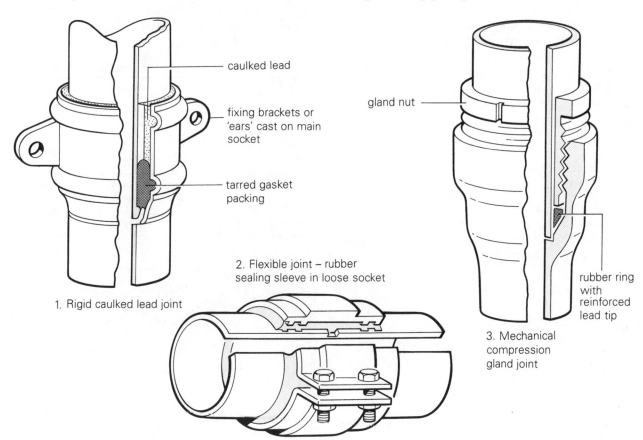

caulked lead

fixing brackets or 'ears' cast on main socket

tarred gasket packing

1. Rigid caulked lead joint

2. Flexible joint – rubber sealing sleeve in loose socket

gland nut

rubber ring with reinforced lead tip

3. Mechanical compression gland joint

*Figure 4.1*   Joints used on cast-iron pipe

## Wrought iron

Pure iron is too soft to have any practical uses but wrought iron has a small amount of other elements added to it making it a useful and durable metal that is also malleable and ductile. It is black/grey in colour.

## Steel

As with the irons described above, steel is a metal composed mainly of iron with the addition of varying amounts of carbon. The amount of carbon added to the iron is governed by its use: the higher the percentage of carbon added, the harder the metal will be. For most pressure pipework, low carbon or mild steel is mainly used, which contains between 0.1 and 0.3 per cent carbon. This makes it malleable to bend yet hard enough to resist impact damage.

## Stainless steel

There are various types of stainless steel available but stainless steel that contains both chromium and nickel is the most popular and is used for the manufacture of pipes and sanitary appliances for public buildings. It is bright silver in colour.

Stainless steel pipe is only available as light gauge in sizes up to 35 mm diameter. It is a durable pipe, resistant to corrosion but difficult to bend due to its thin pipe wall. Most fittings used for copper pipe are suitable for stainless steel although compression fittings are easier and preferable. A special flux is needed if capillary joints are to be used.

## Galvanised steel

This is mild steel with a coating of zinc applied to protect it against corrosion. The zinc can be applied by either electroplating or, for pipes, hot dipping. It is dull silver/zinc in colour. It is a popular form of steel pipe used extensively for cold water supplies. All the main details are the same as for ordinary black steel.

The addition of the following elements can provide steel with even more properties.

**Chromium**  This is used for pipes and vessels carrying corrosive liquids or subject to corrosive conditions. It is a key component of stainless steel.

**Manganese**  This produces steels of great ductility and hardness to resist abrasion, shock and wear.

**Molybdenum**  This is often used to produce steels that will be subject to high temperatures because it produces steels of high tensile strength.

**Nickel**  This produces tough steels which are highly resistant to abrasion. It is often a constituent of stainless steel.

**Tungsten**  This is used to produce very hard tool steels, such as those used to cut metals.

**Vanadium**  This is used to produce steels with a high resistance to fatigue and great tensile strength. This type of steel is mainly used for tools such a screwdrivers and pipe wrenches.

## Steel pipe and fittings

Low carbon mild steel (LCMS) is one of the commonest pipework materials used by the plumber. For domestic water services it must be galvanised to prevent discolouring the water due to corrosion. For other purposes, normal 'black' steel is used; this can be protected against corrosion by the addition of chemical inhibitors to the water.

There are three grades available, each usually identified with a different coloured band near the end of the pipe. The uses of each are shown in Table 4.1. The difference between each is their wall thickness. Because the outside diameter of the pipe must relate to the thread size of the fittings, the outside diameter of all grades is the same. The difference is in the bore of the pipe. It is usual therefore to specify the **nominal bore** for both pipes and fittings.

Steel pipe is available in lengths up to 6 m long, already threaded each end (screwed and socketed), or in random lengths, unthreaded and in sizes 6 mm ($\frac{1}{4}$ inch) up to 150 mm (6 inch) nominal bore.

**Table 4.1** Grades and uses of mild steel tube

| Grade | Colour code | Uses |
| --- | --- | --- |
| Heavy | Red | Steam and underground pipelines |
| Medium | Blue | Water |
| Light | Brown | Gas |

Note: All the pipes will be black unless galvanized, in which case they will be zinc coloured. The colour codes above consist of a painted band about 50 mm wide on one end of the pipe.

Due to its weight great care must be taken when storing steel tubes and fittings. Flooring and shelving may need to be reinforced. Manufacturer's literature always specifies the weight of tubes in kg per metre for pipe and kg per 100 pieces for fittings. Always add 5% for galvanised pipes and fittings. You can joint mild steel by either welding it or using screwed joints. It is unwise to weld galvanised pipe, however, since this generates poisonous fumes and destroys the protective zinc coating. Welding is outside the scope of this book so we will concentrate on screwed or threaded joints.

## Threaded joints

Threads are formed on the ends of the pipes to be joined, on site or in the workshop, using stocks and dies. These are then screwed into proprietary fittings. There are various types of thread but the British Standard Pipe Thread (BSPT) is widely used. The formed thread is tapered but the thread in the fittings is parallel; this ensures a good joint when they are screwed together (Figure 4.2). The front of the dies will only cut an incomplete thread to enable the dies to mount the pipe at the start. As the dies move along, the complete thread is cut by the rest of the die. Because there will always be an incomplete section at the end of any thread, you must make sure that this 'washout' section of thread remains outside the fitting when the joint is made otherwise it may result in a leak. Before screwing the joints on the pipe, jointing tape or hemp and paste are applied to the thread. The method chosen will depend on what the pipeline is used for. For low pressure hot water, cold water and gas pipelines, white linseed oil compound should be used with hemp. For oil and petrol pipelines, red lead haematite compound should be used with hemp. Steam pipelines should be jointed with non-setting black graphite compound but *no* hemp because it may burn out due to high temperatures.

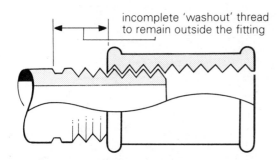

*Figure 4.2* Tapered thread on steel pipe screwed into parallel threaded fitting

Compression joints for use with steel pipe have recently been developed but are not yet widely available outside the specialist oil and gas industries for which they were first developed. Although not a traditional method of jointing steel pipe, the relative speed in jointing may eventually increase its popularity.

They are made of malleable iron and are basically the same as compression fittings for copper and synthetic plastics. Instead of having a soft copper ring that compresses on to the pipe, they have a steel locking ring, washer and rubber seal (Figure 4.3). They can also be used on polythene pipe. They are compact, require minimal pipe preparation, and allow angular movement of up to 6°.

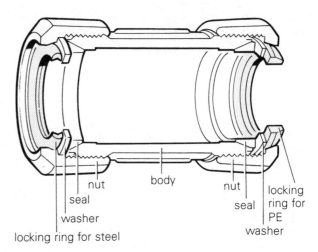

*Figure 4.3* Compression fitting for use with steel or polythene pipe

Screwed fittings for steel pipes are manufactured to various standards covering those made from cast iron, steel and malleable iron, and whether the threads, both male and female, are parallel or tapered. Malleable iron fittings are the most popular because they will accommodate slight deformation on being tightened, without failing. These fittings usually have a parallel thread, with a taper thread being put on the pipe. This creates a tight fit when jointed. Malleable iron fittings can be identified by a reinforcement bead running round the end of the female socket. Some common fittings are shown in Figure 4.4. Steel fittings have a plain end.

## Disconnecting joints

When connecting pipework up to appliances and components that may need to be removed or disconnected for maintenance, such as boilers, cisterns, pumps and tanks, special fittings need to be used that can be undone easily without affecting the surrounding pipework. These include flanges, unions and long threads (Figure 4.5).

### Flange joints
These relatively large ring-shaped fittings are used in pairs. They are screwed on to each end of the pipes to be joined. Holes around each flange must be aligned to enable bolts to pass through for tightening them together. The actual joint is made sound by inserting a jointing ring between the flanges, which may be either compressed fibre, corrugated metal, rubber or sheet graphite depending on the fluid in the pipeline. Some rings cover the full flange, others cover the part inside the bolt hole area. Brass or copper rings are used on gas pipelines and copper nickel alloy rings are used on

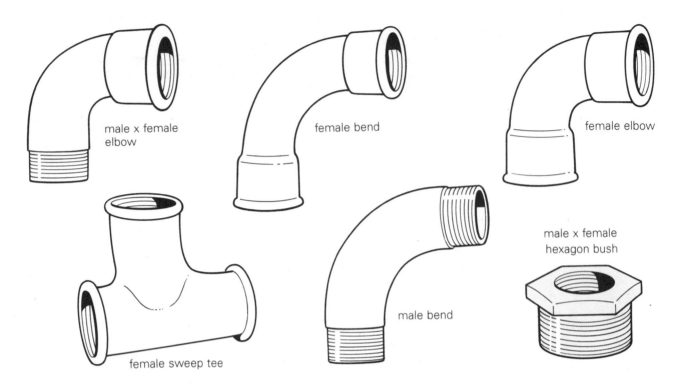

*Figure 4.4*  Threaded malleable iron fittings for steel pipe

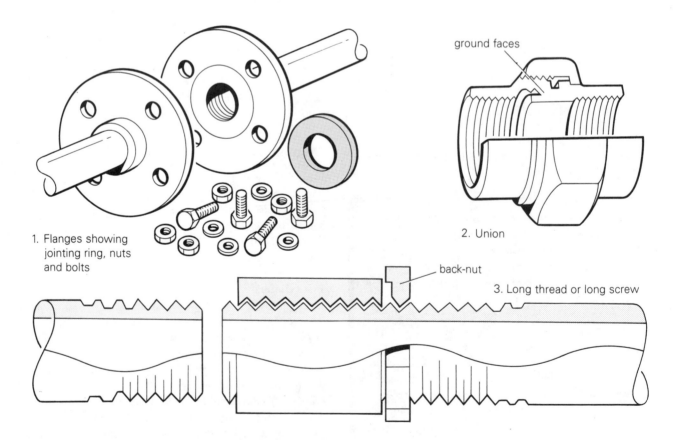

*Figure 4.5*  Disconnecting joints for steel pipe

water and steam pipelines. Stainless steel rings are also sometimes used on steam pipelines.

### Longscrews

These can be made up on site. One pipe end has a parallel thread cut on it, long enough to screw a backnut and socket completely on to the pipe so that the end of the pipe protrudes. A normal taper thread is put on the other pipe end. Hemp and paste or jointing tape are applied to the taper-threaded pipe end and both pipes are aligned. The socket is then unscrewed from the long thread and on to the taper thread until tight. Jointing compound and hemp is then put round the opposite end of the socket and the backnut is tightened against it to make a watertight joint. To remove, simply unscrew both the backnut and the socket.

### Union joints

These fittings are made up of two parts, each part screwing on to the ends of the pipes to be jointed. A large nut screws both parts together. The joint is made sound either by the close fit of machined surfaces on each part and a smear of jointing paste or the insertion of a rubber ring in a space between the surfaces.

# Copper and its alloys

Copper is one of the earliest metals known to man and also one of the most widespread in use today as pipework for hot and cold water supplies. It is reddish brown in colour and is obtained from ores including chalcopyrite and bornite. The relative cost of copper in some countries makes its use prohibitive but its high thermal conductivity, resistance to corrosion and ease of use still makes it one of the most popular plumbing materials.

Copper is used for the manufacture of boilers, cisterns, heat exchangers, storage vessels, sheet roofing and pipes suitable for carrying water, soil and waste, and gas and oil supplies. It is both ductile and malleable enabling it to be worked easily as sheetwork and bent easily as pipework. It will eventually harden during working but can be annealed by heat treatment to soften it.

## Copper pipe

The use of large diameter copper pipes in plumbing for such things as above ground sanitation has now been replaced by other materials due to the cost, but it is still available as large bore up to 159 mm diameter, as well as microbore 6–12 mm diameter, and small bore which includes 15, 18, 22, 28 and 35 mm diameter. It is usually manufactured in 3 grades or tables for different uses. Table 4.2 shows their uses.

There are various ways of jointing copper pipe but most plumbers use either compression joints or capillary joints.

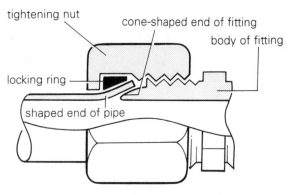

1. Manipulative type

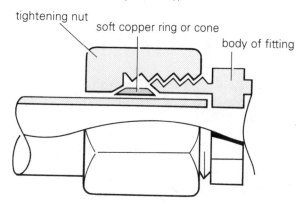

2. Non-manipulative type

*Figure 4.6* Compression fittings for copper pipe

*Table 4.2* Grades and uses of copper pipe

| Grade/description | Table | Uses |
|---|---|---|
| Half hard, light gauge | X | Commonest type, suitable for all fittings, can be bent easily and welded |
| Half hard, annealed | Y | Annealed soft copper tube, usually available in coils for use underground. Can use all usual fittings |
| Hard drawn, thin wall | Z | Cannot be bent. Use only non-manipulative fittings |

## Compression joints

There are two types of fitting available: the manipulative fitting and the non-manipulative fitting (Figure 4.6). With the manipulative fitting, you first place the nut over the end of the pipe, then open up the end of the pipe using a swaging tool and hammer (Figure 4.7). The cone-shaped end of the fitting is then smeared with jointing paste and placed inside the opened end of the pipe, and the nut is tightened on to the thread of the fitting body to form a secure joint. You can use either an open spanner or adjustable spanner to tighten the nuts.

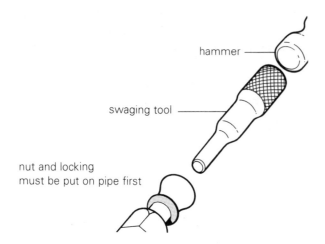

*Figure 4.7* Swaging tool used to open out the ends of copper pipe

This type of fitting has the advantage of not pulling off if the pipeline is subject to extreme conditions of movement or temperature change.

Non-manipulative fittings are similar but the end of the pipe is not shaped. First a nut is placed over the end of the pipe followed by a soft copper ring or cone. Jointing paste is smeared over the cone and the end of the pipe is inserted into the fitting. The nut can then be tightened on to the body of the fitting. This compresses the cone against the pipe wall and the inside of the fitting, making a secure joint.

This type of joint is more popular than the manipulative joint because it is quicker and easier to use and it can be removed with ease, but great care should be taken not to overtighten the joint otherwise removing the cone may be difficult.

## Capillary joints

There are three types of capillary joint: the end-feed fitting, the integral solder ring fitting or 'Yorkshire' fitting and the self-formed swaged socket joint (Figure 4.8). All rely on the capillary action of molten solder to form a sound bond between the outside of the pipe and the inside of the fitting.

First the outside of the pipe and the inside of the fitting must be cleaned with wire wool, a purpose-made wire brush or sandpaper; then the cleaned surfaces should be smeared with a suitable flux to prevent oxidation and to assist the solder to run. Insert the pipe into the socket of the fitting and wipe off any surplus flux with a cloth. With Yorkshire fittings you simply heat up the joint with a blowlamp until you see the solder run around the edge of the fitting, then leave it to cool for a few minutes. With end-feed fittings you will have to feed soft-solder on to the edge of the fitting from a coil when the joint is hot enough. The solder will be drawn up into the joint by capillary action to form the joint. As a guide, a length of solder off the coil equal to the diameter of the pipe should be enough; any more is likely to end up on the

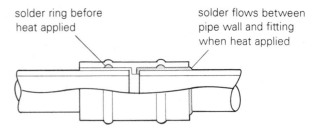

1.   Integral solder ring fitting

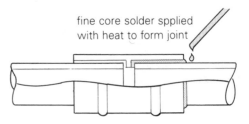

2.   End-feed capillary fitting

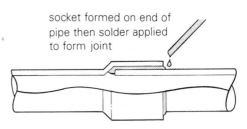

3.   Self-formed socket joint

*Figure 4.8* Capillary joints for copper pipe

floor around the pipe or inside the pipe where it may cause problems in the system.

**Capillary action**

When liquid is introduced between two surfaces close together, the surface tension acting between the liquid and the close surfaces causes the liquid to move and spread between the surfaces. Liquids can travel some distance under these conditions which can cause problems of dampness in buildings, but this phenomenon can be put to good use in capillary fittings.

Self-formed swaged socket joints are manufactured on-site on the end of pipes by using a special swaging tool or pipe expander. The rest of the process is the same as for other capillary joints.

## Sheet copper

Sheet copper is used for both weathering and decorative work on roofs. Because of its high expansion rate, allowances must be made in the joints and fixings. It is highly resistant to corrosion, with a thin green protective coating or patina caused by oxidation forming on exposure to the atmosphere. A special preparation can be applied so that its natural reddish brown colour remains if required. It can be worked and jointed easily using welts, rolls and drips but may need annealing if overworked (see Chapter 13 for details on jointing).

## Brass and bronze

Brass is an alloy of between 50 and 70% copper and between 30 and 50% zinc. It varies between dull gold and yellow in colour depending on the amount of zinc. It is a strong ductile metal which is manufactured as pipe and sheet but its main use in plumbing is for the manufacture of pipe fittings and valves. Several brass fittings and valves are shown in Figure 4.9.

In some situations, the zinc in some brasses may corrode. This is known as **dezincification**. Wherever possible dezincification resistant brass should always be specified.

Bronze is an alloy of copper, tin and zinc. It is similar in colour to brass. The commonest bronze used in plumbing is known as gunmetal and contains 88% copper, 10% tin and 2% zinc. The metal is highly resistant to corrosion and possesses high tensile strength. Its main uses in plumbing are the same as for brass.

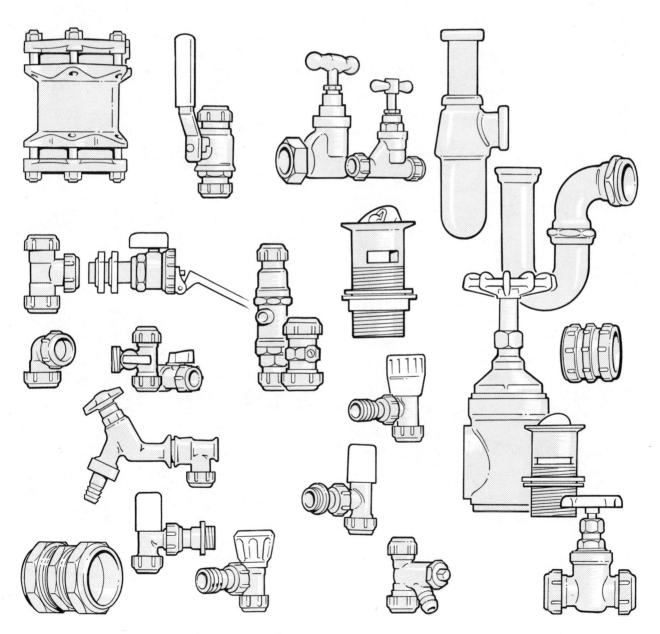

*Figure 4.9*  A selection of brass fittings and valves

# Lead and its alloys

Lead is a heavy metal, yet soft, easy to cut, and both malleable and plastic. Obtained mainly from the ore galena, it is bluish grey. When cut it is bright and shiny but quickly oxidises. These properties, together with its high resistance to corrosion, have made it an ideal material for plumbing but care is needed when fixing because it is also subject to creep. Right from the earliest times lead has been the material most associated with the plumber. It is manufactured as both pipe and sheet.

For water services, the pipes have a thick wall in relation to the bore, making frequent or continuous support necessary (because of their weight), particularly on horizontal runs. Lead soil, waste, vent and gas pipes, by comparison, have very thin walls, which are easily damaged. Partly because of this, and the increased awareness of dangers to health from lead poisoning, and because of the skills associated with jointing lead pipes, some countries no longer use it. However, it is still important for plumbers to be able to joint it for repair and maintenance purposes.

**How to wipe a straight underhand joint** (Figure 4.10)

1. Rasp the spigot end of the pipe down to a fine 'feather' edge.
2. Using a tanpin and hammer, open out a bell-shaped socket just big enough for the spigot to fit inside, then rasp down the edge of the socket to a feather edge.
3. Fit the pipes together and mark out the edge of the finished joint on each pipe. The length of joint will vary according to the size of pipe but an average length of 70 mm for service pipes and 80 mm for waste pipes should be satisfactory.
4. Scribe around the pipes and shave all this joint area with a shavehook; the immediate area beyond the joint is normally painted with black water-based paint known as

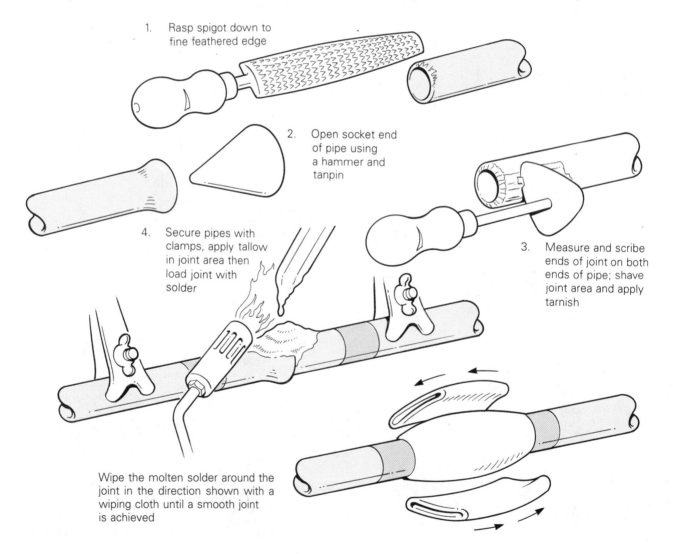

1. Rasp spigot down to fine feathered edge

2. Open socket end of pipe using a hammer and tanpin

3. Measure and scribe ends of joint on both ends of pipe; shave joint area and apply tarnish

4. Secure pipes with clamps, apply tallow in joint area then load joint with solder

Wipe the molten solder around the joint in the direction shown with a wiping cloth until a smooth joint is achieved

*Figure 4.10*  Wiping a straight underhand joint on lead pipe

plumber's **black** or **tarnish** to stop the solder from sticking beyond the joint area. You may need to chalk the surface of the pipe to get the tarnish to stick.

5.  Secure both ends of the pipe together using pipe clamps.
6.  Smear tallow, a flux made from animal fat, over the joint area, then using a blowlamp, gently heat up the joint area and solder together until you can rub the solder stick along the joint leaving a thin coating; do this all round the joint to provide a 'tinned' surface.
7.  Now melt solder on to the top of the joint to leave enough to 'wipe' round the joint – about 0.25–0.75 kg should be enough for most joints.

    Grade D solder should be used for wiped joints. This is approximately two thirds lead and one third tin and is usually available in 0.5 kg bars.

8.  When there is enough solder on the joint, put your wiping cloth under the joint and carefully use the blowlamp to heat the solder up so that it melts and flows down on to your cloth. With the solder now in this plastic state, wipe the cloth around the joint to deposit the solder equally all around the joint area, leaving a raised convex surface around the middle of the joint. The finished joint should be smooth and clearly sealed all around the edges with no

imperfections. When the joint looks alright, wipe off any excess solder by drawing it with the cloth sideways over the joint in the direction of the pipeline.

---

**Points to remember:**
- This is one of the oldest plumbing skills requiring careful manipulation of the blowlamp and the wiping cloth and it takes a long time to perfect. You will need to wipe around the pipe several times to achieve a good looking and sound joint.
- Use a wiping cloth big enough to keep your fingers shielded from the molten solder.
- When you are satisfied the joint is alright, you must then leave it undisturbed for at least 5 minutes to set.

---

**How to wipe a branch joint** (Figure 4.11)

1.  Mark out the position of the branch and use an auger to make a hole in the pipe. If it is a large waste or soil pipe you could use a lead knife to cut a small split into the

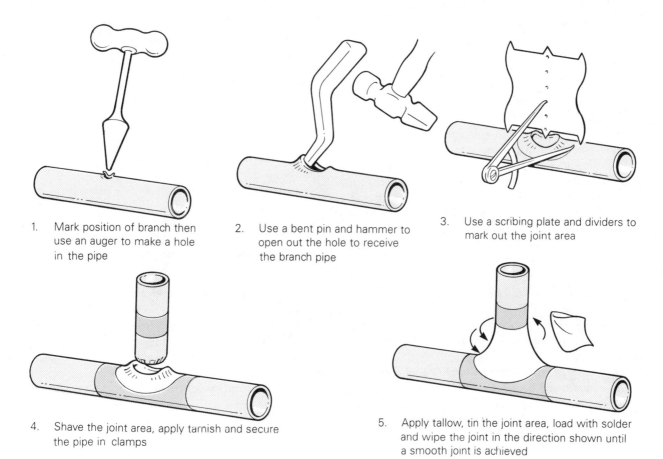

1.  Mark position of branch then use an auger to make a hole in the pipe

2.  Use a bent pin and hammer to open out the hole to receive the branch pipe

3.  Use a scribing plate and dividers to mark out the joint area

4.  Shave the joint area, apply tarnish and secure the pipe in clamps

5.  Apply tallow, tin the joint area, load with solder and wipe the joint in the direction shown until a smooth joint is achieved

*Figure 4.11*  Wiping a branch joint on lead pipe

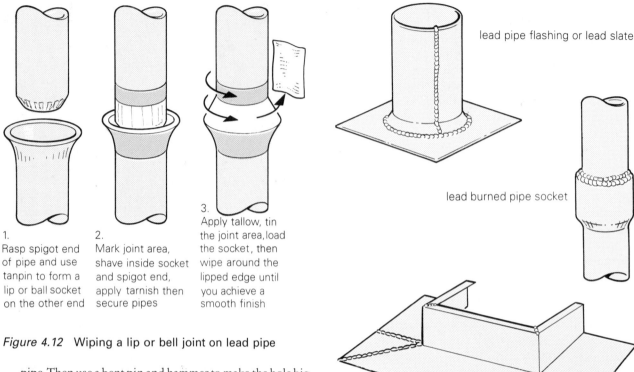

1.
Rasp spigot end of pipe and use tanpin to form a lip or ball socket on the other end

2.
Mark joint area, shave inside socket and spigot end, apply tarnish then secure pipes

3.
Apply tallow, tin the joint area, load the socket, then wipe around the lipped edge until you achieve a smooth finish

*Figure 4.12*  Wiping a lip or bell joint on lead pipe

lead pipe flashing or lead slate

lead burned pipe socket

chimney apron flashing

*Figure 4.13*  Lead components joined by lead burning

pipe. Then use a bent pin and hammer to make the hole big enough for the branch pipe to fit, without it protruding into the pipe to cause an obstruction.

2. Use the scribing plate and dividers to mark out the joint area. The joint should extend to the middle of the main pipe and a minimum of 25 mm up the branch.
3. Shave the joint area and apply tarnish to the area immediately outside this.
4. Secure the pipe and branch with pipe clamps, apply tallow to the joint area then 'tin' the joint.
5. Load the solder up on either side of the branch pipe, then use a small branch wiping cloth to wipe the solder round the joint to give a concave surface at the crotch and a convex surface on the side flanks. When the joint looks sound, as described for the underhand joint, wipe off the excess solder down one of the concave surfaces of the joint.

**How to wipe a 'lip' or 'bell' joint** (Figure 4.12)
This type of joint is normally only suitable on waste, soil or gas pipes which are not subject to high pressures although a well-prepared and applied lip joint can be as sound as an underhand joint.

1. Rasp the spigot end of the pipe to a fine feather edge.
2. Use a tanpin and hammer to open out a lipped socket, giving enough space between the outside of the spigot and the edge of the lip, when the pipes are put together, to provide a good space to apply the solder.
3. Mark out the joint area on the spigot and shave it clean. When the pipes are together this will be a minimum of 25 mm along the spigot from the top edge of the lip.

Shave the inside of the lip then apply tarnish immediately beyond the spigot joint area and beneath the outside of the lip.
4. Clamp the pipes together, apply tallow then tin all cleaned surfaces.
5. Load up the lipped socket with solder and wipe around until the edges are sealed, there are no imperfections and you have a smooth concave surface from the edge of the lip running up the spigot. Wipe off any excess solder as before.

An alternative to wiped solder joints are lead welded or lead burned joints where the lead is welded together using a lead filler rod. This is particularly useful in the chemical industry for pipes and linings to tanks carrying acids because acids will attack solder. It is a popular and alternative method to bossing roof weathering components like aprons and pipe flashings or lead slates. Some leadburned items are shown in Figure 4.13; further details on jointing are shown in Chapter 13.

Sheet lead is still used in many countries for weathering and decorative purposes on roofwork and cladding. It is available in rolls and in different thicknesses or codes according to its use. Each code is traditionally identified by coloured tape or paint on the roll. The various codes, colour and uses are covered in Chapter 13. Due to constant expansion and contraction caused by the weather, allowances need to be made in the jointing and fixing. As with copper, on exposure to the atmosphere it will oxidise, forming a thin coating or patina, whitish grey in colour. This prevents further corrosion, making it ideal for roofwork. It can be worked to fit into most situations cold, and can also be jointed using welts, rolls and drips (see Chapter 13 for details of joints etc.).

## Solder

Solder is an alloy composed of lead and tin in varying quantities depending on its use. It is used for the jointing of pipe, mainly lead and copper, either with or without fittings, and also sheet lead, copper and zinc. The various types are known according to the classifications shown in Table 4.3. Pipework is generally soldered using a blowlamp and sheetwork with a soldering iron.

---

**Points to remember:**
- Before soldering, it is essential to clean thoroughly the area to be jointed. Lead must be shaved and copper rubbed with wire wool. Then a suitable flux must be applied to the cleaned surfaces to help the solder to flow and to prevent oxidation of the cleaned surfaces. A list of common fluxes and their uses is shown in Table 4.4.
- Fluxes can either be 'active' or 'safe' according to their corrosive properties. Read all instructions on the packaging and if in doubt consult the manufacturer. Always protect your hands when using active fluxes and wash excess flux residues off the pipe after soldering.
- **Lead-free solders** are now available, particularly for capillary fittings. They pose less of a health risk and should be used wherever possible.

---

## Aluminium

This is used mainly in pure form (99.99%) as a sheet roofing material. It is shiny white in appearance, malleable, ductile and resistant to most forms of atmospheric corrosion except in extreme salty and sulphurous atmospheres. Obtained from mineral bauxite, it is also extremely light, making it an excellent roofing material (see Chapter 13 for details of jointing etc.). Similar precautions regarding expansion are needed as for copper. The same types of joint can also be used. As an alloy containing other elements such as manganese it becomes much harder and more rigid and can be used for rainwater pipes and gutters and a variety of brackets, supports and fixings.

## Zinc

Zinc is obtained from the ores sphalerite and zinc blende. It is manufactured mainly as sheet for roof weathering, and as an

*Table 4.4* Types of flux and their uses

| Type of flux | Uses |
| --- | --- |
| Resin | Fine solder with capillary fittings |
| Killed spirits/ zinc chloride | Soldering brass, copper and zinc; tinning linings |
| Sal-ammoniac | Soldering brass and copper, and tinning copper soldering iron bits |
| Tallow | Plumber's solder on lead pipe/ sheet |

Note: Most fluxes are bought by specifying the manufacturer's brand name. Examples of fluxes for copper pipe soldering include *Fluxite, Baker's blue, La-co* and *Yorkshire.* Always check to see if they are 'active' fluxes. If so, protect your skin when applying and wash off excess flux from the job after soldering.

*Table 4.3* Grades and uses of solder

| Grade and name | Composition | Uses |
| --- | --- | --- |
| A   Fine solder (capillary solder) | One third lead, two thirds tin *Sets quickly* | Capillary joints on copper pipe |
| B   Tinman's solder | Half lead, half tin (contains some antimony) *More 'plastic' sets slower than grade A* | Used with soldering iron for seams on sheet copper and tinning copper to lead linings |
| D   Plumber's solder | Two thirds lead, one third tin *Long 'plastic' range allows it to be shaped before setting* | Wiping joints on lead pipe |

**Lead-free fine solder** for use with capillary fittings, where available, is strongly recommended for use on drinking water pipes

alloy for gutters and pipes for rainwater disposal. It is not as easy as copper or aluminium to work or joint but has good resistance to atmospheric corrosion, except in areas where sulphur from industrial processes is present. Dull white in appearance, the other main use of zinc is as a protective coating to steel in galvanised pipe and fittings. Zinc is also used for making brass. In the presence of other metals in acidic waters, electrolytic corrosion may cause the zinc to corrode.

## Plastics

The use of synthetic plastics, derived from oil products, has transformed the plumbing industry since the 1960s. They have replaced many traditional plumbing materials for the manufacture of a wide range of products for both the domestic and industrial markets. These include pipes, joints, valves, gutters, cisterns and some san itary appliances. Although there are several types available, most share similar properties of lightness, resistance to corrosion, being non-contaminating and flexible. Their relatively low production cost makes most plastics available worldwide.

Plastics are categorised as either thermosetting or thermoplastic. Thermosetting plastics are very brittle and cannot be resoftened. They are used mainly for the production of work surfaces, bonding agents and glues. Thermoplastics can be resoftened, which makes them ideal for small bore pipework since they can be bent. They are used for above and below ground drainage and hot and cold water supplies, but you must always check the manufacturer's literature about a particular product for details of use and never mix different products together in the same system because the fittings may not match.

While plastics have many advantages over more traditional plumbing materials, they do have limitations. They have a relatively high rate of expansion, so allowances must be made in pipework installations. Most plastics have low impact strength and can fracture, so care must be taken in siting pipe runs, particularly in public places. They can be affected by ultra-violet rays produced by the sun causing degradation, so the plastic becomes brittle and can fail. Most modern plastics are treated to prevent this but in extreme conditions the manufacturer's advice must be sought.

The following list gives brief details of the main plastics used by the plumber. They are all thermoplastics. Figure 4.14 shows a range of plastic plumbing products.

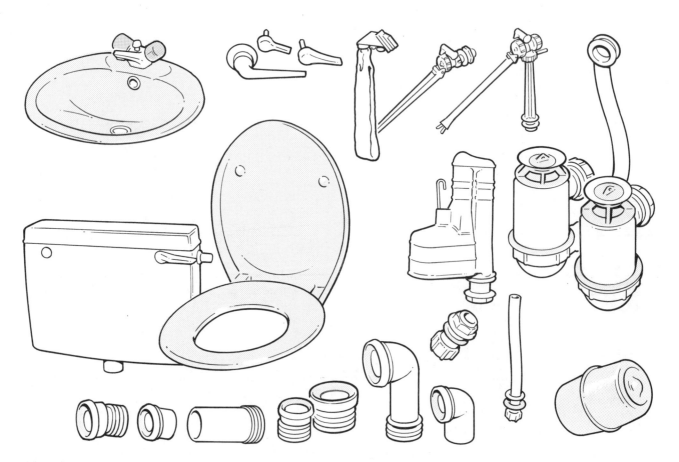

*Figure 4.14*  Common plumbing components made from plastics

**Acrylic**   This plastic can be moulded and coloured easily and is used to manufacture baths and clear corrugated roof sheeting.

**Acrylonitrile butadiene styrene (ABS)**   Generally used for small diameter waste pipes, which are jointed using solvent cement (Figure 4.15). Expansion push-fit joints should be inserted in long straight pipe runs (Figure 4.16).

**Neoprene and nitrile butadiene rubber**   These are both synthetic rubbers used to make the 'O' or 'D' ring joints in push-fit pipe fittings and the sealing joint in rainwater gutters.

**Nylon**   Used to produce spacing washers and other small components.

**Polypropylene**   This plastic is used to produce waste pipes, fittings and traps. It is a rigid material, which makes it useful for the manufacture of fittings for other pipework systems. It can stand high water temperatures for short periods, making it ideal for traps to sanitary appliances. Joints and fittings are either 'O' ring push-fit or compression joints (Figure 4.16).

**Polystyrene**   In its expanded form this is used in plumbing as an insulating material for cisterns, pipes and tanks.

**Polytetrafluoroethylene (PTFE)**   The main use of PTFE in plumbing is as a thin sealing tape for threaded joints.

**Polythene (PE)**   Polythene or polyethylene is generally used for cold water mains and waste pipes. For water mains it is generally jointed using compression fittings and for waste pipes either compression fittings or 'O' ring push-fit joints are used. Bends and offsets can be put on polythene water pipes by the application of heat (see Chapter 3).

**Polyvinyl chloride (PVC or UPVC)**   This plastic is manufactured as a tough, flexible or rigid material designed to resist light degradation and atmospheric pollution. With these qualities it is extensively used for external soil and rainwater systems. It is jointed using push-fit joints (Figure 4.16).

**Post-chlorinated polyvinyl chloride (CPVC)**   This is one of the most versatile of plastics and is used extensively in the food and chemical industries because it can carry a wide range of acids, chemicals and foodstuffs at temperatures of up to 100°. Solvent cement joints should be used and expansion joints or loops should be built into long straight runs.

> ⚠ Great care must be taken when making solvent cement joints. Always make sure there is plenty of ventilation and protect your hands and eyes. Always replace the cap on tins of solvents and cleaners after use.

## Ceramics

These are basically vitrified clay products made from a mixture of minerals, usually quartz sand and a clay binder, hydrated aluminium silicate with impurities, such as chalk, and sulphate plasticised with water. The mixture is shaped, dried to remove water, then fired to produce a glass-like material that is hard, impervious and resistant to most acids and alkalis.

In plumbing, ceramics are used mainly for sanitary appliances and underground drainage pipes. For sanitary appliances a smooth glaze needs to be applied. This glaze needs to be carefully matched to the properties of the clay used otherwise cracking or crazing may occur.

**Earthenware**   This has a relatively high water absorption rate but when glazed it is useful for cheap sinks and WC pans.

**Fireclay**   Glazed fireclay is used to produce sanitary appliances such as urinals and sinks that will be subject to high use and therefore need to be tough and durable, for example in schools and public buildings. The high kaolin content also gives it high fire resistance and unglazed it is used for flue liners and grate-blocks for fires.

**Stoneware**   Stoneware has a similar composition to fireclay but it is fired at a higher temperature to give a higher glass content making it less absorbent and harder. It is used mainly for drainage pipes and fittings either glazed or unglazed.

**Vitreous china**   A higher glass content than earthenware and negligible water absorption even if the glaze cracks makes this the main material used for most domestic sanitary appliances.

A range of vitrified clay products is shown in Figure 4.17. Vitrified clay drain pipes can be joined with either rigid or flexible joints; some examples are shown in Figure 4.18.

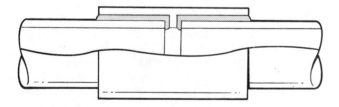

*Figure 4.15*   Solvent cement joint on ABS plastic waste

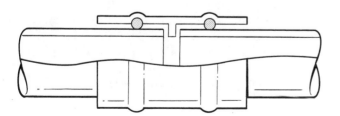

*Figure 4.16*   Expansion push-fit joint for plastic waste pipe

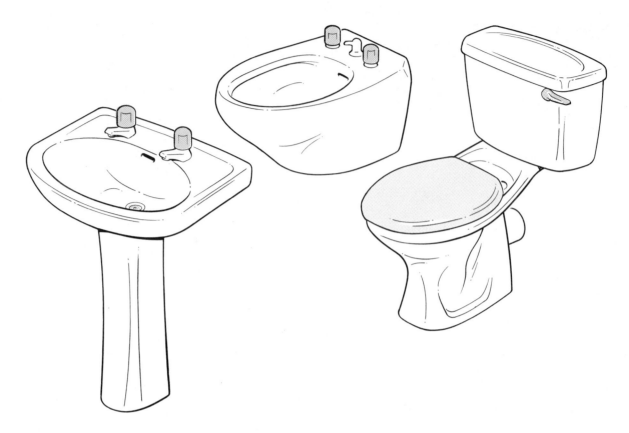

*Figure 4.17*   Common sanitary appliances made from vitreous china

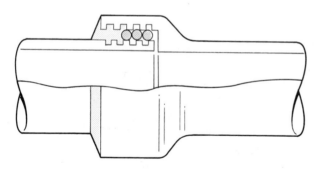

1.   Rigid sand and cement joint

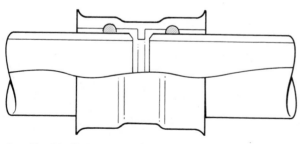

2.   Flexible D ring joint

*Figure 4.18*   Joints on vitrified clay drain pipes

# Asbestos

Asbestos is produced from magnesium silicate which, when split, enables long thin white fibres to be collected. It is manufactured for use in various forms: asbestos cement pipes, fittings and sheet; resin-bonded asbestos sheets; and sprayed asbestos.

It has good resistance to acids, alkalis, neutral salts and organic solvents. It is strong in tension but weak in compression. The main property of asbestos is its heat and fire resistance.

As pipework it is produced in heavy and light grades. Heavy grade only is used for water mains and drains but both grades can be used for rainwater pipes, gutters and boiler flue pipes depending on the diameter. Screwed compression gland joints with rubber sealing rings are used for water mains and rubber push-fit joints are used for drainage and rainwater pipes. Flue pipe spigot and socket joints are sealed with fire cement. It is a popular roofing material in many countries. Corrugated roofing sheets are normally used because they provide added strength. The other main use of asbestos is to fireproof boiler compartments or materials that may be subject to damage by fire or high temperatures.

**Points to remember:**
- Always use roof ladders or 'duck boards' if you need access to asbestos roofs to spread the load, otherwise they may collapse.
- The use of certain types of asbestos for insulation purposes has now stopped due to the risks to health. The stripping off and removal of asbestos insulation from old systems must be carried out by specialist firms, with the area completely sealed. For identification, information and advice, specialist assistance must be sought.
- The inhalation of substantial concentrations of any dust is likely to be injurious to health but exposure to asbestos dust can be reduced by using a respirator or dust extraction system when cutting asbestos products, and damping down the material by spraying with water.

# Glass

In some countries, glazing is part of the plumber's work. In many tropical countries, external window openings in domestic properties are unglazed but internal doors and screens may be glazed. Glass is made from soda, lime, silica and other ingredients, such as alumina and magnesium. These materials are heated to a temperature of between 1490°C and 1550°C, at which point they fuse together in a molten state. The glass sheet is then produced by drawing, floating or rolling. Glass is available clear, obscured in various patterns or wired for security and strength, and in a range of thicknesses from 2 to 6 mm.

Sheet glass is bedded using various types of putty depending on whether the frame is wood or steel. First it is pinned in place with fine wire nails or clips then pointed with putty or beaded with wood or metal strips. Felt strips are sometimes used instead of putty with some forms of beading.

## Glass fibre

Glass fibre is also known as glass wool or fibreglass. It is produced from thin fibres of glass which are then broken up and sprayed with a binding agent. It is supplied in flexible roll or quilt form and also in rigid sheets or pipe cover form. Its main use in plumbing is for insulation purposes (Figure 4.19).

# Pitch fibre

This material is made by impregnating wood fibre pulp with coal tar pitch. It is used mainly for rainwater and drainage pipes. It is relatively cheap and suitable for most domestic drainage systems but can be affected by some trade effluents, including oils and organic solvents. Continuous hot discharges can also be a problem. It is jointed using push-fit rubber ring joints or taper joints which are driven on using a lump hammer and a wooden striking plate or 'dolly' (Figure 4.20). Do not drive taper joints on too tightly otherwise the joint may split. Also, do not use any jointing compounds, lubricants or adhesives.

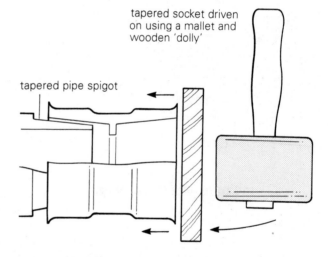

tapered socket driven on using a mallet and wooden 'dolly'

tapered pipe spigot

*Figure 4.20* Rigid taper joint for pitch-fibre pipe

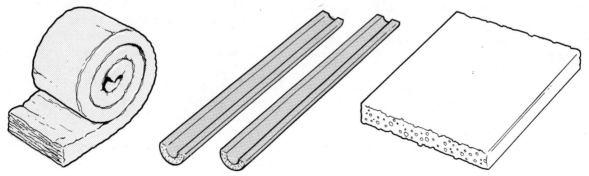

flexible quilt for roof insulation    semi-rigid sections for pipe insulation    semi-rigid sheet for various insulation application

*Figure 4.19* Glass fibre products

# Concrete

Concrete is a common building material made by mixing sand, stone and cement together with water in various quantities. Pre-formed concrete pipes are manufactured, mainly for use in large drainage or sewerage projects. Concrete pipes are available in sizes from 150 mm diameter up to 3000 mm diameter. Pipes are manufactured with socket and spigot ends or with rebated ends. The joints are flexible and made with rubber 'D' rings (Figure 4.21).

Sections through typical flexible joints

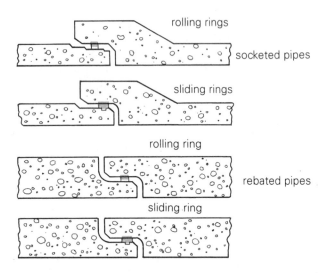

Figure 4.21   Typical flexible joints used on cement pipes

# Taps and valves

These include all the main fittings that are used to control flow, shut-off or isolate, draw-off and drain-off water in hot and cold water systems. There are many types available in a range of materials, shapes and designs to suit a variety of applications. Traditionally, most are made of brass, bronze or gunmetal because of these metals' durability and resistance to corrosion. Increasingly, many are now being made from plastics, including polypropylene, because of its corrosion resistance and relatively low cost and easy manufacture.

As with many things to do with plumbing, the names given to the various flow control fittings varies between countries and even regions. For example, what is known as a ball valve in one country may be known as a ball tap in another one. Some fittings called ball taps in one region are a totally different fitting from a ball tap in another region, which confuses the issue further. Here we have used what are believed to be the most universally accepted names for the fittings described.

## Screw-down taps

These taps are the commonest type in general use and are designed to shut off the flow of water gradually. Water enters the fitting and flows up through a circular hole or orifice. The orifice also forms a seating on to which a valve or jumper rests, making the actual orifice slightly smaller in diameter than the diameter or bore of the pipe the tap is connected to (Figure 4.22). The valve is controlled by a spindle connected to a controlling head. When the head is turned anti-clockwise, to open the tap, the spindle gradually rises, allowing the valve to rise off the seat and let water flow through the tap. When the head is turned clockwise, to shut the tap, the spindle screws down to lower the valve back on to the seat and shut off the water flow. A packing gland and gland nut prevent water leaking up around the spindle. To prevent dirt collecting around the gland nut an easy-clean cover is usually fitted on taps used for drawing off water in kitchens and bathrooms.

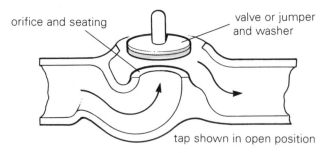

Figure 4.22   Water flow through the orifice and seating of a screw-down tap

**Points to remember:**

- Screw-down taps used on mains cold water should be fitted with loose valves. The pressure of the mains water will force the valve off the seating when the tap is opened and the spindle raised, allowing the water to flow. If back-flow or back-siphonage occurs in the system when the tap is open, the loose valve acts as a non-return valve, the back-flow of water forces the valve back on to the seating to prevent water flowing back into the water main. This prevents the possibility of contaminated water getting into the water main.

- The valves or jumpers on screw-down taps used in low-pressure systems, those that are tank or cistern fed, including those used in hot water systems (hot water draw-off taps), should be fixed to the spindle. This is because there is no risk of back-siphonage and the low pressure may not always be strong enough to lift the valve off the seating (see inset of Figure 4.24).

Valves in screw-down taps are fitted with a replaceable washer on the wearing surface, the part that is in contact with the seating. They are made from synthetic rubber or fibre. Screw-down taps and valves are mainly used on high pressure mains cold water pipelines because their gradual operation is less likely to cause water hammer.

**Water hammer** is caused when water flow is stopped instantly causing the kinetic energy created in the flow to be passed on to the pipes and fittings in the system, causing vibration and noise and possibly damaging the system.

Screw-down taps include the following:

**Bib taps** These are draw-off taps fitted above sanitary appliances such as sinks or on their own to supply water for buckets or hoses (Figure 4.23).

**Pillar taps** These are draw-off taps that are fitted to sanitary appliances like sink units, wash basins and baths. They have a long-threaded shank that allows them to be fitted into the appliance. Pillar taps for sink units should be the high-necked variety to allow buckets to fit underneath (Figure 4.24).

**Stop taps** These are used to shut off flow or control the rate of flow in pipelines. They are commonly fitted to the incoming water main in a building or on the feed pipe to individual appliances or fittings to shut off the water flow for repair and maintenance purposes (Figure 4.25).

**Drain-taps** These are fitted to the low point of all systems for draining down the system. They should have a hose union fitting and are controlled by a removable key or spanner to prevent unauthorised or accidental use (Figure 4.26).

Some drain taps are available without a packing gland and gland nut. Avoid fitting these because they leak when in use.

**Mixer taps** These are basically a pair of draw-off pillar taps, hot and cold, joined together by a common or joint mixing chamber and/or delivery spout to provide a mixed flow of

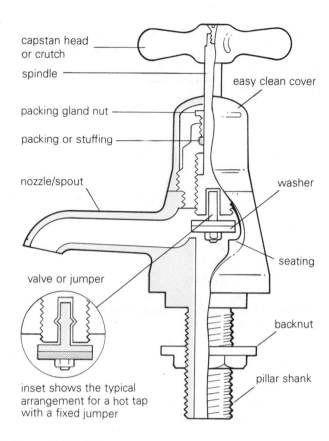

Figure 4.24   Pillar tap

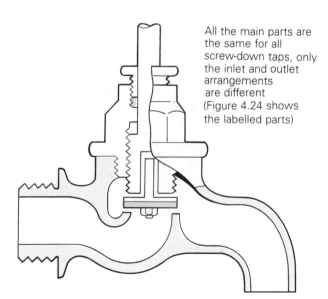

All the main parts are the same for all screw-down taps, only the inlet and outlet arrangements are different (Figure 4.24 shows the labelled parts)

*Figure 4.23*   Bib tap

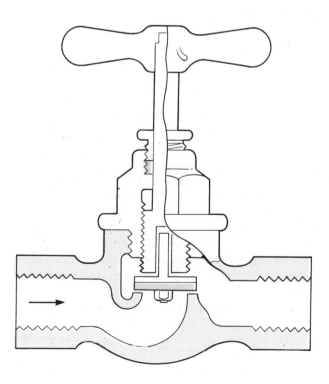

*Figure 4.25*   Stop tap

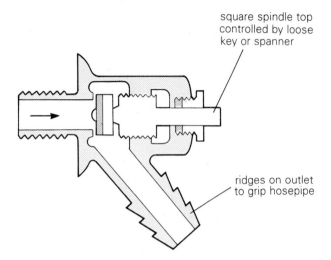

square spindle top
controlled by loose
key or spanner

ridges on outlet
to grip hosepipe

*Figure 4.26*  Drain off tap

hot and cold water. The hot and cold controls are separate,
only the spout is joint. They are used for sink units or baths.
Sink mixers are usually the dual-flow type where the water
only mixes after it has left the spout. With bath mixers,
which often include a shower attachment, the water mixes
inside the body of the fitting itself. Because of the
possibility of back-siphonage of water into the cold water
main with bath mixers, the cold water supply should be
from storage. Back-siphonage cannot occur with dual-flow
mixers so the cold supply can come directly from the main
(Figure 4.27).

> If the hot supply is mains fed and heated in an
> instantaneous mains heater, then the cold
> supply can also be fed directly from the main. It is
> important that, to prevent back-siphonage, both hot
> and cold water must be supplied at the same head
> pressure, i.e. both from storage or both off the main.

**Spray taps**   These are basically wash-basin pillar taps with a
perforated steel disc fitted inside the delivery spout to give a
fine spray. They are used in public toilets to provide a saving in
water. Because the delivery rate is less than a normal tap, a
maximum of 0.05 litres per second, no plug is needed in the
basin outlet. Spray mixer taps are also available with
combined hot and cold supplies to give a blended/mixed
draw-off. They are slightly different in operation from
ordinary spray taps in that the control head also adjusts the
amount of hot or cold water that mixes. Lever handles are
also available for these taps where the wrist or arm can be
used to control the spay; they are often found in clinics and
hospitals. Where spray mixers are fitted, the same restrictions
apply as for sink mixer taps, i.e. both hot and cold water
supplies must be fed into the tap at the same pressure.

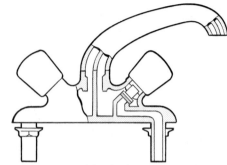

1.  Sink mixers or 'combination' sets are dual flow with no
    mixing inside the fitting

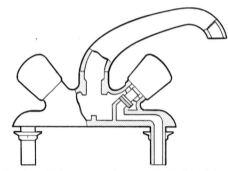

2.  Bath mixer fittings must be supplied with either hot
    and cold from storage or hot and cold from the mains
    (instantaneous  water heater)

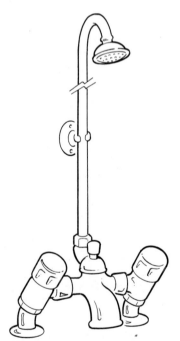

3.  Bath mixer and shower combination, same
    arrangement as in 2, that is hot and cold both from
    storage or both from  mains

*Figure 4.27*  Mixer taps

**Globe valves** These look just like gate valves from the outside but they are screw-down in operation, just like stop taps. They are strong and durable with a wheel head and are used on high pressure pipelines, such as steam supplies, to isolate components or control flow. Because they are used mainly on steel pipe installations, globe valves are usually made with female threaded connections (Figure 4.28).

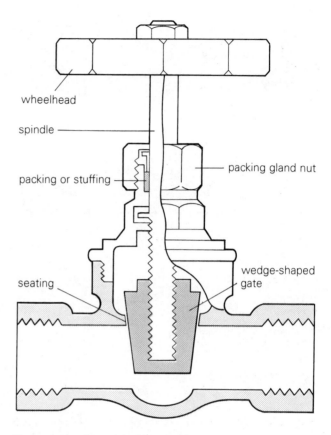

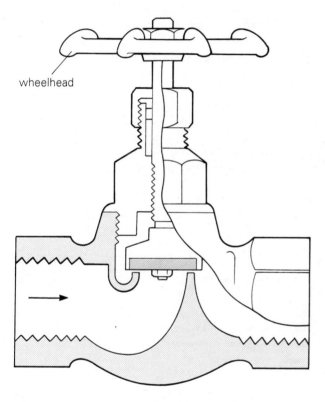

*Figure 4.28* Globe valve

*Figure 4.29* Gate valve

## Gate valves

Gate valves are used in low-pressure systems for shutting off or controlling the flow. When fully open they provide a 'full-way' or full bore flow through the valve, unlike screw-down taps. If a screw-down tap was used in a low-pressure system, the pressure would be further reduced by the friction created by the complicated flow pattern through the seating arrangement. Gate valves do have a seating but the orifice is the same diameter as the diameter of the bore of the pipe connected to it and more importantly it is positioned across the flow so when the valve is opened the water flows straight through the valve with no changes in direction.

A hand-operated wheel head is connected to a non-rising spindle. When the head is turned, a circular disc or gate connected to the spindle will gradually rise or fall depending on the direction of the turn to open or close the valve (Figure 4.29).

## Plug cocks

Plug cocks or quarter-turn cocks are normally only used on low-pressure systems. They are used as either drain-off taps on heating or hot and cold water systems or as control and isolating taps on gas systems. They consist of a tapered plug with a hole drilled through it, which fits into a tapered hole in the body of the fitting. When the hole is in line with the pipe, denoted by a line on the square-headed top of the plug, it is open, and when the plug is turned through 45°, the hole is also moved out of line to leave the metal surface of the plug across the flow shutting it off (Figure 4.30).

A special removable key or spanner is used to control plug cocks. Because the action to shut them off is very quick, they should not be used on mains pressure or high pressure systems because of the risk of water hammer. The metal surfaces of the plug and the tapered hole should be greased to allow easy action and prevent corrosion.

A variation of the plug-cock is the **ball plug tap**. These are small versions of plug taps, but the main fitting consists of a 'ball and socket'. The ball has the hole drilled through it instead of a plug. The action is the same as a plug cock. They usually have a chrome finish with a fixed lever to control the action. They are used mainly as isolating taps on washing machines and dishwashers. Because they are normally kept

cock shown in open position
with line on top of the plug
in line with the body of
the fitting

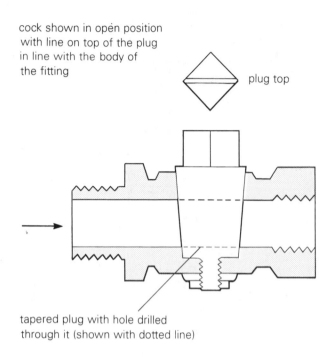

plug top

tapered plug with hole drilled
through it (shown with dotted line)

*Figure 4.30*  Plug cock

in the on position except for periods of maintenance, there is
unlikely to be a problem from water hammer. Washing
machine manufacturers do recommend turning off the
supplies when long periods without use are anticipated, to
protect the plastic or rubber hose connecting pipes.

## Ball valves

These are automatic flow control devices used to control the
incoming cold water supply for storage and feed cisterns and
also flushing cisterns. They work on the principle of a ball

float attached to a lever, which in turn is attached to a valve
which closes as the water level and float rise or opens as the
water level and float drop. There are two types in common
use: the 'Portsmouth' pattern and the diaphragm pattern.

### The Portsmouth ball valve

Water enters the fitting through an orifice and flows down
into the cistern. As the water level in the cistern rises, so
does the float which is connected to a lever arm. The lever
arm is connected to a horizontal valve or piston inside the
fitting. As the float rises, it causes the lever to move the valve
against the inlet orifice. The end of the valve which closes
against the orifice contains a removable synthetic rubber
washer (Figure 4.31). The amount of water allowed into the
cistern before the valve closes can be set by bending the
lever arm.

The orifices are removable and are available in different
sizes. Small orifices are used on high pressure or mains
supplies and large orifices should be fitted on low pressure
or storage fed supplies. Ball valves are often supplied with
both large and small replacement orifices.

A similar type of ball valve with a vertical arrangement of
the valve, known as a Croydon pattern, is also available but is
not commonly used.

On very high pressure water pipelines, another variation of
the Portsmouth pattern is available that reduces the possibility
of water hammer.

### The equilibrium ball valve

This is a larger version of the Portsmouth ball valve. A hole
drilled through the centre of the valve allows the water
pressure to act on both sides of the valve; a washer
connected to the end of the valve contains the water and
therefore the pressure at this end of the valve. Apart from
reducing the force needed by the lever to close the valve it
also reduces problems caused by water hammer (Figure 4.32).

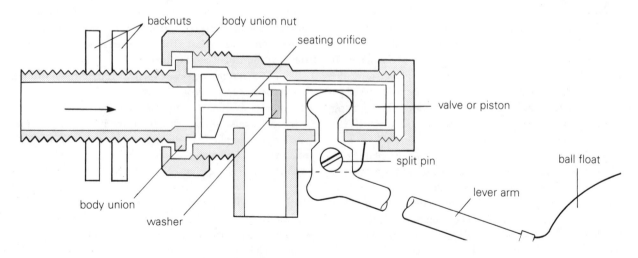

*Figure 4.31*  Portsmouth ball valve

## The diaphragm ball valve

This type of ball valve was developed to overcome some of the disadvantages of the Portsmouth sliding valve pattern. With a Portsmouth ball valve all the moving parts are in contact with the water and over a period of time, salts in the water can build up and prevent efficient action and in some cases can corrode components.

Water enters the fitting and flows through an orifice into the cistern. A ball float attached to a lever arm rises as the water level in the cistern rises. When the lever arm rises, its end pushes against a peg or pin which in turn presses against a flexible rubber diaphragm. As the water continues to rise the rubber diaphragm eventually presses against the orifice which stops the water flow (Figure 4.33). The only moving part of the internal mechanism in contact with water is the rubber diaphragm.

Other design features include: a float adjustment so the arm does not need to be bent; low maintenance; and the action of the lever and pin, which is more direct and therefore the operation is more efficient.

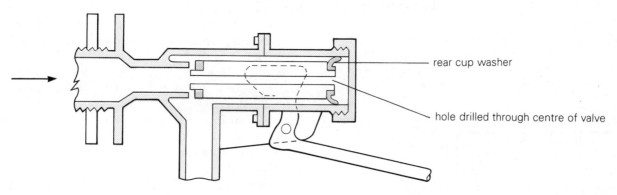

*Figure 4.32* Equilibrium ball valve

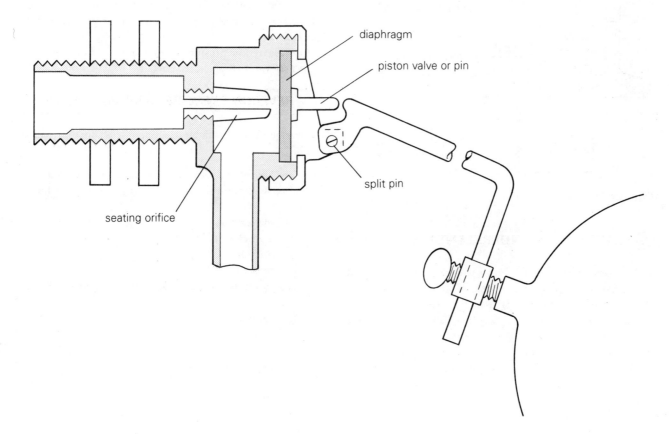

*Figure 4.33* Diaphragm ball valve

The outlet of the diaphragm ball valve is often on top of the valve which reduces the possibility of back-siphonage. Collapsible polythene silencer tubes also help to prevent this. If rigid silencer tubes are attached to ball valve outlets, they should contain anti-siphon holes near the top.

## Safety valves

These are fixed to hot water boilers and heaters to prevent excessive pressure building up. The commonest used by the plumber is the spring-loaded valve (Figure 4.34). A valve with a washer is kept in place over a seating by a spring which is secured by a pressure adjusting nut screwed to the body of the fitting. This is usually pre-set during manufacture. If a certain pre-determined pressure were to build up inside the system, the valve would rise up to relieve the pressure, allowing water to escape through holes in the side of the valve.

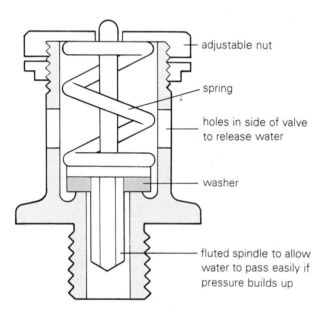

Figure 4.34   Safety valve

▓   CHECK YOUR UNDERSTANDING

● No matter what material you are working with it is helpful to understand the properties it possesses.
● Low carbon mild steel is used for most steel pressure pipework applications but it must be galvanised if used for cold water services to prevent corrosion of the pipe and discoloration of the water.
● Copper is a soft ductile metal, enabling it to be worked easily as sheetwork and bent easily as pipework, but it will harden if overworked.
● Dezincification or corrosion of the zinc content in brass in some waters will leave a porous material, so dezincification resistant brasses should always be used.

● Annealing is a form of heat treatment that can soften certain metals when they become work-hardened.
● There are two main types of plastics available: thermosetting plastics and thermoplastics. Thermosetting plastics cannot be reshaped after initial manufacture but thermoplastics can, which makes them a popular plumbing material.
● Lead is traditionally the material most closely associated with the plumber. The Roman word for lead was *plumbum*. The malleability of lead makes it ideal for use as both sheets and pipes.
● Materials such as copper and plastics have replaced the use of lead for water services in many countries because they are easier to install and carry less risk to health. Many solders are now being manufactured with a low lead content because of health risks.
● Plastic products are popular because they are generally cheaper, easier to install and easier to manufacture than metal equivalents.
● Aluminium in its pure form is ideal as a sheetwork covering because of its malleability, but only alloys of aluminium are suitably rigid for pipes and other components.
● Screw-down stop taps should be used to control flow on mains pressure cold water supplies.
● Full-way gate valves are used on low pressure water systems because they offer little resistance to flow.
● Never use quarter-turn plug cocks on mains cold water supplies inside buildings because they can create water hammer.
● Orifices on low pressure ball valves should be larger than those used on high pressure supplies.

### REVISION EXERCISES AND QUESTIONS

Answer questions 1 to 5 by selecting one of the four options given.

1   The ability of a metal to be worked or rolled into thin sheet without splitting or cracking is a property known as:
    i)    malleability
    ii)   elasticity
    iii)  ductility
    iv)   tenacity
2   Annealing is a form of heat treatment that will make metals:
    i)    easier to work
    ii)   less ductile
    iii)  more conductive
    iv)   harder to scratch
3   The commonest method of jointing steel pipe is to use:
    i)    capillary joints
    ii)   solvent welded joints
    iii)  threaded joints
    iv)   compression joints

4  Brass is a mixture of which two metals?
   i)   steel and copper
   ii)  copper and zinc
   iii) zinc and lead
   (iv) lead and tin

5  Plastics are popular plumbing materials used throughout the world because:
   i)   they are relatively cheap and easy to mass produce
   ii)  they can withstand all forms of wearing and degradation
   iii) they have a low thermal expansion rate and are easy to paint
   iv)  they will not burn and they need fewer fixings

6  Which type of steel pipe is the most suitable for carrying cold water supplies and why?

7  On a screwed joint between steel pipes, where would you find the 'washout' thread and why should it be found there?

8  List the main points to consider when installing thermoplastic pipes for domestic hot and cold water supplies.

9  Why is vitreous china a good material to use for the manufacture of sanitary appliances?

10 List the relative advantages and disadvantages of ceramic materials and stainless steel for sanitary appliances.

11 How does a stop tap prevent back-siphonage of water into the main supply?

12 Which tap, valve or cock should be fitted on a low-pressure cold water pipeline and why?

13 What is the difference between the valves or jumpers in hot and cold water draw-off taps?

14 What flow control device would create water hammer if fitted on a cold water main pipeline?

15 Describe the operation of a Portsmouth ball valve.

# Fixings and fastenings

## Introduction

Plumbers have to fix pipes and other items of equipment to a wide variety of building materials. This means that a good understanding of the various fixing methods that can be used is important if reliable, safe and cost-effective working practices are to result. In this chapter we will explore the basic techniques of fixing and fastening.

## Basic principles of fixings

Fixings can be made using the following methods:
1. By direct fixing into the building structure using screws and nails.
2. By expansion in a drilled hole in brick and concrete.
3. By use of adhesives or by anchoring in cement grout.
4. By embedding bolts in concrete as the building is erected.

### Choice of fixing

The best type of fixing to use in a particular situation depends on a number of factors including: the type and nature of the material to be fixed to; the weight of the item fixed; and the number and size of the fixings that can be used. The cost of the fixings and their ease and speed of use are also important factors to consider.

### Direct fixings

Ordinary steel nails and wood screws are suitable for fixing directly into timber only. Special hardened steel masonry nails are available and these can be driven into brickwork and concrete to fix timber batons and pipe-boards. If a cartridge-powered fixing gun is used, the hardened nails can even be driven directly into steel girders. Great care is needed when using these hardened steel fixings; suitable goggles must be worn and training is necessary before using a cartridge-fixing gun.

### Types of nail (Figure 5.1)

1  **Round wire nail**  Mainly used in carpentry work, for example erecting timber shuttering for concrete. Lengths available from 25 to 150 mm.

2  **Oval brad**  The oval shape of this nail helps to prevent the timber from splitting along the grain. Lengths are the same as for round wire nails.

3  **Lost head nail**  Mainly used for joinery work; it has a small head that can be punched below the surface of the timber. Available from 40 to 75 mm in length.

4  **Clout head nail**  Used to fix roofing sheets, felt and slates. It has a large head to prevent the material from tearing away from the fixing. Clout head nails are usually made from galvanised steel or copper to prevent corrosion. Lengths available from 12 to 50 mm.

5  **Panel pin**  A thin nail used to fix beading and hardboard or plywood panels. Lengths from 20 to 40 mm available.

### Types of screw

Screws offer significant advantages over nails. They have a much higher pull-out strength and can also be easily removed if necessary. Steel wood screws should only be used in dry situations; if the screw is to be fixed in damp areas or for fixing sanitary fittings then it should be protected from corrosion. Black varnished screws offer some corrosion resistance but zinc coated or brass screws are better. Traditional wood screws are tapered, with the thread cut into the metal. This means that the shank is the largest diameter; a pilot hole is often required for the thread and a clearance hole for the shank.

**Twinfast screws** are also available. This type of screw has advantages over traditional wood screws. The basic difference being that the thread of the screw is formed as a double helix; this means that it drives into timber or a plastic plug twice as fast. Furthermore, twinfast screws are made from zinc-plated hardened steel. This means that they are both stronger and more corrosion resistant.

**Mirror screws** can also be useful; these have a chrome-plated dome-shaped top which is screwed into a threaded

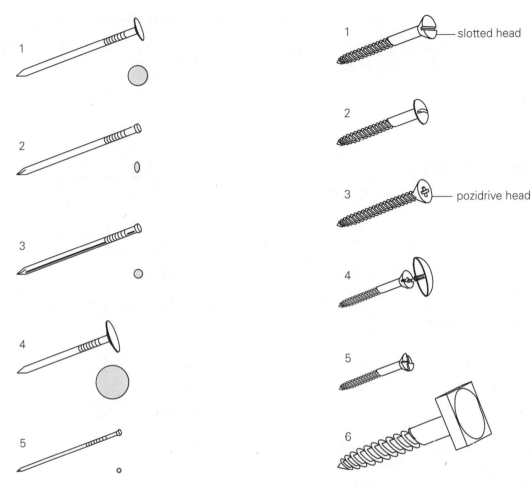

Figure 5.1  Types of nail

Figure 5.2  Types of screw

hole in the screw body. They are used to fix mirrors which have pre-drilled holes and can also be used to good effect for fixing bath panels.

### Screw head patterns (Figure 5.2)
Screws are available with heads shaped for two types of driver: slotted pattern and pozidrive or cross-head pattern. **Pozidrive screws** have the advantage that the screwdriver is less liable to slip and cause injury or damage to fixing surfaces.

**1    Countersunk screw**  The head lies flush with the surface when fixed.

**2    Round head screw**  These are used to fix pipe brackets and other metal components. The shaped head sits on top of the bracket.

**3    Twinfast screw**  These are available in both countersunk and round head patterns.

**4    Mirror screw**  These have a chromed dome-shaped top, which fastens into the screw top.

**5    Security screw**  These have a specially shaped head that enables the screw to be tightened but not unscrewed. They are used in public areas, such as toilets, to form vandal-resistant fixings.

**6    Coach screw**  These are used to fix heavy items and metal plates. The hexagon head enables a spanner to be used to tighten the screw.

### Screw sizes
Screws are available in a wide range of sizes, from 12 to 100 mm in length, and from 2 to 14 gauge in diameter.

## Fixing to solid materials

The basic method used to fix to solid materials, such as masonry, brick and concrete, is by expansion in a fixing hole. This method makes use of a variety of different devices to increase the outside diameter of the fixing, causing it to become wedged tightly against the sides of the hole; it is then held in place by friction.

### Depth of fixings

For best effect, good solid brick or masonry is necessary to resist the expansion pressure of the fixing. Generally, *the deeper the fixing and the larger its diameter, the stronger the fixing will be.* Also, take care to use the correct diameter of rotary percussion masonry drill. If the drill used is too large, the fixing will be weak. Furthermore, take care not to drill fixing holes too close to the edge of the material otherwise the expansion force can burst material off the edge, spoiling the finish and weakening the fixing and structure (Figure 5.3).

## Plastic and fibre plugs

At their most basic, these expansion fixings consist of a colour-coded plastic or a fibre plug that is a snug fit when inserted into a drilled hole. A suitably sized wood screw is then driven into the plug to make a secure fixing in most types of masonry, brickwork or concrete. A range of plug sizes is available to suit screws from number 4 to 22 in diameter (Figure 5.4).

### Using plastic and fibre plugs
1. drill a hole of the correct diameter and depth using a suitable masonry drill;
2. insert the plug;
3. pass the screw through the item to be fixed and into the plug;
4. screw home until tight.

### Plastic plugs for lightweight building blocks
This type of plug fixing has a ribbed, contoured body that can cut into the soft block as the fixing screw is driven home. The ribbed effect stops the plug from turning in the hole while the screw is tightened and the contoured shape resists the load on the fixing, preventing it from pulling out of the block (Figure 5.5).

## Expansion bolt fixings

These offer higher pull-out strengths for fixing heavier items of equipment or large diameter pipe supports. **Shield anchors** consist of a metal bolt which has a cone-shaped end

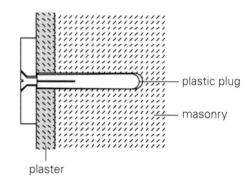

*Figure 5.4*  Plastic plug and screw

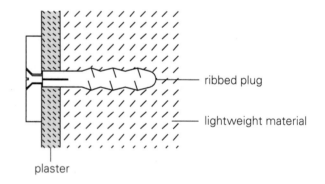

*Figure 5.5*  Plug for lightweight materials

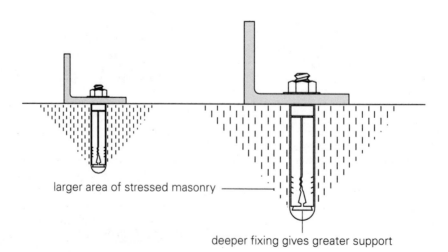

*Figure 5.3*  Effect of depth on the strength of fixings

section or cone-shaped nut. This is pulled into a four-segment metal shield. As the bolt is tightened, the shield expands against the sides of the hole causing it to grip the masonry (see Figure 5.3). The design of the anchor is such that if the load increases, the grip also increases (Figure 5.6).

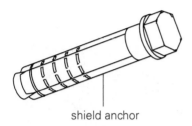

*Figure 5.6* Shield anchor expansion bolt fixing

### Using expansion bolt fixings

1. drill hole of recommended diameter and depth;
2. insert expansion bolt;
3. position the item to be fixed over the bolt;
4. tighten the nut on to the washer to expand the sleeve and secure the fixing.

**Sleeve anchors** are a simpler version of the shield anchor. Because the sleeve anchor is thinner in diameter it can be used to make fixings by drilling directly through the equipment mounting holes. This means that there are no problems of misalignment caused by the fixing holes being out of position relative to the equipment mounting holes (Figure 5.7).

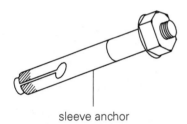

*Figure 5.7* Sleeve anchor expansion bolt fixing

## Chemical anchors

If fixings have to be made close to the edge of the structure then a chemical anchor can be used. This consists of a capsule of chemical resins that can be inserted into a drilled and cleaned hole in any solid material, including low-density blocks. Once the capsule has been inserted into the hole, the stud bolt fixing can be driven into it. This causes the capsule to burst and chemical resin to bond the stud bolt with the structure. *The anchor must be allowed to set before tightening the fixing.* Because the anchor does not use expansion, the fixing can be made close to the edge without danger of bursting.

## Fixing to hollow materials

A wide variety of different types of hollow construction methods are used including hollow concrete blocks, plasterboard and timber studs, and patented partition methods. Because insufficient thickness of solid material is available, the previous methods of securing a fixing by expansion in a hole is impractical. A variety of devices have been developed that can be inserted through a small hole before expanding to a large size in the cavity behind the solid material. **Spring toggle bolts** are one example. When the fixing is tightened, the load is spread over a relatively wide area at the back of the solid material giving a strong secure fixing (Figure 5.8).

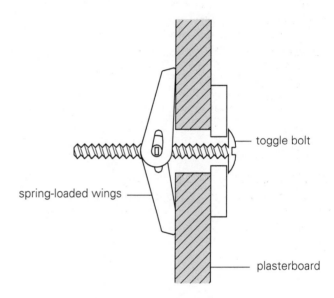

*Figure 5.8* Spring toggle fixing

### Using spring toggle bolts

1. drill a hole of the recommended diameter into the cavity;
2. pass the fixing screw through the fixture and screw a few turns on to the toggle;
3. collapse the wings of the toggle and push them through the hole until they spring apart;
4. tighten the screw until it is firm.

Spring toggle fixings are not suitable for use where the item to be fixed will require removal and replacement. If the fixing screw is removed, the spring toggle will be lost in the cavity of the block In this case a captive collapsible cavity fixing or cavity rivet is better. These have a flanged sleeve which holds them in position after tightening, enabling repeated removal and replacement of the fixing screw as required (Figure 5.9).

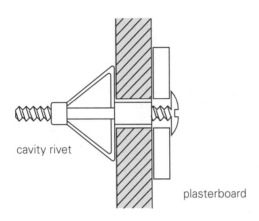

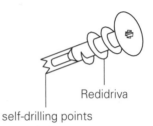
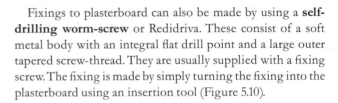

*Figure 5.10*  Self-drilling plasterboard anchor

Fixings to plasterboard can also be made by using a **self-drilling worm-screw** or Redidriva. These consist of a soft metal body with an integral flat drill point and a large outer tapered screw-thread. They are usually supplied with a fixing screw. The fixing is made by simply turning the fixing into the plasterboard using an insertion tool (Figure 5.10).

*Figure 5.9*  Cavity rivet fixing

**Using a cavity rivet**
1.  drill a hole of recommended diameter into the cavity;
2.  insert the fixing sleeve and tighten the fixing screw on to the holding tool (this prevents the fixing from turning in the hole) until the fixing grips the hollow material;
3.  remove the fixing screw and holding tool;
4.  insert the screw through the fixture and into the fixing sleeve;
5.  tighten the screw until firm.

## Bolt fixings

Bolt fixings are often used to secure pipe supports to metal parts of the building structure. They can be inserted through drilled holes or used to clamp brackets on to girders. Bolts usually have hexagonal heads. Zinc-plated roofing bolts are also used to secure sheet roofing materials and gutter joints. Strictly speaking, a bolt has a plain unthreaded section of shank. If it is threaded all the way up to the head it is a **set screw** or **machine screw**. Threaded rod is useful for forming hanger brackets for suspended pipe runs (Figure 5.11).

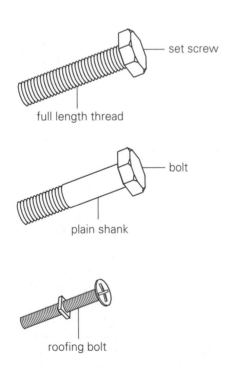

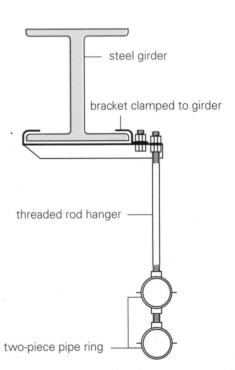

*Figure 5.11*  Bolt fixings

When tightening nuts and bolts, always use the correct size of spanner. This will ensure that the bolt or nut can be tightened with the correct amount of turning force (torque) without stripping the thread or shearing the bolt. These dangers will be present if a large adjustable spanner with the jaws closed down is used. If a small pipe wrench with toothed wide-opening jaws is used there is a danger that the bolt will not be fully tightened. Also, the teeth will bite into the bolt head, damaging it. When using bolt fixings, consider fitting washers under the head and nut. They will spread the load and make a better fixing. If the bolt is fitted to equipment that is subject to vibration then use a spring washer or a lock nut with a nylon insert to prevent the fixing from shaking loose.

## Adhesives and grout fixings

When using adhesive materials it is important to observe the manufacturer's safety and operating instructions if a safe and secure fixing is to be achieved. Adhesives generally require that the surfaces to be fixed are clean and dry. Any dust, oil or grease that is present on the surface will prevent the adhesive from forming a proper bond and a weak joint will result. Even the slight film of grease left by apparently clean fingers is sufficient to cause problems, so once cleaned, do not touch the surfaces before the adhesive is applied. If the adhesive or any cleaning fluids are solvent or petroleum-based and give off inflammable vapours, use them only in well-ventilated areas and take care not to breathe in the vapours.

## Fixing ceramic materials

When fixing ceramic materials use waterproof adhesive in areas such as shower rooms. If cement grout is to be used to fix WC pans to concrete, make sure that the concrete is well moistened so that the cement has time to set before it dries out.

Take care to check the alignment of fixing holes in ceramic sanitary fittings such as washbasins and WC pans and cisterns. These are often made so that the fixing holes are angled and therefore not perpendicular to the fixing surface. If the fixing hole is not drilled at an angle to match the hole in the sanitary fitting, tightening the fixing screw can easily cause the brittle ceramic material to crack. Similarly, over-tightening the fixing screws will create the same problem. To prevent this, try to use a soft plastic or rubber washer (a tap washer is often suitable) between the screw head and the ceramic to allow a little movement (Figure 5.12).

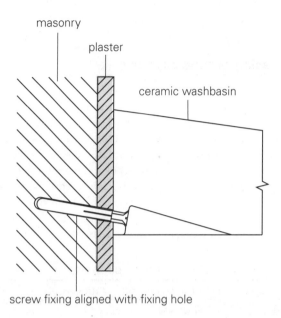

*Figure 5.12*  Aligning fixing screws for sanitary fittings

If pipe brackets or sanitary fittings have to be fixed on the surface of ceramic wall tiles using plastic plugs and screws, always drill slightly deeper than necessary. This will enable the plug to be inserted deeper so that it lies behind the tile, reducing the possibility of the tile cracking when the plug expands as the screw is tightened.

### Silicone sealants

It is often necessary to use silicone sealants around the edge of sanitary fittings to form a water-resistant finish. Use proper sanitary silicone, rather than silicone frame sealant. Sanitary silicone contains a fungicide and will therefore resist the formation of mould growth. Apply masking tape close to the edges before the silicone is smoothed around the joint. If the masking tape is then carefully peeled away, a neat finish will result.

## Fixings for pipe supports

When deciding on the best type of fixing to use for pipe supports, always consider the total weight of the pipe and its contents. This is particularly important where larger diameters of tube are concerned. For example, a 1 m length of plastic soil pipe weights slightly less than 1 kg when empty. If it is filled with water, the total weight of the 1 m length will increase to about 9 kg. If the pipe is vertical and has a height of, say, 6 m then the total force on the base would be over 50 kg. If the pipe has to be supported by a bracket at the base, then the fixings must be strong enough to carry the load.

## Spacing of tube supports

The suggested maximum spacings of supports for a variety of types of pipe materials, for both horizontal and vertical runs, are given in Table 5.1. All tube must be adequately supported and fixed otherwise mechanical damage, sagging or unnecessary movement and noise could be caused. Generally, metal tube is more rigid and therefore more self-supporting than plastic tube; this means that the supports can be spaced further apart. Also, apart from cast iron and ductile iron tube which are relatively brittle, the spacings for vertical runs of tube can be increased by 50%.

## Allowance for thermal movement

Where pipes are installed in long straight lengths of over 12 m, and are subject to significant temperature changes e.g. hot water pipes, the forces of expansion and contraction can be considerable. Care should be taken to allow the movement, without creating too much stress in the pipe, its supporting brackets and their fixings. This can be achieved by installing expansion joints, forming expansion loops or by fitting bends to change the direction of the pipe and to break up the long straight lengths (see the chapter on hot water supply for further details). Where anchor brackets have to be fitted to form fixed points, make sure that the brackets are secured to the structure using fixings, such as shield anchors, that will be able to withstand the forces involved.

*Table 5.1* Spacing for tube supports

| Suggested maximum spacing for tube supports | | | | | | | |
|---|---|---|---|---|---|---|---|
| Tube material | Nominal diameter (mm) | Spacing for horizontal runs (m) | Spacing for vertical runs (m) | Tube material | Nominal diameter (mm) | Spacing for horizontal runs (m) | Spacing for vertical runs (m) |
| Light gauge copper and stainless steel tube | 15 | 1.2 | 1.8 | Poly-ethylene | 15 | 0.4 | 0.8 |
| | 22 | 1.8 | 2.4 | | 20 | 0.4 | 0.8 |
| | 28 | 1.8 | 2.4 | | 25 | 0.4 | 0.8 |
| | 35 | 2.4 | 3.0 | | 32 | 0.45 | 0.9 |
| | 42 | 2.4 | 3.0 | | 40 | 0.45 | 0.9 |
| | 54 | 2.7 | 3.0 | | 50 | 0.55 | 1.1 |
| | 76 | 3.0 | 3.6 | Un-plasticised PVC | 15 | 0.6 | 1.0 |
| | 108 | 3.0 | 3.6 | | 20 | 0.7 | 1.2 |
| | 159 | 3.6 | 4.2 | | 25 | 0.75 | 1.5 |
| Heavy gauge copper and low carbon steel tube | 15 | 1.8 | 2.4 | | 32 | 0.85 | 1.7 |
| | 20 | 2.4 | 3.0 | | 40 | 0.85 | 1.9 |
| | 25 | 2.4 | 3.0 | | 50 | 0.9 | 2.1 |
| | 32 | 2.7 | 3.0 | Chlorinated PVC | 15 | 0.8 | 1.6 |
| | 40 | 3.0 | 3.6 | | 22 | 0.8 | 1.6 |
| | 50 | 3.0 | 3.6 | | 28 | 0.9 | 1.8 |
| | 80 | 3.6 | 4.5 | | 32 | 1.0 | 2.0 |
| | 100 | 3.9 | 4.5 | Poly-butylene | 10 | 0.3 | 0.5 |
| | 150 | 4.5 | 5.4 | | 12 | 0.3 | 0.5 |
| Cast iron and ductile iron tube | 51 | 1.8 | 1.8 | | 15 | 0.3 | 0.5 |
| | 76 | 2.7 | 2.7 | | 18 | 0.5 | 0.8 |
| | 102 | 2.7 | 2.7 | | 22 | 0.5 | 0.8 |
| | 152 | 3.6 | 3.6 | | 28 | 0.8 | 1.0 |

The suggested spacings should prove satisfactory in general service. Where the tube manufacturer recommends alternative spacings, use them in preference to the above.

## CHECK YOUR UNDERSTANDING

● Screw fixings are much stronger than nails and can be easily removed if necessary.

● Use pozidrive head screws whenever possible – the driver is less likely to slip and damage the fixing surface.

● Don't use countersunk screws on flat metal brackets – the raised appearance of the screw head will look shoddy.

● When securing very heavy items use shield anchors – their grip improves as the load increases.

● Ensure that fixings are made deep enough – generally the deeper the fixing the stronger it is.

● Always use the correct sized masonry drill – if the drill used is too large a weak fixing will result.

● Use the correct size of spanner when tightening bolt fixings to ensure sufficient torque.

● When using sealants and adhesives, always ensure that surfaces are clean and dry. Also, don't breathe the vapours unnecessarily.

### REVISION EXERCISES AND QUESTIONS

1   When fixing pipe brackets, what factors must be considered before deciding on the type of fixing to use?

2   Why are sleeve anchors best for fixing very heavy items of equipment?

3   When fixing ceramic sanitaryware using plugs and screws, how can the risk of breakage be minimised?

4   How can a neat finish be achieved when applying silicone sealant around sanitary fittings?

5   What type of fixing would be best to use when securing radiator brackets to plasterboard if the brackets are to be removed periodically to enable decoration behind the radiator?

# Cold water supply

## Introduction

A supply of pure and wholesome potable water is essential for a healthy life. This chapter examines basic aspects of water supply and treatment and the layouts and principles of both storage and non-storage cold water systems in buildings.

## Characteristics and properties of water

Water is a compound of the gases hydrogen and oxygen, its chemical symbol being $H_2O$. When at a temperature of 4°C, it is at its **maximum density** of 1000 kg per $m^3$. At normal atmospheric pressure, water is a liquid between 0°C and 100°C. If it is cooled below 0°C it freezes and becomes a solid (ice). As it freezes, it expands in volume by about 10% and this volume increase can burst pipes. If it is heated to 100°C, it boils and vaporises into a gas (steam), with a volume increase of about 1700 times.

### Force and pressure

Water, like all liquids, pushes on the sides and base of the vessel that contains it. It is also the case that a liquid at rest presses upwards on to things that are put into it. This is easy to prove by simply pushing an empty bottle down into some water in a bucket; as the bottle is pushed down the upward thrust of the water can be felt. The push of the water against the bottle is a **force** and the international unit of force is the **newton** (N). One newton is the force that gives a mass of 1 kg an acceleration of 1 $m/s^2$. The acceleration of objects due to gravity near the surface of the Earth is 9.81 $m/s^2$ so a 1 kg weight has a force of 9.81 N.

We often refer to **pressure** when discussing water systems; to the layman force and pressure might be thought to be the same thing. Plumbers must be more careful. Pressure is measured by the force exerted divided by the surface area on which the force acts. Take the example of a brick 0.2 m × 0.1 m × 0.1 m in size with a weight of 1 kg, resting on a bench. The brick is exerting a downward force of 1 kg × 9.81 = 9.81 N on to the bench due to gravity. If the brick is lying on its side the pressure exerted will be:

$$= 9.81 \text{ N}/0.2 \text{ m} \times 0.1 \text{ m}$$
$$= 9.81 \text{ N}/0.02 \text{ m}^2$$
$$= 490.5 \text{ N}/\text{m}^2.$$

If the brick is then stood on its end the pressure exerted will be:

$$= 9.81 \text{ N}/0.1 \text{ m} \times 0.1 \text{ m}$$
$$= 9.81 \text{ N}/0.01 \text{ m}^2$$
$$= 981 \text{ N}/\text{m}^2$$

The force remains the same but the pressure has doubled because the area is now halved. The international unit for pressure is the **pascal** (Pa); 1 $N/m^2$ is equal to 1 Pa.

> Note: pressure can be quoted in a variety of other units, such as: $kg/m^2$, $kg/cm^2$, $lb/ft^2$; notice that in each case there is a unit for force and another for area. Another useful unit of pressure is the **bar**; 1 bar is equal to 101.3 kPa or standard atmospheric pressure; 1 bar pressure is approximately equal to 10 m head of water.

## Water pressure

Pressure in liquids is directly proportional to the density of the liquid (in the case of water this is normally 1000 $kg/m^3$ but it does vary slightly with temperature) and the depth measured vertically. Imagine a tall vertical pipe sealed at the base. If the area of the base was 1 $m^2$ and the pipe was filled to a depth of 1 m, the pipe would contain 1 m$^3$ of water. This would weigh 1000 kg and exert a force on the base of 1000 kg $\times$ 9.81 $\times$ 1 m$^2$ = 9810 N/m$^2$ (or 9.81 kN/m$^2$) and the pressure on the base would also be 9.81 kPa. If another 1 m$^3$ of water was added, the depth of water would become 2 m, the weight acting on the base would be 2000 kg and the force on the base would double to 19.62 kPa, and so on. Another useful way of expressing water pressure is by the concept of **head of water**. By noting the height of water in pipework, a value for the pressure can be fixed.

It is important to note that the depth of water has to be measured *vertically* from the water surface to the level of the tap or another point in the system even if the pipe slants. In Figure 6.1, the water levels in the tubes are the same even though the sizes and shapes are different. The water is at rest and so the pressure at the point where the tubes join must be equal on all sides even though there is a much greater weight of water in the large tube compared to the small one. It is easy to show that pressure increases with depth by drilling a series of holes in the side of a tall container and filling it with water. The water will spray further out of the holes the lower they are (Figure 6.2).

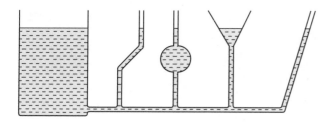

*Figure 6.1* Water finds its own level

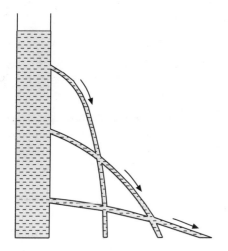

*Figure 6.2* Pressure increases with depth

# Water supply

All our water supplies stem from the oceans; heat from the sun evaporates water vapour from the sea leaving the dissolved salts behind. The water vapour forms clouds which eventually fall to Earth as rain. The rain accumulates into streams and rivers eventually flowing back to the sea; this is known as the **water cycle** (Figure 6.3).

## Water purity

As rain falls through the air, it absorbs oxygen and carbon dioxide gases, causing it to become very slightly acidic. This means that its purity and acidity when it reaches the ground will depend on the air quality through which it falls. Also, in urban areas, sulphur dioxide from burning fuel will often be present in rainwater making it slightly more acidic.

Once rainwater starts to flow along the ground and percolates through the rocks it can dissolve any soluble mineral salts that are present. For example, if water flows through chalk, which is insoluble calcium carbonate ($CaCO_3$), the carbon dioxide ($CO_2$) in the water ($H_2O$) can combine with the chalk and change it to form calcium bicarbonate ($Ca(HCO_3)_2$) which is soluble. The chemical reaction is:

$$CaCO_3 + CO_2 + H_2O \rightarrow Ca(HCO_3)_2$$

and the quantity of calcium bicarbonate that will be dissolved will depend on the amount of carbon dioxide in the water.

Salts of calcium, magnesium and sodium are often found in rainwater. These salts prevent soap from forming a lather easily. To describe this, the idea of **hardness** and **softness** of water has been developed to differentiate types of water depending on the presence, or not, of dissolved salts. Rainwater which has been collected directly from roofs or from ground covered in upland vegetation will generally be soft, while river, spring and well water will vary in hardness depending on the type of ground it runs through.

Apart from the fact that the user might notice a difference in taste and the amount of soap required to form a lather when washing, hard water is not usually a problem in cold water systems. Soft water, on the other hand, being slightly acidic, can be aggressive and corrode metal pipes. For example, certain types of soft water can attack fittings made from brass (a copper/zinc alloy). This is known as **dezincification**; what happens is that the zinc is corroded away by the water, leaving behind a porous, brittle fitting.

## Acidity/alkalinity of water

This is measured on the **pH** scale which has values from 0 (the strongest acid) to 14 (the most alkaline). Pure water is said to be neutral and has a pH of 7. Knowledge of the nature of a water

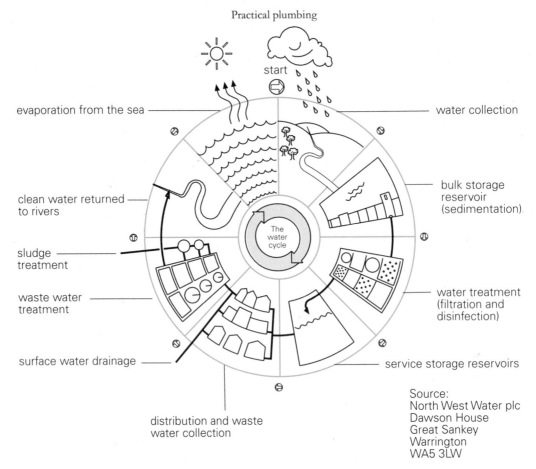

evaporation from the sea

water collection

clean water returned
to rivers

bulk storage
reservoir
(sedimentation)

sludge
treatment

waste water
treatment

water treatment
(filtration and
disinfection)

surface water drainage

service storage reservoirs

distribution and waste
water collection

start

The
water
cycle

Source:
North West Water plc
Dawson House
Great Sankey
Warrington
WA5 3LW

*Figure 6.3*  The water cycle

supply is very useful to a plumber; it allows a better choice of materials and can offer explanations of problems when, for example, corrosion of the pipes in a system occurs. The pH value of a particular water can be checked using **universal indicator paper**. This is simply a strip of absorbent paper that has been impregnated with indicator chemicals. If the paper is moistened with the water to be tested, any colour change can be compared to a reference strip of colours to give a reading of the acidity or alkalinity of the water as a value on the pH scale.

## Sources of water

On a small scale, water can be collected as run-off from roofs and stored in cisterns or tanks for later use. Alternatively, naturally occurring springs, a bore hole and pump or a well can be used as a source of water. On a larger scale, the public water supply authority will use river water or water from lakes if these are available. If necessary, they will drill bore holes or construct reservoirs to store water to maintain the supply in periods of low rainfall. Often the water supply for a town is pumped from a river or lake up to a water tower, from there it can flow down through the mains and is distributed to the buildings.

### Spring water

The nature of the underlying rock strata will determine whether spring water is wholesome. Surface springs are of doubtful quality. Deep seated springs, on the other hand, are more likely to be wholesome because the spring water will have emerged from below an impervious strata through a fault or slip in the rocks (Figure 6.4).

### River and lake water

River and lake water must always be regarded as suspect as it is likely to be polluted by run-off from cultivated fields and by waste water from sewerage or industrial processes.

### Wells and bore holes

Wells and bore holes can be classified as either shallow or deep. A shallow well is one where the well does not pass through an impervious rock strata. A shallow well is of doubtful quality. A deep well will have been drilled through an impervious strata and the water that is extracted will have percolated slowly through the ground over a very long period of time. In doing so, it is likely to have been purified by natural means. Provided the well is lined to prevent surface water entering it, the well water will usually be wholesome. Normally the water from the well will have to be raised or pumped to the surface. However, where the contours of the land happen to form a depression and the surface of the land at the site of the well or bore hole is below the surrounding water table an **artesian well** is formed. In this case the well water will rise to the surface naturally due to the water pressure in the underlying rocks (Figure 6.4).

## Water treatment

Water usually needs to be treated to make it safe to drink. Depending on the nature of the water, the treatment varies but will usually include many of the following processes.

## Sedimentation

Where water can be allowed to remain undisturbed for a period of time (such as in a lake or reservoir), particles of grit, mud or other solid matter can sink to the bottom. Public water suppliers take advantage of this as the initial purification process.

## Filtration

Filtration consists of passing the water through sand to remove any remaining solids; either a **slow sand filter**, where the water passes through a sand and gravel bed (Figure 6.5), or a **pressure filter** (Figure 6.6) will be used.

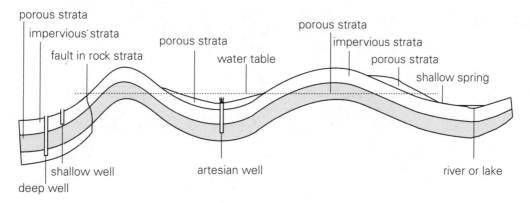

*Figure 6.4* Sources of water

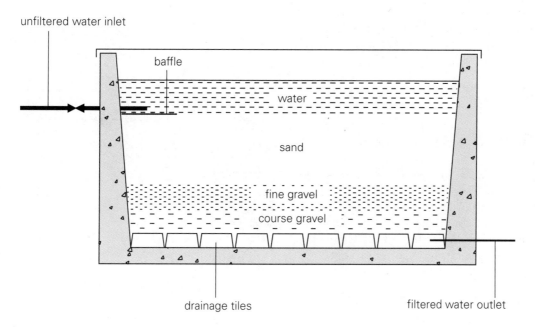

*Figure 6.5* Slow sand filter

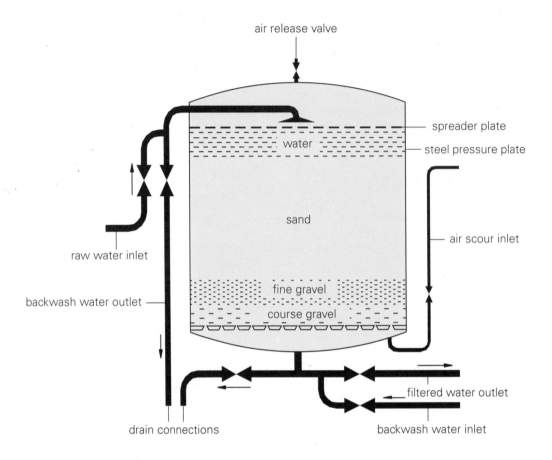

*Figure 6.6*  Pressure filter

The pressure filter is much quicker in operation and so will take up less space. Also, as the filter becomes clogged with debris it is necessary to clean it; this is quickly achieved by pumping previously cleaned water back through the filter, thus washing out the sludge that the filter has trapped.

## Treatment of hard water

### Water softener

Where the water is unacceptably hard a **base-exchange water softener** can be used. These are available as small units for use within a single building as well as larger units for the public water supply; a small domestic unit is illustrated in Figure 6.7. The base exchanger process works by reacting silicates (Si) of sodium (Na), calcium (Ca) and aluminium (Al), known as **zeolites**, with the dissolved salts in the water. For example, where calcium bicarbonate is present in the water the reaction is:

$$Na_2Al_2Si_2O_8 + Ca(HCO_3)_2 \rightarrow CaAl_2O_8 + 2NaHCO_3$$

As the water is softened, the sodium in the zeolite becomes absorbed into the water and is eventually exhausted.

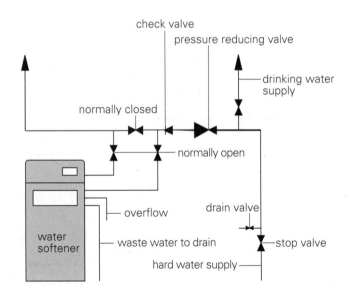

*Figure 6.7*  Base exchange domestic water softener

However, by slowly washing a brine solution made from common salt (sodium chloride – NaCl) through the softener, the zeolite is regenerated. At the same time, the chlorides of calcium or magnesium are washed out with the waste water allowing the zeolite to be reused.

### Water conditioners

There are two types of **water conditioner**: magnetic (where the water passes through an electro-magnetic field) and chemical (where the water flows through a container of polyphosphonate crystals). Water conditioners do not soften the water by removing the hard salts, they change the shape of the salt crystals from jagged to smooth (Figure 6.8). The effect is that the crystals cannot bind together and so do not become attached to the pipes. Water conditioners can be used to treat the supply of water feeding instantaneous water heaters; they help to keep the heat exchanger free from the scale that would otherwise reduce its efficiency.

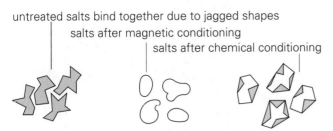

1. View of hardness salts under microscope

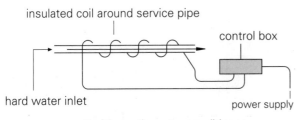

2. Magnetic water conditioner

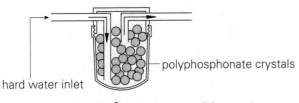

3. Chemical water conditioner

*Figure 6.8* Water conditioners

## Treatment of soft water

Where the water supply is too soft and acidic, problems of **cupro-solvency** or **plumbo-solvency** corrosion can occur. The usual method of treatment in this case is to add an alkali to neutralise the water. This is done by adding controlled amounts of lime or soda to the water to increase the pH closer to 7.

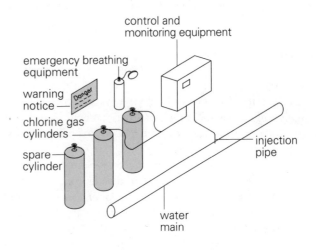

*Figure 6.9* Disinfection by addition of chlorine gas

## Disinfection

Once the water has been filtered, it is usually **disinfected** to destroy any bacteria present. This can be done by adding a very small amount of chlorine gas (Figure 6.9). A very small amount of ammonia is also sometimes added with the chlorine to remove the taste of chlorine from the water.

# Water distribution

## Water mains

Once treated, the water can be distributed through a system of trunk mains to service different areas. Within each area, water mains are used with service pipes running to individual consumers. A simplified layout is illustrated in the diagram of the water cycle (see Figure 6.3). This shows in schematic form the various stages through which the public water supply passes during treatment and distribution.

### Laying water mains

When laying water mains make sure that they are buried sufficiently deep so that any load due to traffic will not cause damage. Normally, the depth under roads should be 0.9 m. In regions where frost protection is necessary, 0.75 m will give adequate protection to the service pipes that run from the water mains into each property. Service mains have to be laid with varying gradients following the contours of the land; this can create problems due to the collection of air at high points. Also, detritus (sludge) can collect at low points. Air release vent-valves and washout-valves can be fitted to the mains to overcome any problems caused by air-locks and enable the mains to be flushed out periodically. The service mains should also be fitted with full-way valves (sluice valves) at suitable locations to enable isolation for repair and maintenance.

### Size of water mains

The diameter of water mains should be large enough to provide sufficient volume flow and pressure to the premises connected to them. Generally, 30 m of head is sufficient for fire-fighting purposes. If the pressure is too great (over about 70 m) then the service pipes within the building will tend to be noisy.

Service mains are usually from 75 to 300 mm in diameter and can be installed using cast iron, ductile iron, reinforced concrete or plastic tubes. Whatever piping material and jointing system is used, it must conform to any local water regulations and be tested to twice its likely working pressure. Note that if the mains is to be tested before the trench is fully back-filled, it is very important to ensure that the joints can withstand the forces involved without bursting off the pipes. Concrete can be placed at the back of bends and branches where necessary, to resist the thrust of the water pressure in the mains during the test. New mains should be disinfected using a solution of sodium hypochlorite before being brought into use (see later section).

### Sources of pressure in water mains

In areas where service reservoirs can be located at a high level, the water pressure in the mains is a result of gravity and the height of the reservoir. For example, if the reservoir is 40 m above the mains, then the formula to work out the pressure will be:

depth of water in m × 9.81 = kPa
= 40 m × 9.81
= 392 kPa.

In areas where the land is flat, a **pump** can be used to raise the water pressure in the mains and fill large tanks fitted at the top of water towers, from where the water can flow by the force of gravity to consumers.

## Pumps

Pumps are mechanical devices for providing pressure or moving water. There are a number of different types

including: lift, lift and force, diaphragm and centrifugal. Atmospheric pressure is one of the factors that determines the height that water can be lifted on the **suction** side of the pump. An ideal pump could, in theory, raise the water by about 10 m up the suction pipe. In practice, this height cannot be reached so in deep wells, for example, it is necessary to position the pump near to the bottom of the well and force the water up from the bottom.

### Lift pump

The **lift pump** consists of a piston fitted with a non-return-valve, or 'clack' valve (valve A, Figure 6.10). This is moved up and down in a cylinder by a lever handle. A second non-return-valve (valve B, Figure 6.10) is fitted at the base of the

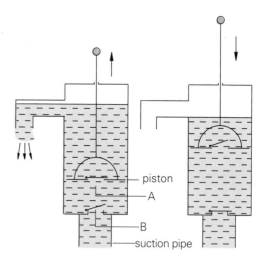

Simple lift pump

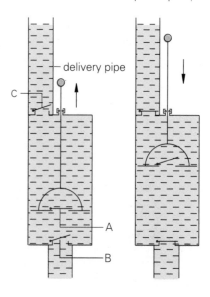

Simple lift and force

*Figure 6.10*  Simple lift pumps

cylinder. On the piston upstroke, water is drawn up into the cylinder through valve B and the water already in the cylinder is discharged through the spout, due to valve A closing. On the down stroke, valve B closes and the water in the cylinder passes through valve A ready for discharge on the next stroke.

### Lift and force pump
By adding another non-return-valve on the pump outlet (valve C, Figure 6.10), and connecting a delivery pipe to the pump outlet, the simple lift pump can be improved so that the water can be forced up from deeper wells and bore-holes. The pump works in the same way as the lift pump but, as the piston is raised, the water above it is forced through valve C into the delivery pipe. Provided sufficient force is available, water can be raised by many metres using the **lift and force pump**.

### Well and bore hole pumps
Modern well and bore hole pumps have been developed so that the pump head can be lowered down the suction tube by the drive shaft and operated from the surface by hand or machine power. When maintenance of the piston seal or non-return-valves is required, the pump head can be pulled back up the tube by withdrawing the drive shaft. Shallow-well pumps use the reciprocating piston method described previously (Figure 6.11), and can lift water up to 45 m. A typical pump will require a bore hole of 100 mm diameter and can lift about 0.4 l per stroke.

### Rotor/stator pumps
Deep well pumps are available that use a different method of pumping – the progressing cavity rotor/stator principle. In this pump, a specially shaped hardened chrome-plated rotor lies inside a moulded nitrile rubber stator. The two touch along a ribbon of contact, and behind this a sealed capsule is created that alternates from suction to discharge as the rotor turns inside the stator. The liquid in the capsule is then forced under positive pressure through the pump element and up the pump riser (Figure 6.12). As the rotor sweeps over the full surface of the stator with each turn, it is impossible for algae to grow; also, iron oxide deposits cannot accumulate inside the pump.

   This pump is designed to be dropped and retrieved through the rising main as before; the pump head contains gears that turn the hand crank movement through 90° to rotate the drive shaft. Only annual inspection and lubrication of the drive-head is required; the pump element itself will usually give many years of service without removal from the borehole. It too requires a 100 mm bore hole and can draw water up from as low as 90 m by hand power, at a rate of up to 0.3 l/s with a steady non-pulsating flow.

### Diaphragm pump
The operating principle of the **diaphragm pump** is similar to the lift pump mentioned previously. However, the piston and

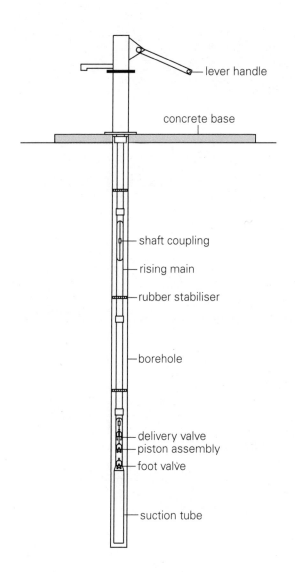

*Figure 6.11*  Shallow well pump

cylinder are replaced by a rubber diaphragm. This makes the manufacture of the pump simpler. Flexing the diaphragm by the operation of a hand lever (or crank shaft and connecting rod if motor driven) creates the suction and pressure that moves the water (Figure 6.13).

### Centrifugal pump
In the centrifugal pump, an **impeller** is rapidly rotated, usually by an electric motor. As it spins, the water at the centre of the impeller is forced outwards by **centrifugal force**. Try spinning a small weight tied on the end of a piece of string to feel the effect of centrifugal force. The impeller spins inside the pump body; this is shaped so that the water is channelled into the centre of the impeller on the pump suction side and around the outside of the body until it is forced out of the pump discharge (Figure 6.14).

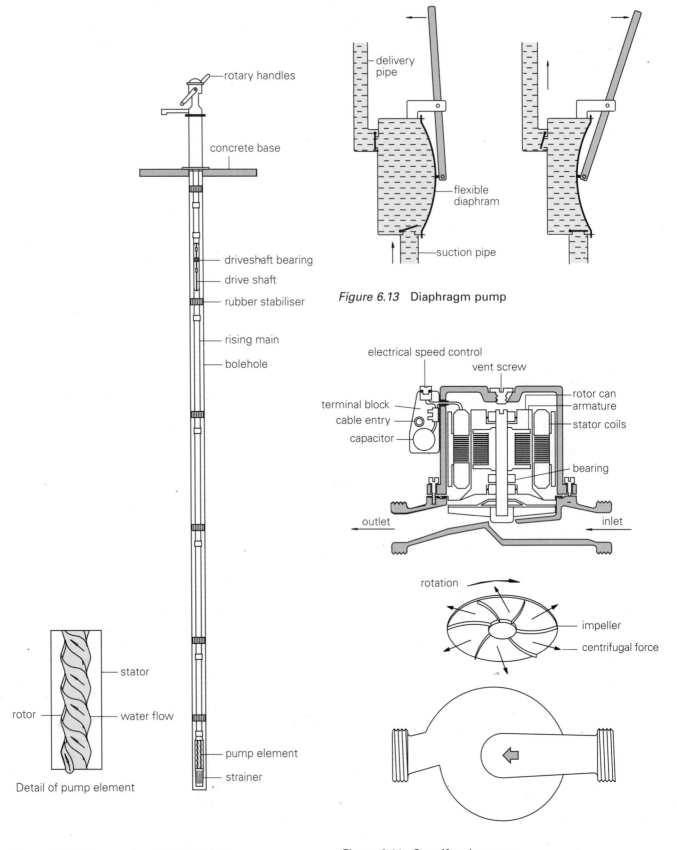

rotary handles

concrete base

driveshaft bearing

drive shaft

rubber stabiliser

rising main

bolehole

pump element

strainer

stator

rotor — water flow

Detail of pump element

Figure 6.12   Deep well rotor/stator pump

delivery pipe

flexible diaphram

suction pipe

Figure 6.13   Diaphragm pump

electrical speed control

vent screw

terminal block

cable entry

capacitor

rotor can
armature

stator coils

bearing

outlet

inlet

rotation

impeller

centrifugal force

Figure 6.14   Centrifugal pumps

## Single and multi-stage centrifugal pumps

A typical small single-stage centrifugal pump can create about 5 to 6 m head pressure. Where it is necessary to raise the water by a greater height, a multi-stage centrifugal pump can be used. In this case, a number of impellers are mounted on to a single shaft driven by a powerful motor. The pump body is designed so that the discharge of one stage becomes the suction of the next. The effect of this is that the pumps act in series with a pressure increase for every added stage. In this way, the multi-stage centrifugal pump can create the high pressures necessary for fire-fighting or to pump water up to the top of water towers and high buildings.

# Cold water systems

Cold water systems in buildings must be installed so that they comply with local water regulations and standards if they are not to create health hazards. Generally, the regulations will specify the types of material and jointing systems that can be used to install pipework and fittings. They will also outline methods of installing water fittings so that the plumbing system does not create a danger to public health by creating problems of contamination due to backflow into the public water mains. The regulations will require control valves, servicing valves and drain valves to be fitted to prevent waste of water and allow for maintenance. They will also specify situations where pipes cannot be installed, such as in inaccessible parts of the building structure, through drain inspection chambers or in foul soil.

## Preservation of water quality

It is important that a plumbing system is installed so that the quality of the water supply is maintained and contamination cannot occur. To this end, there are four areas that should be considered:

● the materials from which the system is made;
● cross connections;
● stagnation;
● backflow of water into the pipework after its discharge.

### Unsuitable materials

If unsuitable materials are used to install the plumbing system, the water quality can be detrimentally affected. Examples of unsuitable materials in potable water systems include: lead pipe; plain steel tube; solders made from lead/tin alloys; linseed oil based jointing compounds; hemp based jointing filler material (the first two items can cause problems of lead poisoning while the last two items promote microbial growth in the water).

### Cross connections

If the pipework is wrongly installed so that water that has been drawn off for use or water from a closed circuit can flow into the cold water supply pipework through a cross connection, then contamination is likely to spoil the water quality. Figure 6.15 shows examples of cross connected pipework systems.

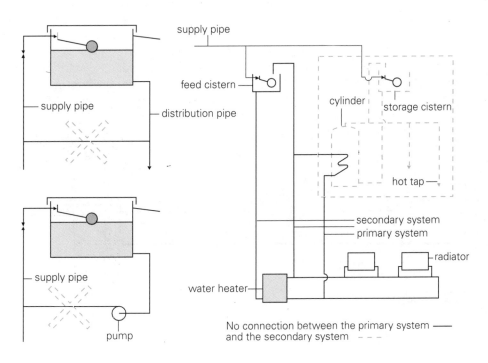

*Figure 6.15*  Examples of cross-connected pipework

**Stagnation**

If water can lie stagnant in the system for long periods, particularly if it is stored at temperatures between 20°C and 50°C, then growth of bacteria, such as *Legionella*, can occur in the system. If this contaminated water is then released as an aerosol, outbreaks of Legionnaires disease can occur.

**Backflow after discharge**

Backflow of water from sanitary fittings and appliances or industrial process plants can be a significant cause of contamination if the pipework system and other water fittings are wrongly installed. If water contaminated with sewage or industrial chemicals is drawn back into the mains then people can be poisoned.

## Service entry pipes

Copper, galvanised steel or plastic (polyethylene or UPVC) are usually used for the **service pipe** that runs from the water suppliers main into the building. The service pipe is connected to the main using a **ferrule valve**; a large radius bend is formed in the service pipe to allow for the possibility of ground movement without damage to the connection. The service pipe is then run to a point close to the boundary of the property where a **boundary stop-valve** is fitted in a chamber to allow access. This section of the water service is known as the **communication pipe**. The remainder of the service pipe, called the **supply pipe**, is then run from the boundary stop valve directly to the building, entering through a duct to become the **rising main** (Figure 6.16).

It is important to bury the pipe sufficiently deep that it will not be damaged by, for example, gardening operations or frost. If the supply pipe is close to the surface (less than 450 mm), it can be protected by running a plastic film as a marker and warning strip above the pipe as the trench is back-filled. If frost protection is required, the supply pipe should be buried to a depth of 750 mm. If the supply pipe is

to be installed using soft coiled copper tube or flexible plastic tube, it should be 'snaked' from side to side as it runs along the trench. This will add a little extra length so that the pipe will not be damaged if ground movement occurs.

The trench base should be free from projecting sharp rocks that could damage the pipe. If necessary a layer of sand can be put down before the pipe is run in the trench. Once laid, the trench can be backfilled and compacted in stages using selected soil that is free from boulders.

## Water meters

A water meter is often installed on the incoming supply pipe to enable charges to be calculated for water supplied. Where possible, the meter should be installed near the boundary of the property in a below-ground chamber that will protect the meter from damage. The chamber should be made of brick, concrete or plastic material and should be fitted with a lid marked 'water meter'. It should be large enough to enable joints to be made and the valves, required on both sides of the meter, to be operated. Where the meter is to be installed inside the premises, it must be fitted downstream of the main stop-valve in a position where it can be read easily (Figure 6.17 shows typical meter installations).

## Direct cold water system

The direct cold water system gets its name from the fact that all the cold taps are connected directly to the mains service pipe. A typical layout is illustrated in Figure 6.18. It is only suitable for the smallest of installations in single dwellings. Its main advantage is that it is the simplest arrangement of pipework and so most economical to install. It also has the advantage that drinking water is available at all taps. However, it has some disadvantages, and should not be installed where the mains water supply suffers from low

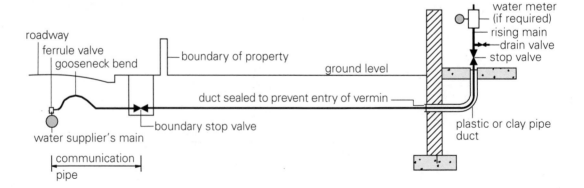

*Figure 6.16*   Service entry detail

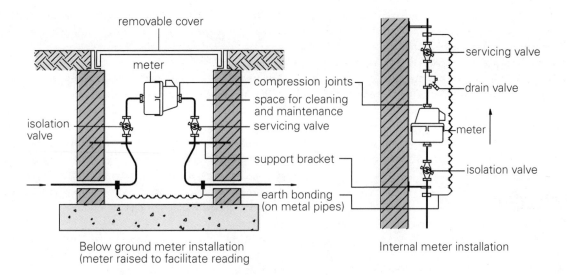

*Figure 6.17*  Water meter installation

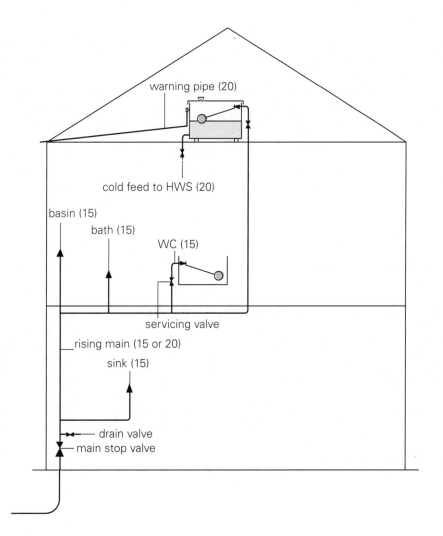

*Figure 6.18*  Direct cold water system layout

pressure or where there are interruptions to the mains supply. This is because there is no storage of water for cold taps or for fire fighting purposes within the building.

Where there is high pressure on the mains, the direct system tends to be noisy in operation causing a nuisance, especially when WC cisterns are flushed in the night. This is because the demand on the mains will be low, so the pressure will be at its highest, causing float-operated valves to hiss loudly as they refill the cistern. Water-hammer can also be a problem when taps are shut-off too quickly.

## Water-hammer

Water-hammer is a loud concussive noise created when a rapid flow of water is suddenly arrested by shutting a tap too quickly. It occurs because water is a virtually incompressible liquid. As the water flows along the pipe it has kinetic energy. When the tap is shut-off quickly, the kinetic energy has to be dissipated and so the loud bang is the result. If the tap is closed gradually, water-hammer will not occur.

In cases of persistent water-hammer, a **hydro-pneumatic accumulator** can be fitted into the pipeline. This is a small pressure vessel containing a rubber bladder into which water can flow (Figure 6.19). The space surrounding the bladder is filled with compressed air. When a tap is closed quickly, the water flow is forced into the bladder and the air is compressed further. The air acts as a shock absorber by soaking up the kinetic energy and preventing the water-hammer.

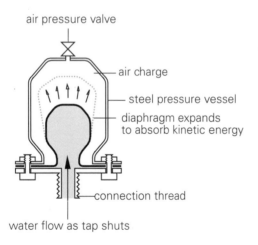

*Figure 6.19*  Hydro-pneumatic accumulator

## Storage cold water system

In the storage cold water system, the main service pipe only feeds the drinking water taps directly (at least one in the kitchen and one on each other floor if possible), as well as supplying water to a storage cistern sited at a high level in the building. The storage cistern then feeds the WC cistern(s), bath(s) and washbasin(s) by gravity flow through a system of **distribution pipes** (Figure 6.20).

### Advantages of storage cold water systems

Although more expensive to install because of the extra pipework, the relatively large pipe diameters and the large storage cistern, the system has some significant advantages, particularly where the mains water supply is not reliable. As well as affording a reserve of cold water in case of mains failure, most of the system operates at low pressure. This means that it will tend to be quieter in operation. Also, tap washers will last longer because they do not have to be closed off as tightly.

Another significant advantage is that most of the system is less likely to cause contamination of the public water main by **backsiphonage** or **backflow**.

## Cold water storage cistern

A **cistern** is simply a vessel for holding water with an unsealed lid. It should be watertight and fitted with a removable lid that has a filtered vent to allow air to enter but that keeps dirt and insects out of the stored water. Where necessary it should be insulated both against heat gain and frost. Cisterns should be made from materials that are sufficiently strong and do not impart toxicity, taste, odour, or colour, or encourage microbial growth in the water. Cisterns can be made from sheet steel welded together and then galvanised to prevent corrosion. They can also be made from glass-reinforced polyester resin (fibreglass) and plastics, such as polyethylene or polypropylene. Cisterns need to be carefully sited on a firm level base to ensure that the weight of the cistern when full does not damage the structure. Sufficient room for access must be allowed – at least 350 mm and preferably 500 mm is needed above the lid for maintenance of the float-valve and cleaning.

## Connections to cisterns

Large galvanised cisterns are usually ordered with threaded connection bosses welded on; they can be supplied as a complete unit or assembled from sections by bolting together on site. Small domestic cisterns are usually drilled on site and then plastic washers are used with tank connectors and back-nuts, which form a seal between the cistern and the tubes. Use plastic washers between the connector fitting and the cistern wall and PTFE tape on the threads as the sealing method on both metal and plastic cisterns. Never use oil-based jointing compounds on plastic cisterns as the oil can soften the plastic and cause the joint to fail after a short period. Where a hole is required in the lid for the open vent pipe from a hot water apparatus, drill this in a corner of the lid; the open vent pipe should only pass

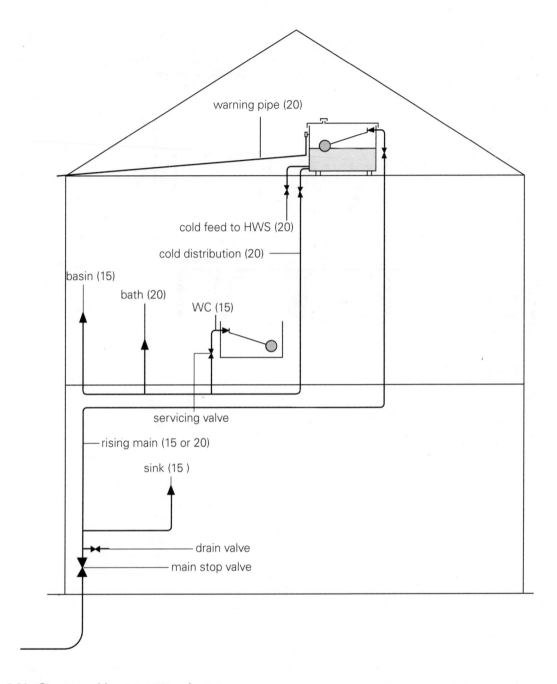

*Figure 6.20* Storage cold water system layout

through a short distance otherwise the lid will be trapped and so not removable for maintenance of the float-operated valve or for cleaning the cistern.

### Water inlet control

The **float-operated valve** controls the inlet of water into the cistern; it should be installed close to the top of the cistern. Once full, the float shuts the valve by a combination of buoyancy and leverage. As water is drawn off, the level drops and the valve opens automatically to replenish it. A servicing valve should be fitted on the pipe feeding the float-valve to enable maintenance and a metal reinforcing plate should be used to spread the load from the lever arm upthrust when fitting float-valves into plastic cisterns (Figure 6.21).

### Warning and overflow pipes

An **overflow** pipe should be fitted to the cistern just below the level of the float-valve and about 25 mm above the normal water level. The pipe should be fitted with a mesh filter screen to prevent the entry of insects into the cistern. If the

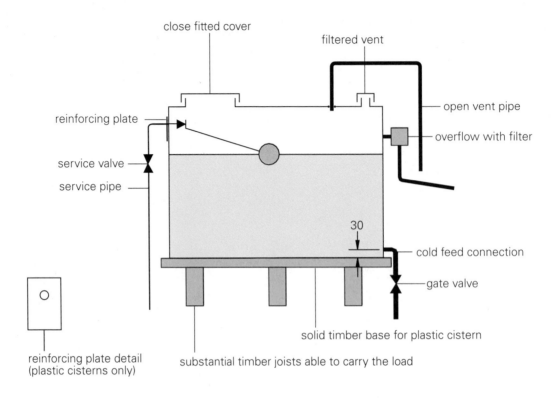

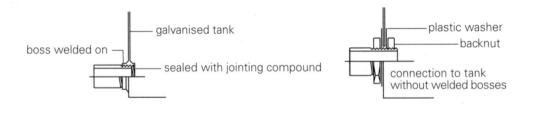

Cistern connection details

*Figure 6.21*  **Cistern details**

float punctures, or the washer in the valve splits and the float-valve starts to drip or run continuously, the warning pipe will carry away the water. It should discharge outside the building in a safe but conspicuous position to prevent damage and draw attention to the waste of water. The warning pipe must be large enough in diameter to carry the full flow from the inlet, so it is usual to install it using tube at least one diameter bigger.

**Outlet connections**
There will be at least one outlet connection to the cistern. It should be fitted on the side opposite the inlet; this is to prevent stagnation of water in the cistern. If the outlet and inlet connections are both at the same end of the cistern, the

water at the other end can remain in the cistern without movement for considerable periods. If it becomes stagnant then microbes and germs can breed.

The outlet connection(s) should be at least 30 mm up from the bottom of the cistern; this is to allow space for debris to collect without blocking off the outlets. Where the cistern outlet also feeds a hot water apparatus, the connection should be at least 25 mm above the connections that feed cold water taps. This is a safety precaution so that the hot taps will stop discharging water before the cold in the event of the cistern emptying.

Servicing valves should be fitted on the outlets to the cistern. These should be **full-way gate-valves** to give maximum flow with minimum resistance. By closing them, maintenance can be carried out on the pipes they serve without wasting the water that would otherwise be lost draining the cistern.

## Determination of cold water storage requirement

When deciding on the capacity of a cistern it is necessary to consider a number of factors including: the nature of the water use in the building; the likelihood of interruption of supply; and whether there will be times when the water pressure is low during the day. In single dwellings, it is usual for cisterns to have a capacity of from 100 l to 150 l for cold taps and double this if the cistern also supplies hot taps. In larger houses, a storage capacity of 100 l per bedroom can be used. Table 6.1 suggests figures for storage of cold water for hot and cold taps based on the type of building and number of occupants.

Take care not to select a storage volume that is much too large; this will increase the risk of stagnation of the water in the cistern. A cistern capacity sufficient for twenty-four hours storage should normally be regarded as sufficient where the building is fed by the public water supply.

### Calculation of cistern storage capacity

Figure 6.21 shows a section through a typical rectangular storage cistern; if it measures 1.2 m long by 0.85 m wide and 0.85 m height overall and has a depth of water in it equal to 0.6 m, it would actually contain a volume of water equal to:

$1.2 \times 0.85 \times 0.6 = 0.612 \text{ m}^3$
or
$0.612 \times 1000 = 612 \text{ l}$

*Table 6.1* Suggested minimum storage of cold water for hot and cold taps

| Type of building and occupation | Storage capacity in litres |
| --- | --- |
| Hotels and hospitals | 200 per bed space |
| Office with canteen facilities | 45 per employee |
| Office without canteen facilities | 40 per employee |
| Restaurant | 7 per meal |
| Nursery or primary day school | 15 per pupil |
| Secondary or technical day school | 20 per pupil |
| Boarding schools and hostels | 90 per pupil |
| Children's home or residential nursery | 135 per bed space |
| Nurse's home | 120 per bed space |
| Nursing or convalescent home | 135 per bed space |

Circular cistern storage capacity can be determined using the formula: $3.14 \times$ radius of cistern$^2 \times$ depth of water contained. A cistern that measures 1 m in diameter and has a depth of water of 0.6 m would contain:

$3.14 \times 0.5 \times 0.5 \times 0.6 = 0.471 \text{ m}^3$
or
$0.471 \times 1000 = 471 \text{ l}$

### Larger cistern installations

It is usual, where a large storage volume is required, to install two or more cisterns each with its own float-valve controlled supply. The cistern outlets then flow into a pipe manifold from where the distribution pipes carry the cold water to the various sanitary fittings and the hot water system. By installing valves on the pipe manifold inlets and outlets it is possible to isolate one cistern for routine maintenance or cleaning while maintaining an uninterrupted supply. Figure 6.22 shows the methods of interconnecting the cisterns and

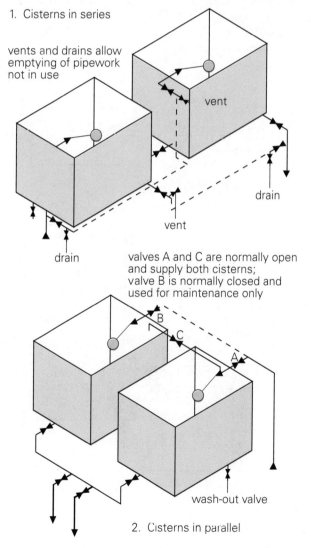

*Figure 6.22* Methods of interconnecting cisterns

associated pipework and Figure 6.23 shows the typical valve opening and closing sequence for cleaning and maintenance.

Where the cistern has a capacity of over 1000 l it is usual to install a **warning pipe** as well as an overflow pipe. The warning pipe is connected to the cistern 25 mm above the normal water level. It is usually installed using 25 mm bore tube and should be run to discharge in a conspicuous position. The overflow pipe will be larger in diameter (at least one pipe diameter larger than the inlet pipe) and connected to the cistern so that it is at a level above the warning pipe and below the float-valve inlet connection. The overflow is run to discharge in a safe position, usually close to a gully or drain. When the float-valve begins to malfunction, any small amounts of water will discharge from the warning pipe. In the event of a major problem, the overflow pipe will carry away the larger volume of water safely.

**Wash-out valves** and pipework are usually fitted to the bottom of large cisterns. These enable the cistern to be emptied and cleaned easily. Full-way valves such as gate-valves or quarter turn ball-valves are suitable types to use in this situation, the outlets being piped away to terminate at least 150 mm above a suitable drain.

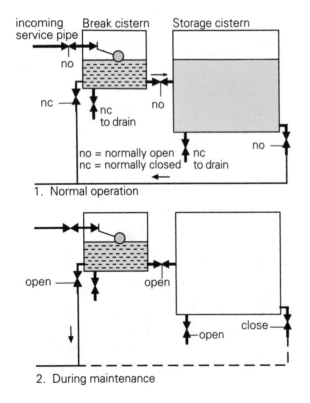

*Figure 6.23* Valve operation for cleaning and maintenance

# Cold water distribution in large buildings

Where long pipelines are fitted in large buildings it is important to ensure that the cisterns and associated pipework are installed so that the risk of contamination due to stagnation or high storage and distribution water temperature is minimised. Figure 6.24 shows a typical arrangement where the risk of contamination is high and contrasts this with a system that will minimise the danger. Stagnation of water in the pipework can be minimised by grouping sanitary fittings close together where possible. Try to avoid installing single sanitary fittings (particularly showers) that will not be frequently used at the end of long runs of pipe.

## Cold water supply in tall buildings

Pumps will often be required to supply water to the top floors in tall buildings. To reduce the size and capacity of the pumps, it is more efficient to supply the lower floors directly from the mains and pump the water up to the higher floors only. Typical pipework arrangements are illustrated in Figures 6.25 and 6.26. It is useful to have some water storage at the top of the building because gravity supply can continue during a power failure. If the high-level storage required is very large, a considerable load will be imposed on the building structure. A compromise is to have both high and low-level storage. The low-level storage cistern creates a break between the pumps and the water supplier's main; this means that the pumps cannot lower the mains pressure to adjacent buildings, which could occur if the pumps were installed directly on to the main service pipe.

Drinking water for the higher floors can be supplied from: a high-level storage cistern; a high-level drinking water header pipe; or a low-level hydro-pneumatic pressure vessel.

Where the drinking water is to be supplied from a high-level storage cistern, it is important that the cistern is carefully sited and installed so that is does not create a danger from stagnation. It must be fitted with a **float switch** to control the pumps.

The high-level drinking water header pipe is simply a large pipe (diameter 100 to 150 mm and about 3 to 6 m long) connected into the pumped riser. It should hold about 5 l of water per dwelling served. It needs to be fitted with an automatic air valve and a **pipeline float switch** that will start the pumps when the header empties.

The low-level hydro-pneumatic storage vessel should also hold about 5 l per dwelling. The vessel consists of a welded steel pressure vessel containing a rubber bladder into which water can be forced by the pump pressure. The space between the bladder and the steel vessel is pressurised with air to balance the pump pressure. The pumps are controlled

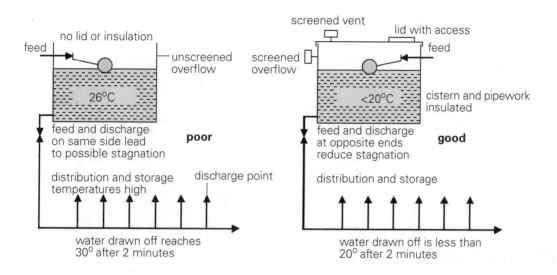

Figure 6.24  Example of good and bad cold water storage and distribution arrangements

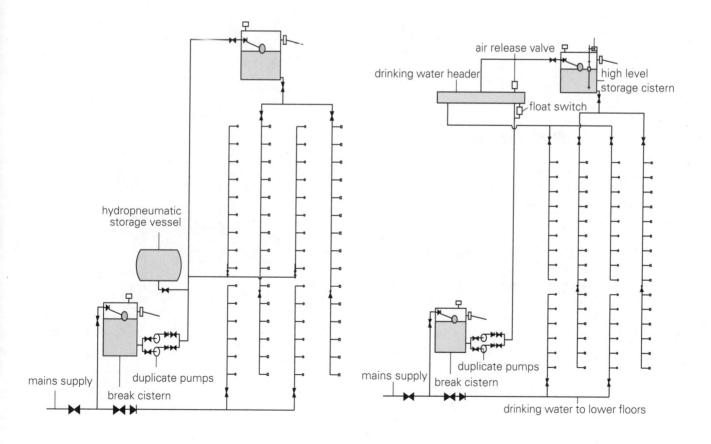

*Figure 6.25*  Pumped cold water supply with pressure vessel

*Figure 6.26*  Pumped cold water supply with drinking water header pipe

by a pressure switch. When the pumps run, the high-level storage cistern will be filled and, at the same time, water will be forced into the pressure vessel. Once the cistern is completely full, a **delayed action float valve** will close off the supply; the water pressure will then rise and operate the pressure switch to stop the pumps.

As users consume drinking water, the air pressure will force water out of the vessel and up the building. When water is used from the storage cistern, the water level in it will drop. However, the delayed action float valve will remain closed until the water level has dropped considerably. This preserves the pressure in the system and reduces the number of pump starts.

Once either the float valve opens, or the pressure in the pumped riser drops below a preset value, the pumps will restart to replenish both the high-level storage cistern and the pressure vessel.

## Insulation of cold water pipes

Insulate cold water service and distribution pipes against heat gain, especially where they run close to hot pipes in ducts. Where cold water service pipes are run through warm humid rooms, such as showers and changing rooms, condensation dripping off the cold pipes will often be a problem. In this case, fitting waterproof insulation will prevent the problem by forming a barrier between the cold pipe and the warm humid air.

## Siphonage

Siphonage is a method of moving a liquid from a cistern or tank, up and over the top of the tank through a tube that runs down to a lower level (Figure 6.27). Siphonage occurs because of atmospheric pressure. We generally do not perceive atmospheric pressure because the air surrounds our bodies. However, the weight of the air is considerable and this creates a pressure of slightly over 100 kPa (equal to about 10 m head of water) at sea level. Siphonage is started by suction at the bottom of the long leg of the siphon. This creates a partial vacuum and atmospheric pressure pushing down on the surface of the liquid in the cistern forces it up the short leg of the siphon. Once over the crown, the long leg fills, and the weight of liquid in it is greater than that in the short leg; this causes the liquid in the cistern to continue to flow until it empties, or air is allowed to enter at the crown of the siphon.

Siphonage can be both useful and a problem in plumbing systems. It is used to good effect to create the flush to clean the WC pan and can be used to drain cylinders where no drain valve has been fitted; it can be a problem where the trap seal

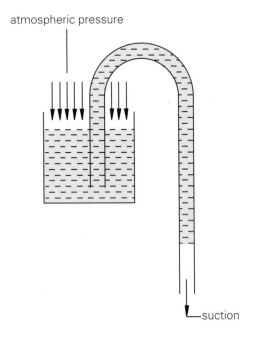

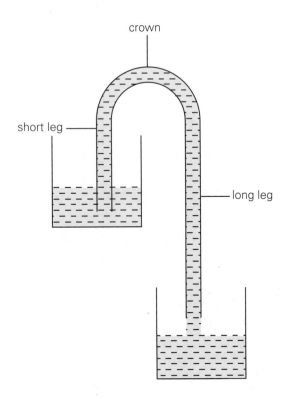

*Figure 6.27* Principles of siphonage

is lost and smells from waste pipes and drains can then enter bathrooms.

## Back-siphonage and backflow

If suction (negative pressure) occurs in a pipework system connected to a sanitary fitting or cistern where the tap outlet is below the surface of any water contained, siphonage (Figure 6.27) can cause the water to be sucked back into the pipe and so contaminate the water supply. To prevent this occurring, backflow prevention measures are required at all cisterns, at taps on sanitary fittings and where hose connections are made.

## Risk associated with back-siphonage

Because the nature of the water that could flow back into the pipes can differ, there are different degrees of risk associated with backflow and back-siphonage. Effectively, three degrees of risk exist. The most dangerous is where the water that could contaminate the system is harmful to health and is constantly or frequently present at the point of use. In this case, a type 'A' air-gap is required at the point of discharge (see Table 6.2 and

Figure 6.28 for details). Alternatively, a cistern can be used to supply water by gravity flow only. A classic example of this type of risk is the WC pan; the flushing cistern is used to prevent the possibility of contaminated water flowing back into the mains. Other major examples of this type of risk include industrial plant involving the use of dangerous chemicals, dental surgeries and hairdressing salons where hoses are used in sinks, or ascending spray bidets (Figure 6.29).

The second degree of risk occurs where a harmful substance may be present at the point of use. This second category of risk can be prevented by the use of mechanical fittings that prevent the backflow, such as a **double-check-valve assembly** (the preferred method of protection, see Figure 6.30). Alternatively, a **single-check-valve** and **vacuum-breaker** or **air-admittance-valve** can be fitted into the feed pipe (Figure 6.31).

*Table 6.2* **Air gap measurements**

| Air gap dimensions in mm at taps and feed-pipe outlets | |
|---|---|
| Nominal size of tap or outlet fitting in mm | Vertical air gap measurement between tap outlet and spill-over level of appliance |
| Up to and including 14 (1/2") | 20 |
| Over 14 (1/2") up to 21 (3/4") | 25 |
| Over 21 (3/4") up to 41 | 70 |
| Over 41 | Twice the bore of the feed pipe or outlet |
| Source of risk | Example of recommended protection |
| Class 1 risk | |
| WC pan | Flushing cistern |
| Bidet | Type A air-gap |
| Class 2 risk | |
| Taps on sinks | Type A air-gap recommended |
| Hose union taps | Inline check-valve and anti-vacuum valve |
| Clothes washing machine | Type B air-gap |
| Class 3 risk | |
| Hot and cold mix tap | Any of the above or a single check-valve, or an inline anti-vacuum valve |
| Domestic Water softener | |

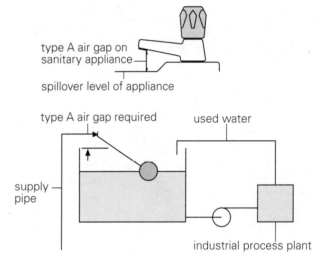

*Figure 6.28* **Type 'A' air-gap**

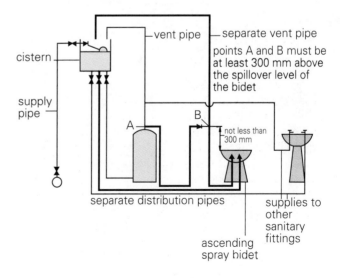

*Figure 6.29* **Ascending spray bidet connections**

Examples of this type of risk include: a domestic tap where a hose-pipe can be fitted for garden watering purposes; in this case a double-check-valve-assembly in the supply pipe will safeguard the supply. Another example is the WC cistern; in this case a type 'B' air-gap is required (see Figure 6.32 for details).

The third and lowest category of risk includes fittings such as washing machine hose-connections, and sink and shower mixer-taps. Washing machine manufacturers usually incorporate a type 'B' air-gap into their design and no further protection is required. Mixer-taps, on the other hand, come in two basic forms: the safest is where the hot and cold water supplies do not mix inside the tap. This type of mixer is often used on kitchen sinks and no further protection is required even when the water supplies are unbalanced (Figure 6.33).

The second type of mixer, used on showers and spray-taps in washbasins, allows hot and cold water to mix inside the body of the tap. In this case, the mixer should be fed using **balanced water supplies**. This means that both the hot and

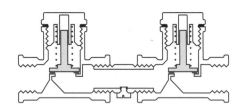

*Figure 6.30*  Double-check-valve assembly

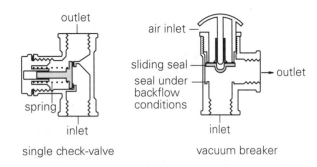

single check-valve                     vacuum breaker

*Figure 6.31*  Single-check-valve and vacuum breaker

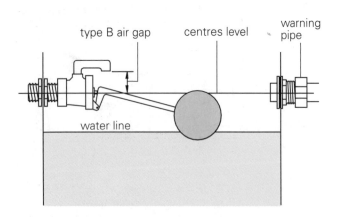

*Figure 6.32*  Type 'B' air-gap

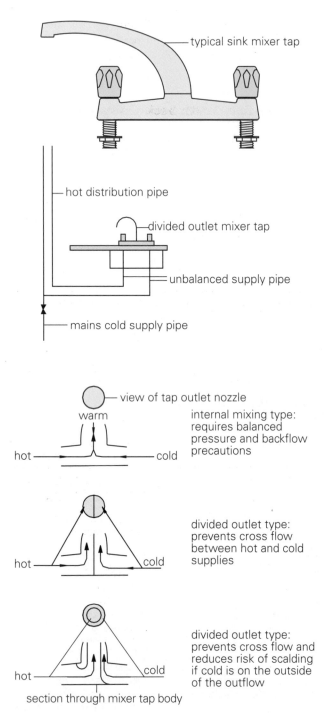

*Figure 6.33*  Sink mixer and unbalanced water supplies

cold supplies should be mains fed or both should be cistern fed (Figure 6.34). If they are unbalanced, with for example mains fed cold water and cistern fed hot water, then single-check-valves are required in the supply pipes to protect the mixer tap. Furthermore, if the shower rose is connected using a flexible hose and can be submerged in the water in the tray, the outlet needs to be protected by a double-check-valve-assembly.

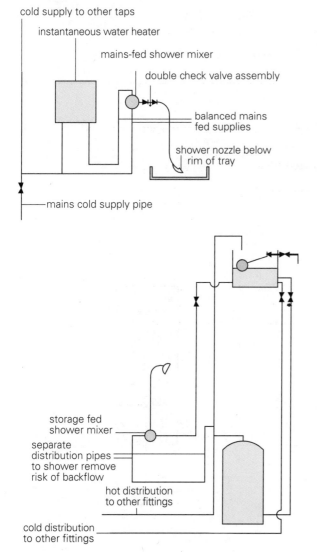

*Figure 6.34* Shower mixer and balanced water supplies

## **Water economy**

When designing cold water systems it is important to consider ways of minimising water usage. Excessive pressure at the taps tends to increase water consumption, by limiting working pressures to no more than is necessary, water will be saved. Metering water for charging purposes tends to produce

good savings compared to water use from unmetered supplies.

Leakage from faulty joints and pipework will obviously waste water, especially if these are buried underground or in the building structure or below suspended ground floors. Always carry out a hydraulic pressure test on new pipework in large buildings. In small installations, visually inspect every joint for leaks.

Where the pipes are buried underground, look for wet patches or areas where the vegetation is greener than that surrounding it along the line of the pipe, and check stop-valve chambers for standing water. With all taps turned off, listen with a stethoscope or your ear touching the stop-valve key while it rests on the valve. If water flow can be heard, turn off the stop-valve and listen again. If the flow noise has stopped, the leak is on the installation supply pipe.

If a water meter is fitted, leaks can be found by taking test readings during times when no water is being used. The procedure is as follows:

1. Check all isolating valves for effective shut-off.
2. Turn off all discharge points and record the rate of flow using the meter and a watch; if the flow rate is nil, there is no detectable leak.
3. If water is flowing, turn off isolating valves in turn, starting with the furthest from the meter. Note the rate of flow after each valve is closed.
4. Continue until all isolating valves are closed back to the meter.
5. Calculate any changes in the rate of flow.

Leaks exist in any section of pipe where closing the isolating valve produces a reduction in the rate of flow (see Figure 6.35 and Table 6.3).

In public toilets, fitting **self-closing taps** and **spray outlet taps** can also save water. However, spray taps are only suitable for rinsing hands; where the basins are likely to be heavily fouled by grease or dirt they should not be fitted.

All sinks, washbasins and baths must be fitted with a plug to seal the waste outlet, except for basins where spray taps that cannot flow at more than 0.06 l/s are fitted, and special medical or dental sinks.

Urinals can use considerable amounts of water if unregulated automatic flushing cisterns are fitted. At most, there should be no more than 3 flushes of 2.5 l per bowl, stall or 700 mm length of slab per hour. This rate can be achieved by timing flush intervals and adjusting a lock-shield-valve fitted on the inlet to the cistern. Even more water can be saved if a time-clock and motorised-valve are fitted to cut off the supply when the building is unoccupied. Alternatively, a valve that opens on pressure variations in the cold water pipe can be fitted. Where the urinal is used infrequently (less than three times an hour) a user-operated flushing cistern will show a water saving compared to automatic flushing.

*Table 6.3* Typical valve operation and rate of flow change

| Valve operation sequence | Rate of flow (l/min) | Change in flow rate (l/min) | Leak suspected (remarks) |
|---|---|---|---|
| Start of procedure | 120 | – | All water fittings turned off |
| Close valve 1 | 120 | 0 | |
| Close valve 2 | 90 | 30 | Leak in canteen/toilets |
| Close valve 3 | 90 | 0 | |
| Close valve 4 | 80 | 10 | Leak in factory workshop |
| Close valve 5 | 80 | 0 | |
| Clove valve 6 | 45 | 35 | Leak on underground pipe |
| Close valve 7 | 45 | 0 | |

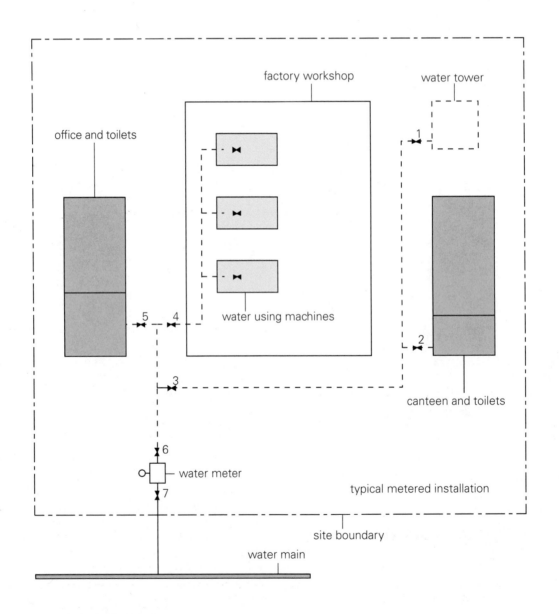

*Figure 6.35*  Typical pipe layout for meter leak detection

# Noises in cold water systems

Noise in cold water systems is caused by vibration – many materials used in their construction transmit noise very effectively. Good design and workmanship are the key to avoiding the creation of a noisy system.

## Water flow noises

Noise created by the water flowing along the pipeline can become a nuisance where the velocity is greater than about 3 m/s. By choosing correct diameters, the water velocity in the pipe can be kept below this figure. Note, however, that the pipes should not be oversized so that the water velocity is below 0.5 m/s, otherwise detritus can settle in the pipes. Always de-burr the inside of tube that has been cut using wheel cutters. If the burrs are left on the pipe ends, turbulence will be created; this can result in vibration and noise. The bore of the pipe will also be reduced (by about 20% on a 15 mm tube) resulting in reduced water flow. Figure 6.36 illustrates how flow noises can be created in pipes.

### Cavitation

Turbulent water flow at velocities of over about 7 m/s can result in erosion or wear of the materials from which the pipe and fittings are made. This is known as cavitation and noise will often be generated during the process. Outlet taps and float-valve orifices usually have abrupt changes of diameter and direction; these can create sudden drops in pressure which then causes cavitation and so result in, for example, a squealing noise from the float-valve as the cistern fills (Figure 6.37).

Some common causes of noise are easily remedied, such as:

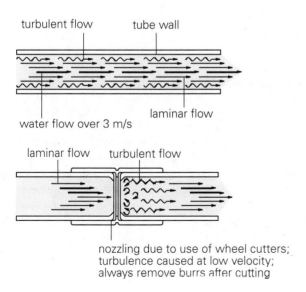

Figure 6.36  Flow noises in pipes

- stop-valves that are partially closed;
- stop-valves that are partially blocked with debris;
- partially blocked float-valve orifices;
- water-hammer due to wear allowing taps to close too fast.

Fully opening or cleaning and maintaining the valves will remove the cause of the noise.

## Noise caused by resonance

All solid objects have a natural frequency of vibration; where this happens to coincide with the frequency of waves set up as a result of water flow then very loud, sometimes damaging, resonant vibrations can build up in the system. These often sound similar to quickly repeated loud bangs or sometimes they can be similar to the noise of an electric motor. The banging noise usually results from waves formed as water flows from the float-valve into circular cisterns (Figure 6.38). If the frequency of the waves happens to coincide with the

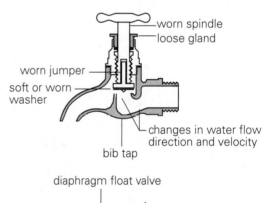
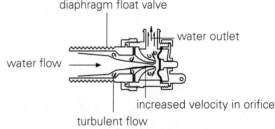

Figure 6.37  Noise in taps and valves

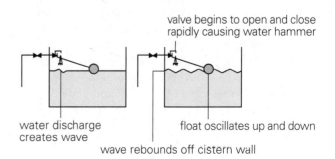

Figure 6.38  Vibration in cisterns

distance to the side of the cistern, they can bounce back towards the float and be magnified, causing the float to oscillate up and down. This in turn creates larger waves compounding the problem. The float then causes the valve to open rapidly and close and water hammer results. Various ways of curing the problem can be tried, for example: increasing the length of the lever arm; increasing the diameter of the float valve; or fitting a baffle plate into the cistern to stop the waves hitting the ball.

Another cause of this type of resonance induced noise is incorrectly supported tube. If the supporting brackets and clips are too far apart then, sometimes, the tube can begin to vibrate from side to side damaging the pipework in the process. Suggested maximum spacings for tube supports are given in Chapter 5, Table 5.1. This type of resonance-induced pipe noise should not occur if these measurements are not exceeded and the clips or brackets are properly tightened on to the pipe and structure.

## Noise from faulty tap washers

Sometimes worn tap and valve washers can create loud resonant vibrations that sound similar to an electric motor as the water flows through the tap (Figure 6.39). The cure is simple – change the worn, soft or split tap washer.

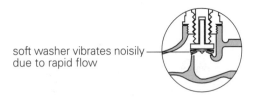

soft washer vibrates noisily
due to rapid flow

*Figure 6.39*  Tap or valve washer oscillation

## Commissioning cold water systems

On completion of the system installation, it must be inspected to see that it complies with all relevant local water regulations. It also needs to be tested to ensure that it is leak free and operates correctly in accordance with the design specification.

All pipework and fittings should be visually checked for correct supports, unsealed open ends or any other problems. The storage cistern(s) should be checked and cleaned so that debris cannot be flushed into the pipes when they are filled. All isolation and servicing valves should be closed so that the system can be filled and tested in stages. The boundary stop-valve can be opened and the service pipe filled as far as the main stop-valve. A hose can then be connected to the

adjacent drain valve, which should be opened before turning on the main stop-valve to allow the service pipe to be thoroughly flushed. This will help to prevent float-valve orifices becoming blocked as the remainder of the system is filled.

Once the water is running clean, the drain valve can be closed and the remainder of the service pipe can be allowed to fill. Water flow should stop after a short while. As the service pipe is filling, it should be visually inspected for leaks and trapped air should be vented through draw off points. Once full, the other sections of the installation can be brought into service. The storage cistern(s) can be filled and the float-valve(s) adjusted to shut-off at the correct water level. The cistern(s) should also be deliberately over-filled to test the operation of the warning and overflow pipes. Next, the cistern outlet valve(s) can be opened to fill the distribution pipework, again allowing trapped air to vent off through draw off points. A thorough check for leaks must be made at each stage of the process and any leaks found must be repaired.

If the specification calls for hydraulic pressure tests of the pipework, these should be carried out. Usually the test pressure will be 1.5 or 2 times the working pressure. If necessary, fit blanks or valves in the place of any items of equipment that cannot withstand the test pressure without damage before connecting a suitable pump and gauge. Pressurise the system carefully, ensuring that all air is allowed to vent, up to the test pressure required and observe the gauge for the test period, usually 1 hour is sufficient. Once satisfactory tests have been achieved, any necessary certificates should be completed and signed by the appropriate witness.

Once tested and full, each section of pipework should be thoroughly flushed to remove any remaining dirt and debris and taps can then be run to check for adequate pressure and flow rate. WC cisterns should also be checked for speed of fill and float-valve operation.

## Disinfection of water systems

In large buildings, the water regulations or the contract specification might call for the system to be disinfected before it is put into use. If this is required, the following guidelines can be followed, as well as the chemical suppliers handling and safety instructions. The water supplier should be notified before disinfection using sodium hypochlorite is carried out. (Note: ordinary household bleach powder contains approximately 5% available chlorine.)

- Flush the system to remove all visible dirt and debris then add sufficient sodium hypochlorite to give a measured strength of 50 ppm in water in the cistern.
- Leave this to stand for 1 hour then open taps in turn, working away from the cistern, until the water smells of

chlorine; then close the taps. During this process, the cistern should be regularly checked and topped up with 50 ppm chlorinated water.

- Once the pipework system is full of chlorinated water, leave it to stand for 1 hour.
- The level of residual chlorine at the furthest tap should then be measured. If this is less than 20 ppm the process should be repeated.
- Finally the system should be thoroughly flushed out with clean water until all the residual chlorine is removed.

## Final checks

Once the system is operating satisfactorily and all problems have been corrected, cistern lids can be fitted and isolation valves marked up as to their use and whether they should normally be open or closed. Any site drawings can be marked up to show the system 'as installed' before the job is left clean and tidy.

# Maintenance of cold water systems

Planned routine inspection and maintenance can keep the system operating correctly and help to avoid the possibility of faults causing expensive damage to the building structure and its contents. By drawing up a maintenance schedule or check list it is less likely that certain items will be missed and a record can easily be kept of the results of the inspection; a typical form is illustrated in Figure 6.40. It lists the items to be checked and has space for signatures and notes so that necessary remedial actions can be flagged.

### CHECK YOUR UNDERSTANDING

- Water pressure is a result of the 'head' available. Head in this sense refers to the vertical height difference between the cistern or reservoir and the tap it serves; the greater the height difference, the greater the pressure.
- All our water for drinking and washing is part of the 'water cycle' and it is returned to the cycle after use; we must be careful to install plumbing systems so that the purity of our water supply is always maintained.
- Knowledge of the nature of the water being used, whether it is hard or soft, acid or alkaline, enables a better choice of suitable materials and jointing systems for use within an installation, and an understanding of why things might have gone wrong if problems do occur.
- Water usually needs to be treated to make it safe to drink and depending on the nature of the water, the treatment varies. New private water supplies should always be tested and assessed for safety before use, and periodically while in service.

- It is important that the plumbing system is installed so that the quality of the water supply is maintained and contamination cannot occur. To this end there are four areas that should be considered: the materials from which the system is made; cross connections; stagnation; and backflow of water into the pipework after its discharge.
- In the direct cold water system, all the taps and discharge points are connected to the main service pipe, so if the water supply is interrupted or turned off, there will be no reserve of water during the interruption.
- In the storage cold water system, at least one drinking water tap will be connected to the service pipe, while cold water for the bath, WC cistern and washbasin is supplied by gravity flow from a storage cistern.
- Take care to ensure that the storage cistern is correctly installed, in line with the detailed guidance given earlier, to preserve the water quality in the storage cold water system.
- Stagnation of the water in distribution pipework can be minimised by grouping sanitary fittings close together where possible. Try to avoid installing single sanitary fittings (particularly showers) that will not be frequently used at the end of long runs of pipe.
- Take particular care to assess the degree of risk of backsiphonage and backflow when connecting items of industrial plant, shower fittings, ascending spray bidets, or sanitaryware in hospitals and dental surgeries. Use the appropriate method of creating an air-gap or backflow prevention device wherever necessary.
- Consider ways of minimising water usage, for example, by installing spray taps and valves to shut off urinal flushing in temporarily unoccupied buildings and public toilets.
- When installing pipes, ensure that the burrs are removed after cutting, that the pipes are adequate in diameter, and that the pipes are correctly supported, to minimise problems of noise in cold water systems.
- When commissioning a cold water system, close all isolation valves so that the system can be filled and checked for leaks and flushed in a controlled methodical manner.

### REVISION EXERCISES AND QUESTIONS

1   List the factors that should be considered when laying an underground service pipe.

2   Where should underground water service pipes *not* be buried?

3   Make a labelled diagram of a direct cold water system to serve a sink, washbasin, bath, WC cistern and the feed cistern for a hot water installation.

4   A cistern is to be installed to supply water for domestic purposes.
    i)   List the requirements for the cistern.
    ii)  What are the specific requirements relating to access to the cistern for repair of the float-valve?

| Maintenance and service schedule | Location _____ | Date _____ | Inspected by _____ |
|---|---|---|---|
| Item | Checks | Satisfactory (Y/N) | Notes |
| Water meter / boundary stop-valve | Read meter, check for excessive usage, check access and operation of boundary stop-valve | | |
| Water analysis (where bulk storage >1000 l) | Take water sample and send for chemical / bacteriological analysis | | |
| Duct and inspection covers | Check for ease of opening and clean out if necessary, look for signs of leakage or corrosion | | |
| Storage cisterns | Check for cleanliness/stagnation (dust on water surface). Check operation of float-valve and overflow. Check supports, lid, filters, insulation & c. | | |
| Control and servicing valves | Check for ease and effective operation. Check valve labels if required. Check emergency valve keys correctly fitted. | | |
| Pipework | Inspect for signs of corrosion, leakage &c. Check support brackets, provision for thermal movement, thermal insulation. Check labels/colour codes still correct. Check fire stopping to sleeves is maintained. | | |
| Sanitary fitting taps and terminal valves | Check operation and effective closing. Check/adjust float-valve water level in WC cisterns. Remove shower heads and descale. | | |
| Pumps | Bleed air or prime if necessary. Check flow setting, pump noise levels and anti-vibration mountings if fitted. | | |
| Safety valves | Open test lever to free stuck valves. Check discharge pipes not blocked. Check pressure reducing valve operation and downstream pressure. | | |
| Pressure vessels | Check for signs of damage, corrosion or leakage. Check and adjust gas pressure. | | |
| Filters | Remove gauze, clean and replace. | | |
| Electrical controls and earth bonding | Check operation of float control, pressure switch, motorised valves. Check for pipe alterations maintain bonding. | | |
| Signature of inspector _____ | | Signature of client _____ | |

Figure 6.40  Water services inspection and maintenance form

5   Where should service valves be fitted to the pipework in a cold water system?

6   Where should drain-valves be fitted in a cold water supply system?

7   How should a cistern of over 1000 l capacity be protected in case of float-valve failure?

8   When considering water economy, what is the maximum rate of fill for an automatic flushing cistern supplying:
   i)   a single urinal bowl;
   ii)  1400 mm of urinal slab?

9   Explain how cold water system flow noises can be minimised when installing system pipework.

10  How can a bib tap supplying water for a garden hose be protected against back-siphonage?

# Hot water supply

## Introduction

An adequate supply of hot water can improve the quality of life considerably. In this chapter, we shall cover the basic theory and practical considerations regarding the installation of a variety of hot water systems.

## Heat

Heat is a form of energy. We can use a thermometer to measure the temperature of an object or substance, and the reading will give us a measure of the intensity of the heat energy. However, this does not give us any information about the total quantity of heat energy held within the object. For example, compare a cup of boiling water at 100°C with a bucket full of warm water at 25°C. The cup has a higher temperature, but the bucket contains much more water and therefore has more energy. If the cup's water was poured into the bucket it would make hardly any difference to the temperature.

### Heat measurement

We can use the **Celsius** system to measure temperature. This is based on two properties of water: the ice point, when liquid water turns to ice, at 0°C; and the boiling point, when water (at normal atmospheric pressure) turns to steam, at 100°C. The difference between these two points is divided into 100 parts – each being 1 degree (°C).

### Quantity of heat

From experiments of many kinds it has been found that the quantity of heat that needs to be put into, or given up by, a substance so that its temperature is changed is in proportion to three things: the mass (or weight) of the substance, the

amount that its temperature changes, and a characteristic called **specific heat capacity**.

### Specific heat capacity of water

Compared with other substances, water requires a relatively large amount of heat energy to change its temperature. The actual amount required to change 1 kilogram (kg) of water by 1°C is 4.18 kilojoules (kJ) (Table 7.1).

Knowing the value of water's specific heat capacity enables us to determine both the total amount of heat energy needed to heat up a certain amount of water and the boiler or heater power required to heat the water in a certain time.

To find the total amount of energy required in kJ the formula is:

kJ of energy = 4.18 × mass of water in kg × temperature change in °C

In the cylinder shown in Figure 7.1, the capacity is 100 litres (1). As 1 l of water has a mass of 1 kg, then to raise the water's temperature from 20°C to 60°C will require:

$4.18 \times 100 \times (60 - 20) = 16\,720$ kJ of energy.

**Table 7.1** Specific heat capacities

| Specific heat capacity of common materials (kJ/kg/°C) | |
|---|---|
| Substance | Specific heat capacity |
| Water | 4.18 |
| Alcohol | 2.75 |
| Iron and steel | 0.46 |
| Copper and brass | 0.38 |

## Boiler power

The power of the boiler needed to heat the cylinder depends on the total amount of energy required and the time available to heat it. Power is measured in watts (W) or kilowatts (kW). When energy is used at the rate of 1 Joule per second (J/s), the

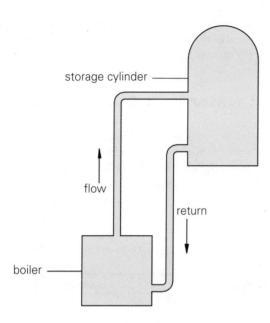

*Figure 7.1*  Simple boiler/cylinder

power used is 1 watt. Similarly, if the rate of energy used is 1 kJ/s then the power used is 1 kW.

To find the boiler power required in kW the formula is:

kW boiler power = energy required in kJ/time in seconds

So, if we want to heat up the cylinder in 1 hour (3600 seconds) we will need a boiler with a power of:

16 720 kJ / 3600 s = 4.64 kW (or 4640 W)

When using electricity to heat the water, the power required can be found using the same method. Once this has been determined then the amount of electric current required can be found. In an electrical circuit the current that is consumed depends on the power required in watts divided by the voltage at which the circuit operates. For example, the cylinder previously mentioned required 4.64 kW of power; if the electrical supply operates at 240 V then the current flow would be:

4640 W / 240 V = 19.3 amps

and the supply cable, its fuse and all the other equipment used would have to be able to carry the load safely.

### Calorific value of fuel

This term describes the amount of heat energy that is produced when a given mass of fuel is completely burnt. Some calorific values are given in Table 7.2. Knowledge of the calorific value of different fuels enables an estimation to be made of the quantity of fuel likely to be required for a given boiler and a comparison of running costs between different fuels.

*Table 7.2* Calorific value of fuels

| Fuel | Calorific value |
| --- | --- |
| Coal (anthracite) | 32 MJ/kg |
| Wood | 19 MJ/kg |
| Domestic fuel oil | 45 MJ/kg |
| Natural gas (90% methane) | 38 MJ/cubic metre |
| Propane | 95 MJ/cubic metre |
| Butane | 121.5 MJ/cubic metre |
| Manufactured coal gas | 19 MJ/cubic metre |
| Electricity | 3.6 MJ/kW |

### Transfer of heat

Heat energy can move from a relatively hot place to a colder place by three methods:

- conduction;
- convection;
- radiation.

### Conduction of heat

Conduction is the transfer of heat through solid materials. If you hold a short length of copper tube at one end and heat the other with a blowtorch, the heat rapidly conducts along the copper causing it to become warm at the other end. Heat travels through all solid materials, but the speed at which it passes through varies.

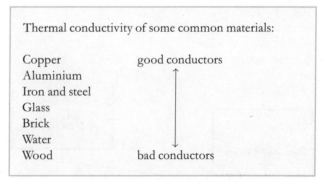

Thermal conductivity of some common materials:

| | |
| --- | --- |
| Copper | good conductors |
| Aluminium | |
| Iron and steel | |
| Glass | |
| Brick | |
| Water | |
| Wood | bad conductors |

Conduction occurs in a hot water system when the heat from the fuel burnt in the boiler passes through the copper or cast iron of the boiler plates into the water.

### Convection currents

Convection currents can also be called gravity circulation or natural convection. They are a form of heat movement in hot water systems. One of the effects of heating substances is that they expand in size, making them less dense. When a boiler is firing, hotter and therefore less dense water is pushed up the flow pipe. This is due to the colder more dense water from the bottom of the storage cylinder flowing down the return pipe because of the pull of gravity (Figure 7.2).

The temperature difference between the flow pipe and the return pipe determines the difference in density of the water. This in turn, together with the circulating head (the vertical height difference between the boiler and the storage vessel) determines the **circulation pressure** that causes the water to flow through the pipe circuit. Table 7.3 gives values for the density of water at different temperatures. For example, in the boiler circulation pipes and storage vessel illustrated in Figure 7.2, if the circulating head is 3 m and the temperatures of the flow and return pipes are 80°C and 60°C respectively, then the circulating pressure will be: (density of return – density of flow) × 9.81 × circulating head:

$$= 983 - 972) \times 9.81 \times 3$$
$$= 11 \times 9.81 \times 3$$
$$= 323.73 \text{ Pa } (N/m^2)$$

Provided the circulation pressure created by the density difference is greater than the resistance resulting from the pipes and fittings, even though the circulating pressure is small, the water will flow around the circuit.

### Radiation

Radiation is the transfer of heat in the form of infrared rays. It is the heat we feel from the sun or when we stand in front of a fire. Radiant heat will pass through the air or space until it hits a solid object that will absorb it and be heated by it. The surface of an object determines how good it is at both absorbing and emitting radiant heat; matt black is best and shiny silver worst. In a hot water system, the heat from the burning fuel in the boiler is radiated into the metal of the boiler heat exchanger.

# Hard water in hot water systems

Hard water can be a problem in hot water systems. If the dissolved salts in the water are driven out of suspension by the heat from the boiler they can reduce the efficiency of the system. In the worst cases they can even result in the danger of boiler explosion if the circulation pipes become blocked with scale (Table 7.4).

*Table 7.4* Water classification according to its hardness

| Designation | Parts per million (ppm or mg/l) |
| --- | --- |
| Soft | 0–50 |
| Moderately soft | 50–100 |
| Slightly hard | 100–150 |
| Moderately hard | 150–200 |
| Hard | 200–300 |
| Very hard | over 300 |

### Temporary and permanent hardness

Temporary hard water can cause problems in hot water systems. This is because the dissolved salts can be precipitated out of the water when it is heated. **Temporary hardness** is common in areas with a chalky subsoil. The salts form a rock-like scale inside the boiler, circulation pipes and storage cylinder. The scale prevents heat transfer, making the system less efficient, wasting energy, and causing blockages that can lead to potentially dangerous situations. **Permanent hardness**, on the other hand, describes water containing salts that remain dissolved even after heating. So, permanently hard water is not a problem in hot water systems.

# Corrosion

There are two forms of corrosion that can occur in hot water systems: **rusting** or **oxidic corrosion** of iron and steel due to the presence of dissolved oxygen in the water, and **electrolytic corrosion**.

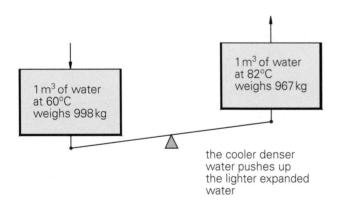

*Figure 7.2*  Effect of temperature on density of water

*Table 7.3* Density of water at different temperatures

| Temp °C | 10 | 20 | 40 | 50 | 55 | 60 | 65 | 70 | 75 | 80 | 85 |
| --- | --- | --- | --- | --- | --- | --- | --- | --- | --- | --- | --- |
| Density kg/cubic metre | 1000 | 998 | 992 | 988 | 986 | 983 | 980 | 978 | 975 | 972 | 969 |

## Oxidic corrosion

Because the water in the secondary side of the system is constantly being replaced when hot taps are run, dissolved oxygen is always present. It is important, therefore, that all the materials that come into contact with this water are corrosion resistant, for example galvanised steel, copper or plastic. If ordinary plain steel tube was used it would rapidly be corroded into rust and this would appear as a red iron oxide stain on the surfaces of sanitary fittings.

## Electrolytic corrosion

This occurs where there are two (or more) different metals in contact with an electrolyte. In the case of a hot water system the electrolyte is water. Also, because the system gets hot, the rate of corrosion is increased.

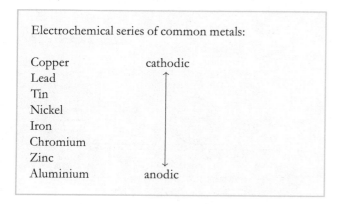

Electrochemical series of common metals:

| | |
|---|---|
| Copper | cathodic |
| Lead | ↑ |
| Tin | |
| Nickel | |
| Iron | |
| Chromium | ↓ |
| Zinc | |
| Aluminium | anodic |

The metals are listed in the order of their ability to resist corrosion. Metals higher on the list will become the **cathode** and destroy those lower on the list, which form the **anode**.

If a piece of plain uncoated steel is connected to copper where there is an electrolyte, the steel is more likely to corrode. Normally the corrosion occurs where the metals join. However, if the water can dissolve the copper and this then becomes deposited on the surface of the steel away from the joint, remote corrosion cells can be set up (Figure 7.3).

## Prevention of corrosion

Corrosion in hot water systems can be prevented by choosing suitable materials and keeping oxygen out of the system. Try to choose materials that are corrosion resistant; in direct hot water systems this means at least galvanised steel and preferably copper or a suitable plastic for pipework. The primary side of the indirect hot water system can be installed using plain steel tube, and mild steel or cast iron for the boiler heat exchanger because the water remains in the system.

# Thermal movement

When any object is heated or cooled its size changes. The actual change depends on three things: the length of the object, the change in temperature, and the material from which it is made.

## Coefficient of thermal expansion

The coefficient of thermal expansion is a number which gives the amount of increase, or decrease, by which a 1 m length of material will expand or contract if it is heated, or cooled, by 1°C (Table 7.5). Take for example, a steel hot water circulation pipe. If its temperature rises from 25°C to 85°C when the

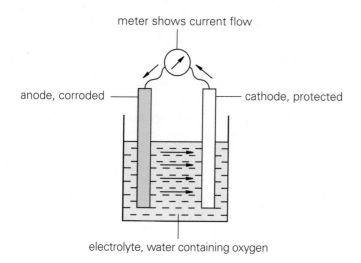

meter shows current flow

anode, corroded — — cathode, protected

electrolyte, water containing oxygen

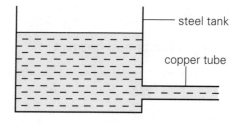

steel tank

copper tube

electrons flow from steel to copper resulting in the steel corroding

*Figure 7.3* Electrolytic corrosion

*Table 7.5* Coefficients of thermal expansion

| Material | Coefficient per 1°C |
|---|---|
| Aluminium | 0.000026 |
| Cast iron and steel | 0.000011 |
| Copper | 0.000016 |
| Lead | 0.000028 |
| Zinc | 0.000029 |
| Plastic | 0.00018 |

boiler is running, and the straight length of the pipe is 20 m, then the increase in length will be:

= length of tube × temperature change × coefficient of expansion
= 20 × (85 − 25) × 0.000011
= 0.013 m or 13 mm

If the pipe is installed so that the expansion cannot easily occur, problems can arise. In long runs of tube it is sometimes necessary to incorporate expansion joints or expansion bellows. Alternatively, the run of tube can be broken down into shorter sections by using bends or elbows to form expansion loops (Figure 7.4). Where branches will form anchor points as they pass through walls, then 'cross-over' tee arrangements can be used.

## Bracing long runs of tube

On long runs of tube with fixing supports such as hanging brackets, anchor bracing should be used at 12 m centres to avoid swaying. The distance between anchor fixings used for bracing and expansion joints in hot water lines is determined by the type of expansion joint used and the amount of movement the joint can accommodate. Figure 7.5 shows how a long run of tube can be anchored by means of supports at each change of direction. The expansion can then be accommodated by an expansion joint or by fabricating an expansion loop, either from fittings or by bending the tube. If an expansion loop is used, it should be installed and supported in the horizontal plane to prevent airlocks.

## Expansion joints and bellows

Where a gland-type expansion joint (as shown in Figure 7.6) is used on a run of copper tube, and the tube is subjected to a temperature difference of 60°C, then if the expansion joint can accommodate 25 mm of expansion, the length of straight tube each side of the joint to an anchor fixing can be up to 12.5 m. This is because each 1 m length of copper tube will change in length by approximately 1 mm when its temperature is changed by 60°C. So, 1 mm of movement

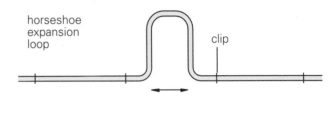

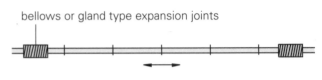

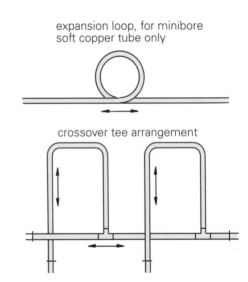

*Figure 7.4* Provision for expansion

within the expansion joint permits 1 m of pipe length between the expansion joint and the anchor points. The same approach should be used if a bellows-type expansion joint is fitted. Note that the tube should be installed so that it stretches the bellows slightly when cold. By applying 'cold draw' in this way, the bellows will be able to accommodate the expansion (Figure 7.6).

In order to avoid possible breakdown of branch joints connected to a heating or hot water main, it may be advisable to use the branch joints as anchor fixings. However, where the branch is connected to a tube that will itself be moving due to thermal expansion, the leg of the

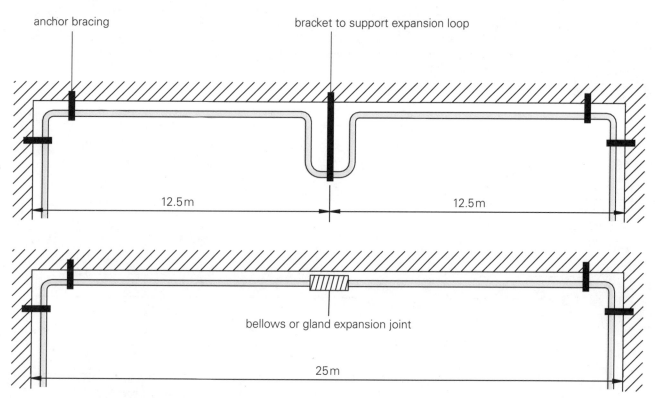

*Figure 7.5* Anchor fixings for bracing long runs of tube

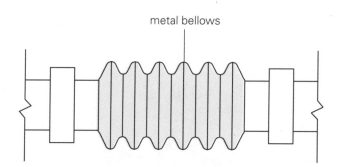

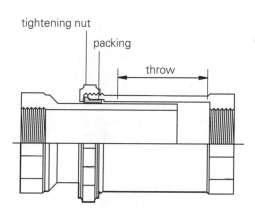

*Figure 7.6* Expansion joints and bellows

branch should also be able to move. In this situation, **cross-over tees** can be used to permit the movement, as shown in Figure 7.4.

Thermal expansion also has useful applications, for example in rod-type thermostats. These make use of the fact that different metals expand at different rates. This differential movement can be used to operate a switch or open a valve.

# Hot water systems

A hot water system should provide an adequate flow of water at the correct temperature required by the user, at minimum overall cost. The cost factors to be taken into account include: the capital cost of installation, maintenance of the system, and fuel and running costs.

## Choice of hot water system

The type of building, its size and the number of occupants all have to be taken into account if the most appropriate type of hot water system is to be installed. The types of system available fall into two categories: a localised system, where the water is heated close to its point of use, or a centralised system, where the water is heated and then stored in a vessel for distribution through the building via a system of pipes (Figure 7.7).

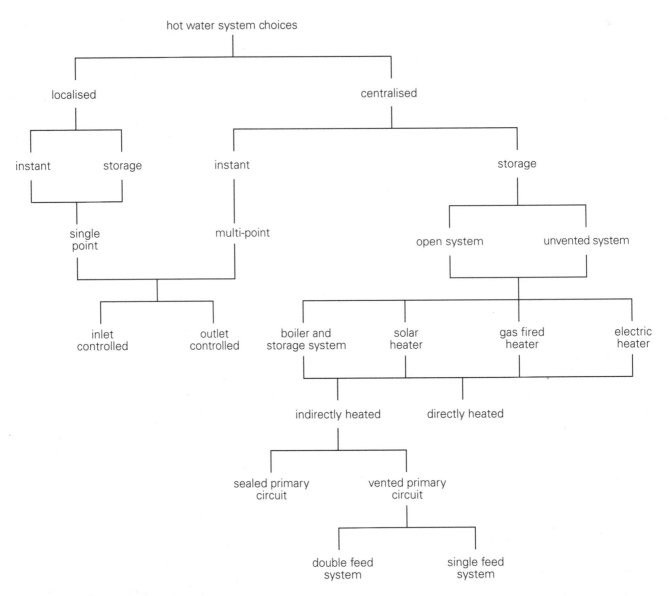

*Figure 7.7*  Choice of hot water system

## Storage hot water systems

### Stratification

Because water is a poor conductor of heat and hot water is less dense than cooler water, stratification occurs in hot water storage vessels. Stratification is the floating of hot water on top of the cold feed water that enters at the bottom of the storage vessel. Provided that the storage vessel is correctly connected to the pipework, stratification enables all the hot water to be drawn off from the vessel without the water mixing to any great extent. Furthermore, some hot water will have collected ready for use before the entire vessel is heated. For stratification to operate effectively it is important that the storage vessel, regardless of its shape, should be installed with its longest side vertical. The ratio of height to width, or diameter, should not be less than 2:1. The position of the cold feed and draw off pipe connections are also critical. The cold feed should enter horizontally just above the base of the vessel. The hot water draw off should connect at the very top of the vessel and run horizontally for at least 450 mm; this is to prevent heat loss due to **one-pipe circulation**. Figure 7.8 illustrates stratification and connection details for typical hot water storage vessels.

### Storage capacity

The storage capacity necessary to provide an acceptable level of hot water flow and an adequate temperature depends on two factors: the rate at which heat can be put into the storage vessel and the pattern of hot water use in the building.

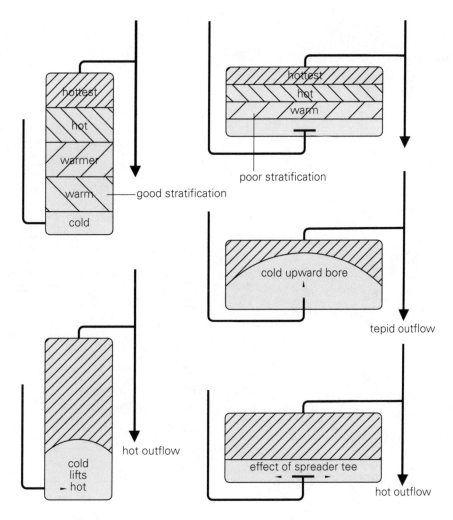

*Figure 7.8*  Stratification in hot water storage vessels

## Hot water storage vessels

These can be rectangular or cylindrical in shape. A cylindrical hot water storage vessel with domed ends is the best shape; this is because it can withstand the internal water pressure without distorting. In a rectangular storage tank, the flat sides will tend to bulge out even if they are made from a thicker material (Figure 7.9). The storage vessel needs to be large enough in capacity to contain sufficient hot water at a suitable temperature to supply the likely maximum demand. Small domestic storage cylinders can be made from sheet copper; they might be fitted with an aluminium **sacrificial anode** inside at the bottom. This will lengthen the life of the copper cylinder in areas where the water is very soft and therefore aggressive. Storage vessels are also made from steel by welding; they are then galvanised after fabrication. They will usually have female threaded connection bosses welded in. These comprise a hot draw off and vent connection at the very top of the vessel. There might also be a larger female threaded boss for an electric immersion heater; this could be

at the top for a vertical heater or on the side near the bottom for a shorter, horizontally mounted heater. The cold feed connection will be fitted close to the bottom of the vessel; this will be the same diameter as the hot draw-off, connection. There will be two connections on the side of the vessel; one for the primary flow, the other for the primary return.

Always connect the flow pipe – the circulation pipe that comes from the top of the boiler – to the top connection and the return to the bottom; otherwise, if the connections are crossed, gravity circulation will be stopped and the vessel will not get hot. A bolted access hole, sealed using a rubber gasket, might also be fitted. This is used to clean out and de-scale the inside of the vessel in temporary hard water areas.

If secondary circulation is to be installed then another boss is required. This will be fitted on the side of the vessel about a quarter of the way down. Figure 7.9 shows typical cylindrical and rectangular storage vessel connection details. To avoid one-pipe circulation up the hot water draw-off, make sure

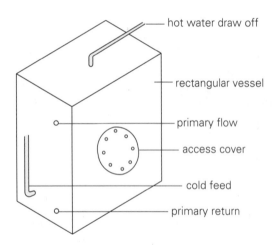

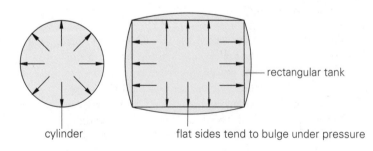

*Figure 7.9* Hot water storage vessels

that a section of horizontal pipe at least 450 mm long is fitted immediately after the connection, otherwise heat will be lost as the vent pipe gets hot.

## Hot water usage

Hot water usage varies with the type of building and the number of occupants. In modern dwellings, hot water (60°C) use can average between 35 and 45 l per person per day.

- A bath can use about 60 l at 60°C plus 40 l at 10°C or 100 l at 40°C
- A shower requires 0.05–0.1 l/s at 40°C
- A washbasin hot tap requires 0.15 l/s at 40°C
- A kitchen sink requires 0.20 l/s at 60°C

In other types of building, typical usage rates for domestic hot water might be as indicated in Table 7.6.

*Table 7.6* Hot water usage

| Typical hot water consumption rates (litres per person per day) | |
| --- | --- |
| Boarding schools and colleges | 115 |
| Day schools and colleges | 15 |
| Factories and offices | 15 |
| Hotels | 115 to 135 |
| Sports pavilions | 35 |
| Hospitals | 135 to 230 |

## Heat recovery period

The time in minutes taken to heat a given quantity of hot water through a certain temperature rise can be found using the following formula:

$$M = L \times T / (14.3 \times P)$$

where:
M = the time in minutes
L = the volume of water to be heated in litres
T = the temperature increase in °C
P = the boiler power or rate of heat input in kW

Note: 14.3 is the ratio between the number of seconds in 1 minute (60) and the specific heat capacity of water (4.18 kJ/kg/°C).

For example, a rectangular storage tank with a capacity of 122 l has to be heated from 20°C to 65°C by a 3 kW electric immersion heater, so the time required is:

$$= L \times T / (14.3 \times P)$$
$$= 122 \times 45 / (14.3 \times 3)$$
$$= 5490 / 42.9$$
$$= 128 \text{ minutes}$$

*Table 7.7* Minimum sizes of hot water storage vessels

| Heat input to water | Minimum storage capacity for dwelling with 1 bath | |
|---|---|---|
| | with stratification | with mixing |
| 3 kW | 109 l | 122 l |
| 6 kW | 88 l | 88 l |
| 10 kW | 70 l | 70 l |
| 15 kW | 70 l | 70 l |
| Heat input to water | Minimum storage capacity for dwelling with 2 baths | |
| | with stratification | with mixing |
| 3 kW | 165 l | 260 l |
| 6 kW | 140 l | 200 l |
| 10 kW | 130 l | 130 l |
| 15 kW | 120 l | 130 l |

Suggested minimum sizes of storage vessels are shown in Table 7.7.

## Hot water system feed-cistern

The capacity of the hot water system feed-cistern should be at least the same as the capacity of the hot water storage vessel. This will enable the use of all the hot water, even if the main supply happens to be interrupted. If the cistern also supplies cold water to sanitary fittings it should have a larger capacity; possibly twice the volume would be satisfactory.

Connection details for the feed-cistern are covered in Chapter 6. Figure 6.11 shows a typical cistern.

## Hot water storage vessel capacity

The volume, in m³, and capacity, in l, of rectangular hot water storage tanks can be found by multiplying together the length, width and overall height. For example, Figure 7.9 shows a rectangular hot water storage tank; if this measures 0.8 m long by 0.4 m wide by 0.8 m high its volume would be:

$$0.8 \times 0.4 \times 0.8 = 0.256 \text{ m}^3$$

There are 1000 l in l m³, so the tank would contain:

$$0.256 \times 1000 = 256 \text{ l}$$

The volume of cylindrical storage vessels can be found by the following formula: 3.14 × radius of vessel² × height. Most cylindrical vessels have both a convex domed top and a concave domed base. By measuring the height to the shoulder we can regard them as being simple plain-ended cylinders. This is because the increased volume of the top is more or less cancelled out by the reduction due to the concave base. For example, if the cylinder illustrated in Figure 7.9 was 0.9 m high to the shoulder with a diameter of 0.4 m, then its radius would be 0.2 m and its volume would be:

$$3.14 \times 0.2 \times 0.2 \times 0.9 = 0.113 \text{ m}^3$$
or
$$0.113 \times 1000 = 113 \text{ l}$$

# Open-vented hot water systems

## Direct storage hot water system

This is the simplest storage hot water system. It gets its name from the fact that the water that comes from the hot taps will have been heated directly by the boiler. This is because the storage vessel does not contain a heat exchanger (Figure 7.10).

In this system, some of the water that circulates around the boiler and circulation pipes is replaced by fresh water containing oxygen each time the taps are turned on. Because of this, it is important that all pipework and the boiler, cistern and storage vessel are made from corrosion resistant materials such as galvanised steel, copper or brass. If the water supply is temporary hard, the direct hot water system is not recommended because it will gradually become clogged with limescale.

## Indirect storage hot water system

In an indirect hot water system, the water that circulates between the boiler and the storage vessel is kept entirely separate from the water that issues from the hot taps. This is achieved by using a storage vessel which has a heat exchanger, either a coil of tube or a small inner cylinder, inside it (Figure 7.11).

From the outside there appears to be no difference between the indirect storage vessel and those used in the direct system. Inside, however, the heat exchanger allows heat from the boiler, or 'primary' side of the system, to pass through into the water in the 'secondary' side of the system. The benefit of this arrangement is that the water that circulates inside the

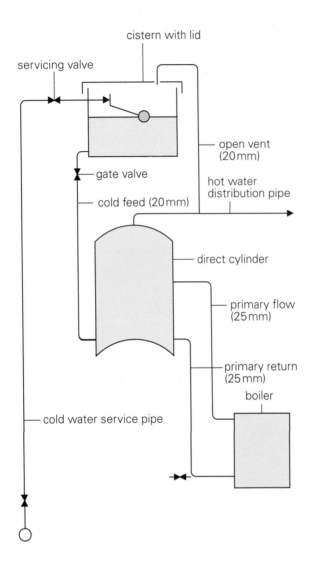

Figure 7.10   Direct hot water system

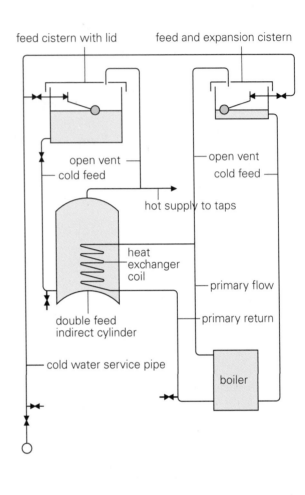

Figure 7.11   Indirect storage hot water system

boiler, circulation pipes and heat exchanger never changes. Once the system has been filled and heated, any temporary hardness that the water contains will be driven out, but there will be no measurable effect owing to the small quantity of water contained in the system.

## Feed and expansion cistern

In the indirect system there are two feed cisterns: one relatively large feed cistern for the secondary side, supplying water for the hot taps, and a second, usually smaller, cistern to keep the boiler and primary side of the system full. This second cistern also has to accommodate the expansion volume created when the boiler and its water heat up. When heated from 20°C to 90°C water will expand by about 4%; if

the primary side of the system holds 100 l when cold, then this will become about 104 l when hot (see Figure 7.12). Because of this, the float valve in the feed and expansion cistern should be adjusted to allow the expansion volume to flow back into the cistern without overflowing.

## Single-feed indirect hot water system

This type of system makes use of a storage cylinder that has a specially designed heat exchanger inside. The cylinder is 'self-priming' because it enables the filling of the primary side of the system by a single cistern, cold feed pipe and open vent.

As the system is filled for the first time, water is allowed to run through the heat exchanger into the primary circulation pipes and boiler. Once the primary side is filled, two air

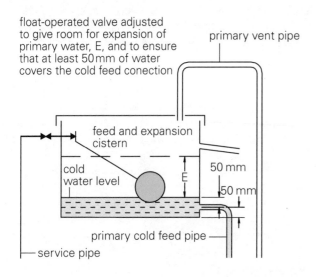

float-operated valve adjusted
to give room for expansion of
primary water, E, and to ensure
that at least 50 mm of water
covers the cold feed conection

primary vent pipe

feed and expansion
cistern

cold
water level

50 mm

E

50 mm

primary cold feed pipe

service pipe

*Figure 7.12*   Feed and expansion cistern

bubbles are trapped within the heat exchanger due to its shape. Water then continues to flow into the cylinder to fill the remainder of the system. The primary and secondary water are kept separate by the air bubbles (Figure 7.13). Each time the water in the system is heated by the boiler it expands in volume. The expanding primary water causes a pressure increase that results in the large air bubble being forced down into the bottom chamber in the heat exchanger. The secondary water is, at the same time, forced away and this expansion goes up the cold feed pipe into the feed cistern. Once the system is allowed to cool, the water contracts and the air bubble is able to return to its original position. Provided that the volume of water in the primary side of the system is not greater than the cylinder manufacturer states in the installation instructions, then the cylinder is able to keep the water in each side of the system separate. If there is too great a volume of primary water, then the air bubble will be forced too far down into the bottom chamber and will escape through the cylinder and open vent. The primary and secondary water will then be able to mix and corrosion will occur.

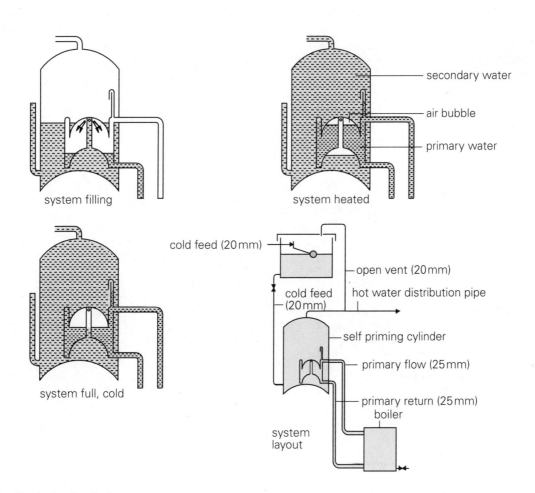

system filling

secondary water

air bubble

primary water

system heated

system full, cold

cold feed (20 mm)

open vent (20 mm)

cold feed
(20 mm)

hot water distribution pipe

self priming cylinder

primary flow (25 mm)

primary return (25 mm)

boiler

system
layout

*Figure 7.13*   Single feed cylinder system

If the air bubble is only lost occasionally, say due to the primary water boiling, then it can be replenished. This occurs because the fresh water that enters the system each time a hot tap is run contains dissolved gases. These are driven out of solution from the water in the secondary side as it is heated, and they bubble up the flow pipe to collect in the heat exchanger.

# Components of hot water systems

The relative positions of the major components of the direct and indirect hot water systems are important if the systems are to operate satisfactorily. If the water circulates between the boiler and storage vessel by convection currents (gravity circulation) the storage vessel must be fitted above the boiler. About 2 m would be the recommended minimum to give reasonable circulation. It must also be kept fairly close horizontally, otherwise the circulation will be sluggish and the vessel will take a long time to heat up (Figure 7.14). Furthermore, the primary circulation pipes between the boiler and the storage vessel must be installed so that they rise continuously without forming any airlocks, which would stop the circulation completely.

The system is kept full of water by the cistern that contains a float-operated valve. The position of the cistern also determines the pressure available at the hot taps. It must be fitted higher than all the hot taps and the storage vessel. Ideally it will be about 2 m above them to provide a good flow of water.

## Open vent and cold feed pipes

These are two very important safety pipes; they must be fitted correctly and be adequate in diameter for the size of the system. In a small system they should be at least 20 mm bore.

If the boiler thermostat malfunctions, so that the water in the system starts to boil, the open vent pipe will allow any steam formed to discharge into the cistern. The cold feed pipe replaces the water lost as steam with cold water to keep the system full. The open vent also allows the system to fill up without becoming air-locked during initial filling. Furthermore, because the system contains water that is constantly replaced while the taps are turned on, the open vent allows the dissolved gases, which are driven out of the water during heating, to bubble away without forming an airlock in the top of the storage vessel.

## Height of vent pipe

It is important that the vent pipe rises sufficiently above the top of the cistern before turning down and ending just inside the lid. The vent pipe can contain hot water and so have a level of water in it that is higher than the level of the denser cold water in the cistern (shown as the difference 'd' in Figure 7.15). Also, when a hot tap is shut off a surge can occur in the vent pipe. If the vent pipe turns down too quickly, water can discharge from it each time a hot tap is turned off.

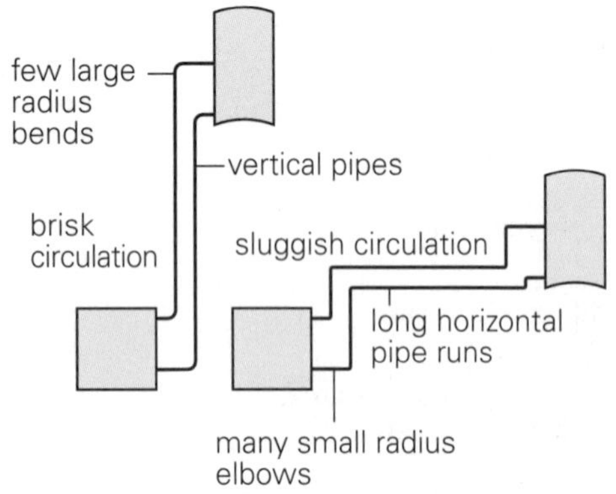

![Figure 7.14 diagram]

*Figure 7.14* Factors affecting gravity circulation

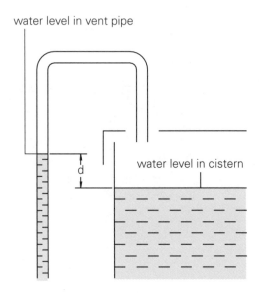

*Figure 7.15* Detail of open vent height

The height by which the vent pipe should rise above the top of the cistern can be found by allowing 40 mm for each 1 m by which the water level in the cistern is above the base of the boiler, plus a further 150 mm.

For example, where the distance from the base of the boiler to the water level in the cistern is 6 m, the vent pipe should be carried up at least $40 \times 6 + 150 = 390$ mm above the water level in the cistern.

## Sealed primary circuit

An alternative to the use of a feed cistern, with open vent and cold feed pipes, is to use a sealed primary circuit, as in Figure 7.16. This has the advantage that air cannot become mixed with the primary water, so corrosion is reduced significantly. There is, however, a slightly increased level of danger with a

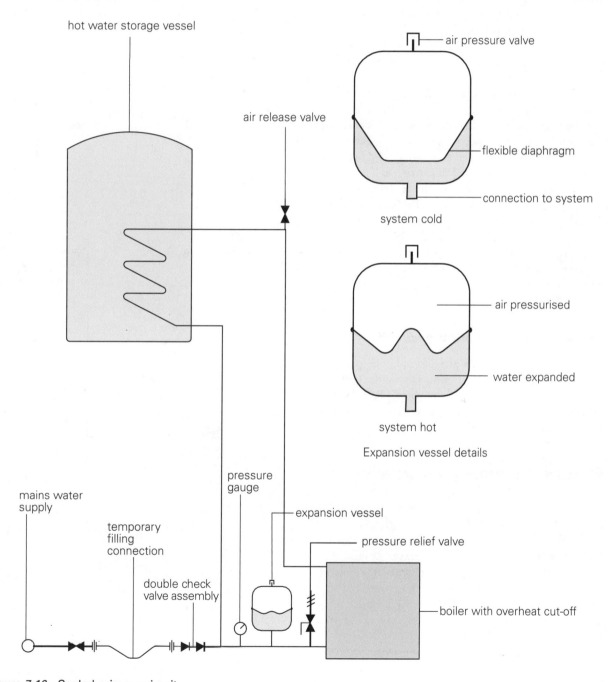

Figure 7.16   Sealed primary circuit

sealed system. If the thermostat on the boiler fails so that the boiler continues to run, the pressure can build up in the system and an explosion can occur.

To prevent this, sealed systems must only be used with boilers that have a second 'overheat cut-off' thermostat fitted. This will shut off the boiler if the normal thermostat fails. A pressure relief valve must also be fitted to allow any dangerous build up of pressure to escape. The outlet from this valve should be piped away to terminate and discharge in a safe place using metal, not plastic, piping.

A pressure gauge is also required. This will enable the circuit to be filled to the correct pressure, and, if leaks occur, the gauge will show a drop in pressure.

Because the water in the circuit will expand on heating, an 'expansion vessel' is fitted to the circuit. This consists of a steel cylinder containing air under pressure and a rubber bladder or diaphragm. As the water is heated and expands, the expansion forces water into the bladder. This compresses the air in the vessel and so the expansion is allowed to occur without causing a pressure build up. The expansion vessel must be big enough to accept the volume increase of water. It should be sized to accept 5% of the total water volume in the primary circuit.

A connection for filling and another, at the top of the circuit, for venting, are required. Once the circuit has been installed, the air pressure in the expansion vessel must be checked and adjusted to the manufacturer's recommended pressure using the tyre valve fitted to the top of the vessel. The circuit can then be connected temporarily to the mains cold water supply for filling and venting. This connection should be removed after filling.

## Maintenance of sealed primary circuits

If a sealed circuit is fitted, the air pressure and water pressure should be checked annually at the same time as the boiler is serviced. Also, the pressure relief valve should be manually opened briefly to ensure that it has not corroded shut; any water lost should be replaced.

## Pumped primary circulation

Where the hot water storage vessel and the boiler cannot be fitted to enable convection currents (gravity circulation) to occur, a small electric-powered circulator pump can be fitted. This will force the water to travel around the primary circuit much faster, enabling smaller diameter primary circulation pipes to be fitted. The heat recovery period will probably be reduced. Also, the cylinder does not have to be fitted above the boiler, giving greater flexibility in the design of the system. If fitted to an indirect system, the pump body can be made from cast iron, but in a direct system it should be corrosion resistant and so a bronze-bodied pump is used.

### Overpumping

It is important to ensure that the primary cold feed and open vent are connected correctly if a pump is installed. If the pump outlet forces water towards the vent and the pump suction tends to draw water down the cold feed, overpumping can occur. The term 'overpumping' describes circulation up the vent pipe, through the feed and expansion cistern and down the cold feed pipe. The problem is that the water, as it gushes out of the vent, is able to dissolve air. This then causes corrosion inside the boiler and primary circulation pipes. Overpumping happens when the pump is installed between the feed and vent connections. Figure 7.17 shows how to connect the vent and cold feed so that overpumping will not occur.

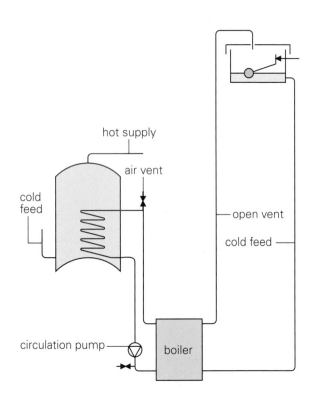

*Figure 7.17* Feed and vent connections to pumped primary system

# Hot water distribution pipes

Hot water distribution pipes feed the hot water from the top of the storage vessel to the various taps. In a cistern fed hot water system, it is important to install the system so that the distribution pipes are kept within the hydraulic gradient. Figure 7.18 shows what could happen to the water pressure if the pipework is too long for the head pressure available.

If the distribution pipework goes outside the gradient line, spluttering taps can result. This is because air can be drawn into the pipework, either through the open vent or through another tap when it is opened. When this occurs, the air and water will emerge from a lower tap. Keeping the pipe runs as short and direct as possible by grouping the sanitary fittings close together and near to the cylinder wherever possible will prevent this problem.

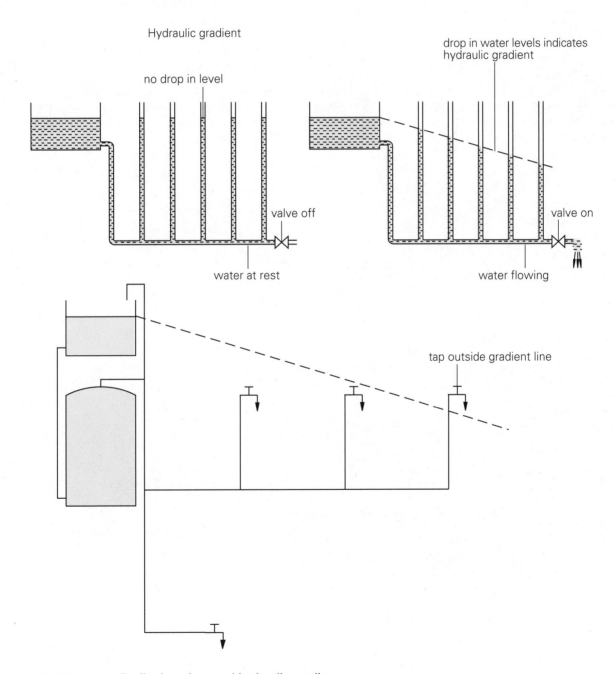

*Figure 7.18*  Hot water distribution pipes and hydraulic gradient

## Secondary circulation

In large buildings, the waste of water and fuel, and the length of time people would have to wait before hot water reaches the tap, would be excessive with the simple systems described so far. This is because the hot water supply pipes from the top of the storage vessel to the various taps are 'dead legs' (as shown in Figure 7.19).

A dead leg is simply a length of tube that does not have water circulating through it. After use, it will contain hot water; this will then cool down when the tap is turned off. Once the water has cooled, the next user will have to run off cold water until the hot from the vessel has replaced it. This is simply wasted, as is the fuel that has been used to heat it.

To prevent the waste of water, but not fuel, a system of secondary circulation pipes is fitted so that water can circulate continuously from the top of the storage vessel, around the secondary circuit and back to the storage vessel. If the building is big enough to require secondary circulation, it will probably not be possible to arrange the pipes to make use of gravity circulation for the secondary circuit. A bronze-bodied pump can be fitted in the return, close to the storage vessel, to cause the circulation. Towel rails or drying coils can also be connected into the circuit; this can be an advantage as these can then be heated all the year round Figure 7.20.

## Boilers for small hot water systems

There are a number of different types of boiler that can be installed to power direct and indirect storage hot water systems. They can be fuelled by:

- gas: natural gas (methane) or liquefied petroleum gas (LPG) (propane or butane);
- solid fuel: coal, coke or wood;
- oil: kerosene or gas-oil.

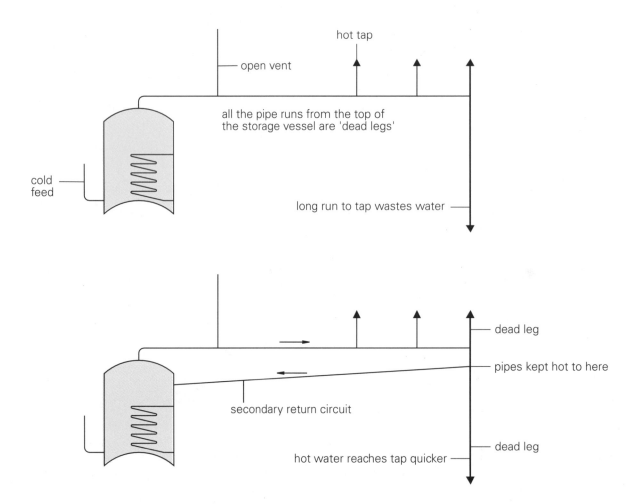

*Figure 7.19* Detail of single 'dead legs' and simple secondary circulation

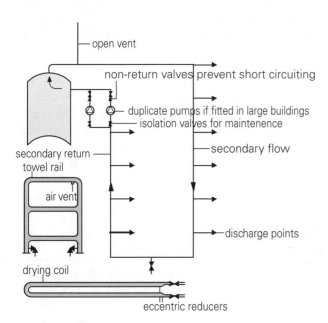

*Figure 7.20* Pumped secondary circulation system

In general, all boilers comprise the following major components: heat exchanger, combustion chamber, flue, hearth and controls for safety and temperature.

### Heat exchanger

This can be made from steel, cast iron or copper. The purpose of the heat exchanger is to collect heat from the radiation and hot gases that are generated as the fuel is burnt. The heat exchanger will work more effectively if it has a relatively large surface area through which the heat can pass easily into the water inside. This will make the boiler more fuel efficient and will consequently save fuel and running costs. Also, the heat exchanger must be robust enough to withstand the conditions under which it must operate.

For example, the heat exchanger in a solid fuel boiler might have to withstand rougher treatment, as fuel is added and ash is removed, than a gas-fired boiler, which does not require manual operation. So, solid fuel boilers usually have heat exchangers that are made from cast iron, whereas a gas-fired boiler could have a heat exchanger that is fabricated from finned copper tube. This would be very efficient in collecting heat but would not be suitable for the solid fuel boiler, as it could not withstand the rough treatment, and the small gaps between the fins would soon become blocked with dust and ash.

The simplest solid fuel boiler is the 'range' or back-boiler. This is a rectangular hollow box that has two threaded tappings on one side. It is fitted into an open fireplace or hearth. It can only supply a limited amount of hot water owing to its low output. Some fireplaces have their back and

sides replaced with a more elaborate higher output boiler; this can also have an internal flueway to further increase the surface area. Free-standing or independent boilers are more efficient, and can be installed in situations where a chimney is not available.

### Combustion chamber

In solid fuel and some oil boilers, the combustion chamber will be lined on one or more sides with refractory heat resistant concrete. Fuel and air burn inside the combustion chamber creating heat. In the solid fuel boiler, the combustion chamber is simply a space for the fuel to burn with a door that is sometimes at the top of the boiler, to enable fuel to be added and ash to be removed. There will also be some form of damper or air-shutter. This enables control over the burning rate of the fuel. By starving the fuel of air, it will burn more slowly and so the boiler will generate less heat. A typical solid fuel boiler is illustrated in Figure 7.21.

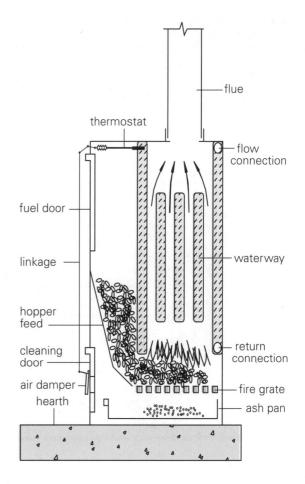

*Figure 7.21* Hopper-fed solid fuel boiler

## Oil-fired burners

In the oil-fired boiler the burner assembly will either use heat to vaporise the liquid oil so that the oil vapour and air can mix and burn, or it will have an atomising or pressure jet burner (as in Figure 7.22). This uses an electric motor to drive an air fan and oil pump. The pump pressurises the oil to about 7 bars pressure and forces it through a specially designed nozzle. The hole in the end of the nozzle is very small. As the oil escapes from the end, its pressure suddenly drops back to normal atmospheric pressure, causing the oil to be atomised into a mist of very small particles. Air can then mix easily with the oil mist and this mixture can be ignited by means of a high voltage spark, which is generated by means of a step-up transformer. The correct conditions for safe combustion are created by a control box which, together with a photocell and thermostat, give fully automatic operation of the boiler. By varying the oil pressure and/or volume of air entering the combustion chamber (within the limits set by the manufacturer) clean safe combustion can be achieved and also heat input to the boiler can be matched to the heat required by the system.

## Gas-fired burners

Because the fuel for this type of burner is already a gas, it is in the ideal state for combustion. The methane, propane or butane can be mixed directly with approximately 50% air for combustion inside the burner. This mixture is formed by using a specially designed injector and burner assembly. The gas flow rate, and in proportion the heat input, depends on the gas pressure and the size of the hole in the end of the injector. Because the different gases have different calorific values, that is a different amount of heat energy in a given volume of gas, it is important to make sure that the correct type of gas is matched to the correct size of injector. Also, it is important to check that the gas pressure at the injector is set to the correct pressure. This can be measured by using a water gauge or manometer and is adjusted by turning the appropriate screw on the governor or multifunction-gas-valve on the appliance. The gas burner is often designed to have many small flames each just touching its neighbour. This is necessary to ensure that the flame is retained on the burner. Two typical gas boilers are illustrated in Figure 7.23.

## Boiler flue

The boiler flue carries away the smoke and fumes (products of combustion) from the top of the heat exchanger to the outside air. It can be a brick or masonry chimney, or made from suitable cast iron, steel or aluminium pipe. It must be installed so that it does not create the danger of fire, by being kept a suitable distance away from combustible parts of the building. It must also terminate in a position where the products of combustion can vent away safely without creating the danger of carbon monoxide (a deadly poisonous gas) re-entering the building through openings such as windows or air vents.

Flues operate because the hot products of combustion are lighter than the cold air surrounding the flue. They make use of convention currents as in circulation pipes. So, to ensure that the flue operates effectively, it is necessary to keep it warm by positioning it inside the building if possible. Keep

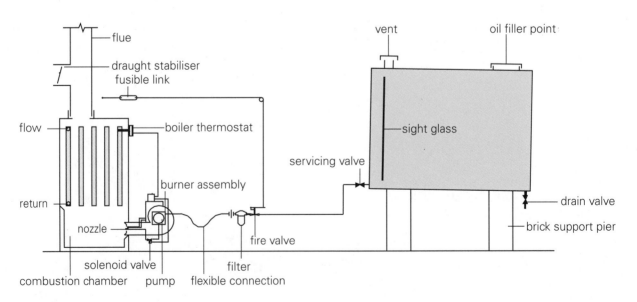

*Figure 7.22*  Pressure jet oil boiler and tank

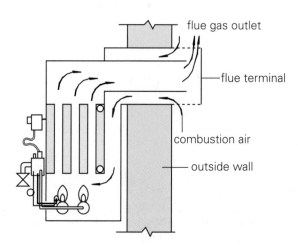

Balanced flue gas boiler

it short, but not so short that there is insufficient draught to pull the fumes away from the boiler. A flue that is too tall can suffer from condensation problems because it loses too much heat before the fumes can vent away.

Because the products of combustion are slightly acidic, the flue must be kept warm so that the water vapour that is created as a result of combustion of the fuel does not condense inside the flue and drip down on to the heat exchanger causing external corrosion and so shortening its life.

The flue should be kept as vertical as possible, using 135° bends wherever possible. If horizontal runs of flue pipe must be used then they must be kept as short as possible so that they do not create too much resistance. All flue joints should be correctly sealed; if using socket and spigot flue pipes, they should be installed with the sockets uppermost so that any condensation formed when the boiler is first fired from cold cannot run out of the joints.

## Room-sealed boilers

Many types of small gas-fired boiler, and some small pressure jet oil boilers, are supplied with **balanced flues**. The balanced flue comprises a pair of ducts, one often inside the other larger outer duct, as shown in Figure 7.23. The purpose is to supply air for combustion, and carry away the products of combustion. Because the air inlet and flue outlet are close together, the air pressure acting on them is balanced. The difference in temperature between the hot flue gases and the colder combustion air is sufficient to cause the flue to operate. Also, because the appliance does not take air from the room it is safer.

## Boiler hearth

Depending on the type of boiler being used, a fireproof hearth may be required. Because they operate at higher temperatures, solid fuel and most oil boilers require a concrete or masonry fireproof hearth. This must be large enough to accommodate the boiler and allow for the possibility of hot ashes spilling out. It must also be thick enough to prevent heat travelling down through it into combustible materials below.

## Local building regulations

All boilers must be installed strictly in accordance with local building regulations and with due regards to the manufacturer's instructions. It is important that they are correctly commissioned and regularly maintained if they are to be kept safe and give long service. Also, it is important to install the boiler in a suitable location, one that has sufficient space to enable safe operation as well as giving room for maintenance and repair.

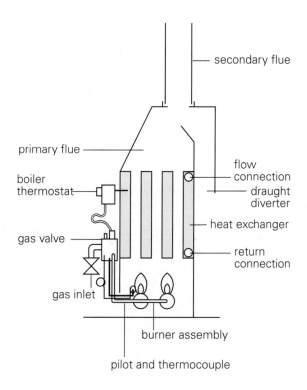

Open-flued gas boiler

*Figure 7.23*   Open flue and room-sealed gas boilers

## Boiler controls

Some form of temperature control is fitted to all but the most basic of solid fuel boilers. Depending on the type of boiler, the complexity of the controls will vary. The boiler thermostat will control the temperature of the boiler water, turning on the burner when the water is cooler than the setting on the thermostat and off once this temperature is reached. Boiler thermostats make use of expansion, usually of a liquid that is trapped in a hollow tube or probe connected by a fine capillary tube to a metal bellows. When the probe is heated and cooled, the liquid expands and contracts and this volume change causes the bellows to lengthen and shorten in sympathy. This then operates a switch that controls the burner.

## Flame failure controls

Flame failure safety controls are fitted to automatic oil and gas boilers. In the case of the oil boiler this is usually a photocell (a light-dependent resistor or 'magic-eye' that can detect the light given off by the oil flame. If the boiler control box starts the ignition sequence and the flame is not established correctly, the boiler will then shut down. The control box will go to its 'lock-out' condition and will not attempt to reignite the burner until someone has pressed the reset button. This is usually in the form of a red illuminated push button switch. The control box will also go to lock-out if the flame goes out for any reason during the firing run before the boiler thermostat is satisfied; this could be due to burner breakdown or simply because the boiler has run out of fuel.

The safety control on most simple gas boilers consists of a permanently lit pilot flame and thermocouple. The pilot flame ignites the main burner when the multifunction-gas-valve opens a solenoid-valve under the control of the boiler thermostat. If the pilot flame is extinguished, the thermocouple cools down and this causes the interrupter valve in the multifunction-gas-valve to shut. It is necessary for someone to press in and hold a manual starting button to reopen the interrupter valve while the pilot flame is ignited. The button must be held down for about 30 seconds after the pilot is lit so that the thermocouple can be heated sufficiently for it to generate the electric current that holds the interrupter valve open.

## Boilers and their controls

### Traditional large water content boilers

The traditional boiler has a cast iron heat exchanger that has a large water content, an open flue and a multifunction-gas-valve with a thermocouple and a boiler thermostat. The flame failure device is the thermocouple; a permanent pilot is used for ignition purposes.

These boilers are very reliable and can last for many years; they usually only require an annual clean of the burner, the heat exchanger and, possibly, replacement of the thermocouple. They are not as efficient as more modern boilers. Because of their large water content they are slow to react to their controls. Furthermore, there is a lot of residual heat trapped in the boiler when the system shuts down and this is often wasted. However, they are slow to cool down to freezing point and the permanent pilot helps to prevent frost bursts of the heat exchanger when installed in temperate latitudes.

**What can go wrong with this type of boiler?**
The thermocouple/gas-valve interrupter or the boiler thermostat/gas-valve solenoid can become faulty.

If the pilot will not stay alight, disconnect and check the thermocouple with a multimeter to see if it produces the correct voltage (about 30 mV open circuit) when heated. If the boiler is receiving its correct electrical supply, isolate then check the gas-valve interrupter or gas-valve solenoid for correct resistance with the multimeter, or check the boiler thermostat with a thermometer and the multimeter to see if the switch inside makes a circuit when the thermostat is cold and breaks the circuit when the thermostat is heated.

**How can the boiler be made more efficient?**
Reduce the water content so that the boiler responds more quickly to its controls. A low water content boiler will be more responsive to its controls. The heat up time will be reduced and, more importantly, the boiler will retain less heat energy when the controls are satisfied and so it will be more efficient.

The controls used on this low water content boiler are very similar to those on the traditional boiler: a thermocouple, a gas valve and a boiler thermostat. However, there is one important addition. The fast response to heat is an advantage as far as energy efficiency is concerned, but this can lead to problems of overheating, causing noises (kettling and implosion banging) and damage to the heat exchanger if the boiler thermostat becomes faulty. To prevent this, a bypass is usually required on the pipework to allow circulation round the heat exchanger at any time, and an overheat thermostat is added to the controls. This is a second thermostat that, when heated to above its operating point (usually about 90°C), opens a switch to break the thermocouple circuit and extinguish the burner and pilot. The overheat thermostat is self-resetting when it cools, but because pilot outage shuts the interrupter in the gas valve, which itself shuts down the pilot gas supply, the boiler is totally shut down and will not relight until the pilot has been manually re-established.

If the pilot is prone to outage on this type of boiler there are three possibilities:

1. a faulty thermocouple or gas valve interrupter;
2. a faulty boiler thermostat, causing overheating and thus pilot outage;
3. a missing or badly adjusted bypass.

The controls can be checked as before and the customer can be questioned to see if the boiler is noisy or whether the main burner tends to be on until the pilot goes out. Also, a thermometer can be used to check the boiler flow and return temperatures, so that the bypass can be adjusted to comply with the manufacturer's recommended setting (probably an 11°C drop across the flow and return).

## Fanned flue boilers

The most modern boilers are room-sealed and use a fanned flue. They will also have spark ignition and no permanent pilot. Dispensing with the pilot will give a fuel saving over a boiler with a permanent pilot. The controls are also different: on a fanned flue boiler, the burner must not be allowed to fire if the flue fan is not running correctly and moving air through the boiler. You cannot be sure that the fan is running even if it is receiving an electrical supply. The motor could be burnt out or seized or the flue could be blocked. So a pressure switch is used to detect whether air is flowing through the boiler before the repeating spark is started and the burner is supplied with gas. A quick-acting flame failure device is also needed because it would not be safe to supply gas to the burner unless the flame is properly established. Flame rectification is usually used to detect whether the burner is lit in this case.

### What might go wrong with this type of boiler?
1. The fan might not run/the pressure switch could be faulty.
2. The spark ignition system could become faulty.
3. The flame failure electronic circuit or the flame electrode (its position relative to the flame or its associated cable and connections) could become faulty.
4. The boiler control board (electronic) could become faulty.

Use a manometer (connected to the burner pressure point) to see whether the case is properly fitted. If the case is properly sealed there will be a small (0.5 mbar approximately) change in the water level on the manometer as the fan starts before the main burner attempts to ignite. If there is too much air leakage around the case seals, the boiler will not run. Check the pressure switch with a multimeter to see if the switch makes a circuit when there is an air pressure difference between the boiler case and the surrounding atmosphere. Check the fan to see if the impeller runs freely; check the fan motor windings for resistance to see whether it is burnt out.

## Condensing boilers

By increasing the surface area of the heat exchanger, the boiler can be made more efficient. If the heat exchanger is able to take out sufficient energy from the hot flue gases passing through it, the water vapour will be condensed back into liquid, giving up further heat in the process. In the condensing boiler this is designed to occur. The heat exchanger will be made from corrosion resistant materials and will be shaped to cause the condensate to collect and be discharged through a small drain pipe to a gully or soak-away. Condensing boilers have fanned flues because the flue gases are cooled to such an extent that a conventional open flue would not operate. Their controls are usually the same as are found on the fanned flue boiler mentioned previously.

## Fault-finding in boilers

When checking the electrical systems of boilers, refer to the manufacturer's detailed instructions for fault finding. This is to ascertain the correct sequence of checks to carry out and their associated multimeter readings, in order to rectify the fault or establish what the correct action is.

Remember that *electrical safety* requires that you carry out this type of work in a way that does not create *danger*. So ensure that, as far as possible, the work is carried out with the system totally disconnected from both the gas and electricity supplies. Also remember to carry out preliminary gas and electrical system tests before re-establishing the supplies.

## Boiler mountings and connections

Depending on the size (power) of the boiler, its complexity and the type of hot water system it serves, the boiler will have one or more of the components illustrated in Figure 7.24 fitted. The drain valve is essential for maintenance, as is the safety valve or pressure relief valve if the boiler is connected to a sealed system. Also necessary in a sealed system is a pressure gauge; this will show if any small leaks are gradually losing pressure from the system. A thermometer might also be mounted on the boiler.

Boilers are usually supplied with female threaded tappings, two on each side. Always use demountable union, compression or flange joints to make the connections. The diameter of the tappings will depend on the power of the boiler. This can give an indication of the diameter of primary circulation pipes required. If these are to use gravity circulation, the boiler manufacturer will probably recommend that the diameter of the circulation pipes should be equal to the tappings. If pumped circulation is to be fitted, the circulation pipes can probably be reduced in diameter. If the diameter is to be reduced, the flow and vent pipe connections at the top of the boiler should be reduced using eccentric reducing couplings, as in Figure 7.25. These will allow the boiler to vent properly without trapping a bubble of air in the top of the boiler. Ordinary concentric screwed bushes can be used to change the diameter if these are fitted to vertical pipes.

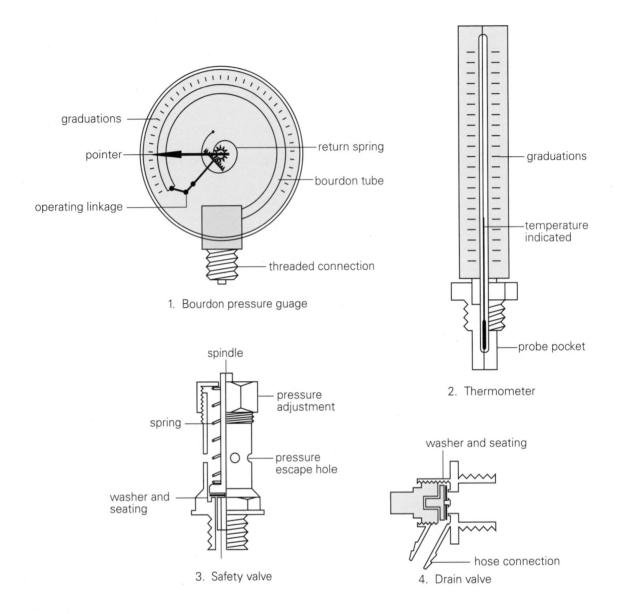

*Figure 7.24*  Boiler mountings

# Water heating by steam

If a supply of steam is available, say in a factory, then this can be passed through the heat exchanger of a **calorifier** (a hot water storage vessel, which contains a tube type heat exchanger) to produce hot water for use at sanitary appliances. In a steam boiler (unlike a hot water boiler in which the water does not boil), water is heated until it boils to create steam. This steam is then distributed via a system of steam pipework to the various pieces of equipment that the boiler serves. Once the steam has given up its heat energy, it condenses back into liquid water and is returned to the boiler plant by way of condensate pipes.

The reason steam is used in certain processes, rather than hot water, is because it can carry considerably more heat energy than liquid water, at a much higher temperature if required. Consider the case of liquid water, that requires 4.18 kJ of energy for each kg of mass to raise its temperature by 1°C. When 1 kg of water cools by 1°C it gives up the same quantity of energy. If the same 1 kg mass of water was heated until it reached 100°C and heating was then continued, the

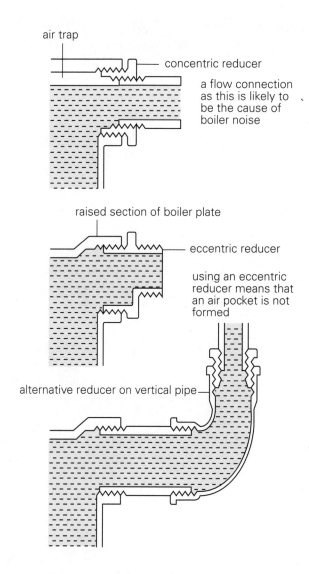

air trap

concentric reducer

a flow connection as this is likely to be the cause of boiler noise

raised section of boiler plate

eccentric reducer

using an eccentric reducer means that an air pocket is not formed

alternative reducer on vertical pipe

*Figure 7.25*  Boiler connection details

temperature of the water would not increase but steam would start to be generated, with a volume equal to 1670 l for each litre (kg) of water that was completely boiled into steam at standard atmospheric pressure. In fact, to convert the 1 kg of water completely into steam, still at 100°C, would require 2257 kJ of energy. This energy, which is latent or hidden heat energy, is called the **specific latent heat of vaporisation**, and is available to be given up and must be lost by the steam before it can condense back into liquid water.

The boiling point of water varies with its pressure and so the water in a steam plant that operates at a pressure of 1 bar above atmospheric pressure would start to boil at a temperature of 120°C. Because of this, the steam generated in this plant would have to give up even more energy before it condenses back into liquid water at 100°C. By reference to steam tables, the total quantity of heat energy available from

steam at various pressures and temperatures can be determined.

Steam is a very efficient method of carrying heat energy and is very suitable as a source of heat for water heating. In order to control the production of hot water in the calorifier the steam entering the heat exchanger must be controlled. Figure 7.26 shows a typical arrangement of the equipment.

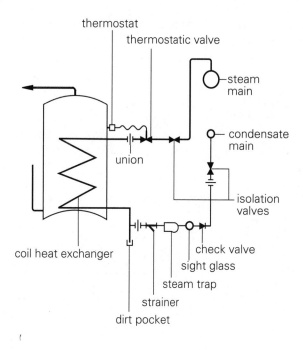

thermostat

thermostatic valve

steam main

condensate main

union

isolation valves

coil heat exchanger

check valve

sight glass

steam trap

strainer

dirt pocket

*Figure 7.26*  Small steam-heated calorifier

## Fittings and components required

**Isolation valves**  These are installed at the steam inlet and condensate outlet of the equipment to facilitate maintenance.
**Strainer**  An in-line strainer is fitted into the pipeline wherever there is a danger of scale and dirt affecting he operation of sensitive valves such as steam traps or thermostatic valves.
**Thermostatic valve**  This, together with a thermostat, is fitted on the steam side of the heat exchanger to control the water temperature of the stored hot water. The thermostat senses the temperature of the water and shuts the thermostatic valve thus preventing further steam from passing through the heat exchanger and so limiting the temperature of the stored hot water.
**Bypass**  This is sometimes fitted so that manual control and a continuation of supply of hot water is possible if the thermostatic valve malfunctions.
**Dirt pocket**  This is simply a short leg of pipe fitted with a cap end into which dirt and scale can fall before reaching the strainer that is fitted just before the steam trap.

**Steam trap** This device, of which there are many different patterns each with its own particular application, is fitted to prevent steam simply blowing through the heat exchanger and away into the condensate mains. In use, the valve in the steam trap stays closed while there is steam in the pipe at the inlet to the steam trap. When the pipe fills with condensate, the valve opens and the condensate is blown out of the pipe by the pressure of the steam behind it; the steam trap then shuts down again until the pipe refills with condensate.

**Sight glass** This is a pipeline fitting that has a thick glass window in its side. It is fitted to enable a visual inspection of the condensate in the pipe, after the steam trap, to see if the steam trap is operating correctly and not passing steam indiscriminately.

**Materials** Steam pipes are installed using heavy gauge mild steel tube with welded joints or screwed joints and wrought iron fittings sealed with black graphite compound. Steam mains are installed with a slight fall so that the condensate that forms in the pipe will trickle towards steam traps that are fitted periodically along the mains. Condensate pipes can be made from galvanised mild steel pipe and fittings.

Steam and condensate pipes are usually painted silver as an identifying colour and are normally insulated to reduce heat losses that would otherwise be considerable.

# Gas and electric storage water heaters

There are many types of purpose-designed storage water heaters powered by both gas and electricity. Their capacities range from a few litres, to serve a single sink, to many hundreds, serving more taps. The advantage of having a purpose-designed heater is that site installation is simplified; also they are usually very well insulated making them economical to run. Because they are neat and have a clean appearance they can be installed in situations where a storage vessel and pipework would not be visually acceptable.

## Electric immersion heaters

These consist of a length of **resistance wire** inside a copper sheath, the space between being filled with mica electrical insulation. The heater element is fitted into the hot water storage vessel through a female threaded boss, and so is immersed in the water. A rod type thermostat is usually also incorporated to give temperature control. See Figure 7.27 for details of a typical immersion heater installation. When the electrical supply is turned on, the resistance wire becomes hot and so heats the water in the storage vessel directly.

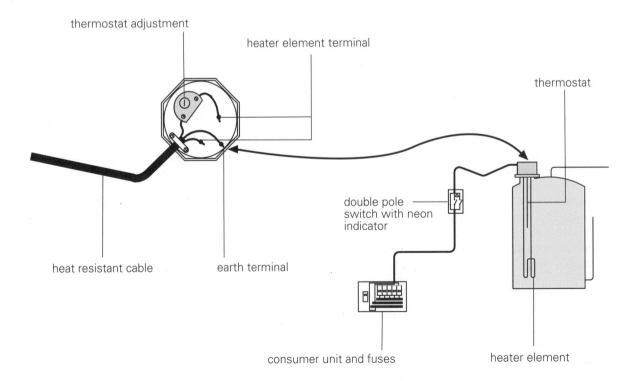

*Figure 7.27* Electric immersion heater

Immersion heaters use about 3 kW of power and must be correctly fitted and wired in accordance with local regulations if they are to be safe and give long service.

## Single-point storage water heaters

These supply water to one sink only; they are often fitted with a swivel outlet and have the water flow controlled by a valve on the inlet supply. Figure 7.28 shows details of a typical small thermostatically controlled electric-powered storage water heater.

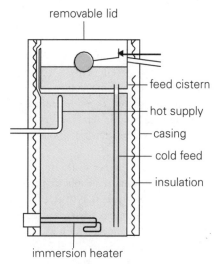

1. Electric storage water heater unit

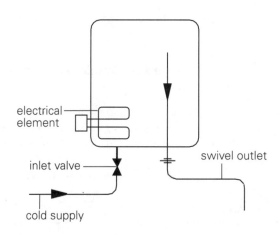

*Figure 7.28* Single-point electric storage water heaters

## Multi-point storage water heaters

These have a larger capacity and can serve more than one tap. Multi-point heaters therefore have the water flow controlled by the taps they serve. Figure 7.29 illustrates typical gas and electric multi-point storage water heaters.

Gas storage heaters are often purpose-designed vessels with a gas burner incorporated directly underneath the storage cylinder in the base of the unit. The burner flue goes up the centre of the vessel and is surrounded by the water; the flue has baffles inside it to increase the rate of heat transfer. This type of unit is very fuel efficient owing to its thermostatic control and the factory fitted insulation.

It is important to site the heater close to the taps it serves; long runs of pipe will simply waste heat and reduce the amount of hot water available. If there are a number of taps close together, supply them from the multi-point heater. If the taps are spread through the building, consider using a combination of smaller capacity heaters.

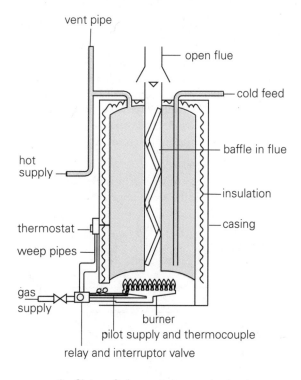

2. Cistern fed gas storage water heater

*Figure 7.29* Multi-point storage water heaters

# Unvented domestic hot water storage systems

In areas where the mains water supply is sufficiently reliable to satisfy the demand for both hot and cold water then, provided local regulations permit, it is possible to install an unvented domestic hot water storage system. This is comprised of a cylindrical storage vessel made from copper, or steel lined with vitreous enamel or rubber, together with controls to regulate the water pressure and the temperature, and a vessel to accommodate the expansion that occurs as the water is heated.

The temperature at which water boils depends on the pressure of the water. At normal atmospheric pressure, 1 bar absolute, the boiling temperature is 100°C. If the water is under pressure inside the storage vessel, then its boiling point will be increased (Figure 7.30). Provided the temperature controls operate correctly, the water in the cylinder will never reach temperatures where there is any danger, because the control thermostat will turn off the power at, for example, 60°C. Unfortunately, as with all things mechanical, there will be occasions when things go wrong. If the storage cylinder was operated at 2 bar gauge pressure and the thermostat malfunctioned, the water could reach a temperature of over 130°C and still not be boiling. If the pressure in the system was then to drop to atmospheric, for example because the cylinder fractured, the water would flash to steam with explosive force! This could easily be sufficient to demolish the building. For this reason, a combination of safety controls *must* be fitted on a mains unvented hot water system. If the storage vessel is directly heated, three levels of control are required:

- thermostat – set to 60–65°C;
- energy cut-out – set to operate at no more than 90°C;
- temperature relief valve – set to operate at 95°C.

A pressure relief valve on its own does not have the capacity to eliminate the danger of explosion as it would still allow a dangerous build up of heat energy to remain in the storage vessel after blowing off. The temperature relief valve has a sensing element that *must* protrude into the top, and therefore the hottest water, of the storage vessel. If this gets too hot then the valve will open and allow a discharge of hot water to continue until it has been cooled down to a safe level by cold water entering the system.

Figure 7.31 shows a typical unvented domestic hot water storage system with all the controls and fittings necessary to ensure complete safety in operation. It is important to make sure that all the controls are matched to the capacity of the unit and power of the heater that feeds it. It is best to fit a 'package' unit because the manufacturer will assemble the components correctly and safer installation will be more likely.

## Controls for unvented domestic hot water storage systems

**Isolating valve**   This is necessary for maintenance purposes.

**Line strainer**   This prevents solid matter entering the system and possibly blocking the operation of the other controls (Figure 7.32).

**Non-return valve**   This prevents back-flow of water, that may be hot or contaminated, into the mains cold water pipes (Figure 7.33).

**Pressure reducing valve**   This reduces the pressure of the mains to that required by the storage cylinder. It gives a close and accurate control to its outlet by the action of back pressure on to a diaphragm (Figure 7.34).

**Pressure limiting valve**   This is a simpler alternative to the pressure reducing valve. When the mains inlet pressure goes above the preset outlet pressure, the valve operates and closes. It does not give such close control and is usually fitted to systems with steel storage vessels (Figure 7.35).

**Expansion vessel**   This accepts the increased volume of water when it is heated up without allowing a build up of pressure (see Figure 7.16 for details).

**Expansion relief valve**   This is a valve that discharges water if the pressure in the system exceeds a predetermined level. If the expansion vessel loses its air pressure, this valve will dribble water each time the system heats up (Figure 7.36).

**Temperature (and pressure) relief valve**   This protects the system from failure of the thermostat and energy cut-out and is the last line of defence against explosion. If the storage vessel overheats, the probe expands and opens the valve allowing cold water into the system until the temperature drops to a safe level. It should be supplied preset and fitted directly into the top of the storage vessel. It must operate at below 100°C. It might incorporate a vacuum relief valve; this will allow air into the system if the pressure drops below atmospheric and the cylinder is in danger of implosion. It also has a

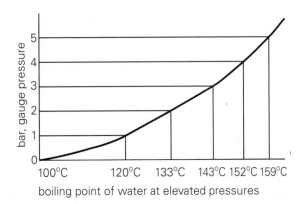

*Figure 7.30*  Graph of boiling point at various pressures

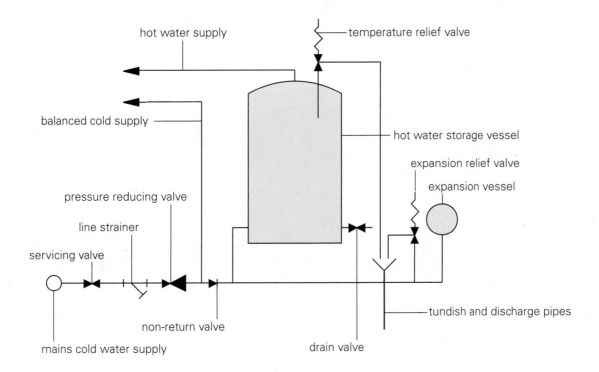

*Figure 7.31*   Unvented domestic hot water storage system

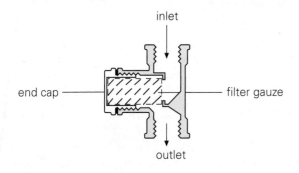

*Figure 7.32*   Section through a line strainer

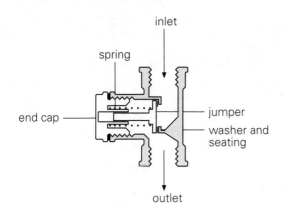

*Figure 7.33*   Section through a non-return valve

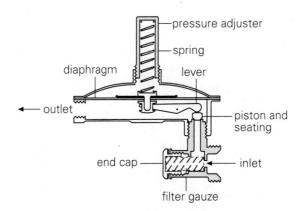

*Figure 7.34*   Section through a pressure reducing valve

bursting disk built in; this should vent if the valve fails to operate (Figure 7.37).

**Discharge pipework**   Both the expansion relief valve and the temperature relief valve are designed to discharge water if the system malfunctions; the discharge pipework must carry away the near boiling water safely. It must be made from metal pipe to withstand the heat. It should not be too

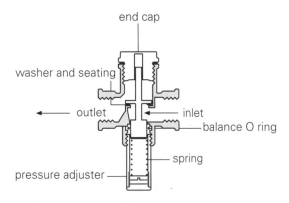

Figure 7.35   Section through a pressure limiting valve

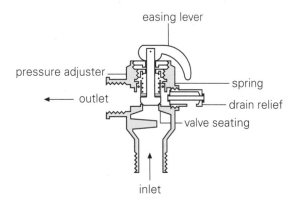

Figure 7.36   Section through an expansion relief valve

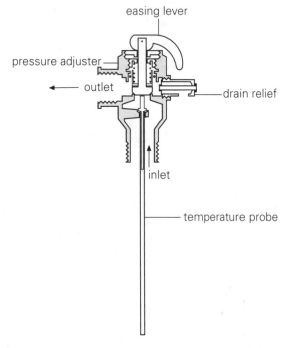

Figure 7.37   Section through a temperature relief valve

long, 9 m maximum, and not have too many 90° bends fitted, three being a safe limit. It should also fall continuously throughout its length, and its diameter must not be smaller than the valve outlets it serves (Figure 7.38).

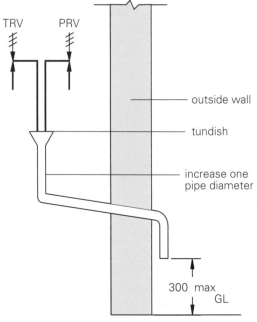

Figure 7.38   Detail of discharged pipework

## Commissioning unvented domestic hot water storage systems

Once installed, it is very important that the hot water storage system is tested and brought into service properly following the manufacturer's recommendations. These will probably include the following:

1. Flush out the system, the unit and all its pipework.
2. Check the connections for water tightness.
3. Check the immersion heater thermostat at 60°C, and that it is the correct type with an energy cut-out fitted.
4. Check the air pressure in the expansion vessel.
5. Make sure that any drain valves have been closed and then open the highest hot and cold water taps.
6. Open the cold water supply stop valve and allow the cylinder to fill with water; continue to fill until water reaches the taps and then shut these off.
7. Check for any leaks.
8. Manually open the relief valves and ensure that water flows away through the discharge pipework.
9. Switch on the immersion heater and check its operation.

## Maintenance and servicing

Once per year it is important to check that the expansion vessel still contains the correct pressure of air. The relief valves must also be manually opened to make sure that they still operate correctly, all in accordance with the manufacturer's recommendations.

### Reliability and safety of the system

Provided that the system is properly designed, correctly installed and commissioned and then correctly maintained, the unvented domestic hot water storage system is a reliable and very safe system. To ensure the above, it is best if only fully trained and competent personnel install and maintain it.

## Solar hot water systems

Radiant heat from the sun can be used to provide hot water in areas where the climate is favourable. A solar hot water system consists of an area of heat collectors, a pipework circulation system and a storage vessel. It is an advantage if the collectors can be sited below the storage vessel; the heat can then be carried from the collectors to the storage vessel

by gravity circulation. If the collectors are above the storage vessel, a circulation pump and temperature sensing controls to turn the pump on and off will be necessary, as in Figure 7.39.

### Solar collectors

Solar collectors absorb solar energy and produce heat. They can be used for heating water for buildings or industry. The flat-plate type of collector is made from a copper, aluminium, or steel heat-absorber plate, the surface of which is painted black to make it more efficient in absorbing solar energy. Tubes are soldered or clamped to the plate to allow heat transfer, usually by means of a water-and-antifreeze solution, to circulate and carry heat from the plate to a storage vessel; as an alternative, the liquid may simply flow across the surface of the collector.

One or two layers of glass or transparent plastic, separated by an air space, are placed above the plate; for low-temperature applications, such as swimming-pool heating,

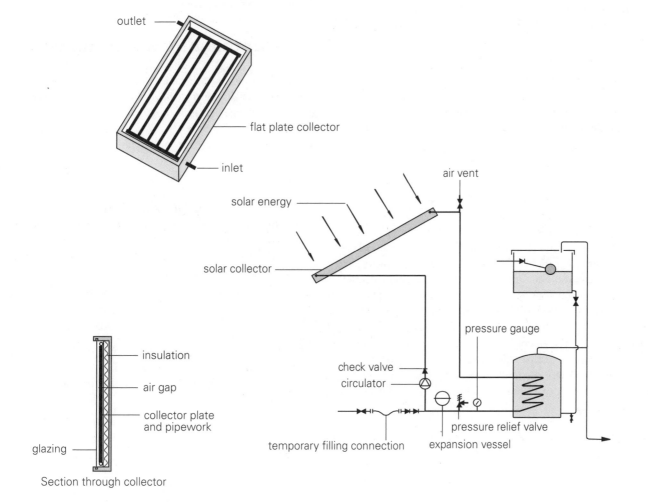

*Figure 7.39*  Solar hot water system

no layers may be used. The air space minimises convective and conductive heat losses to the atmosphere. The glazing also minimises heat radiation from the collector. Heat losses are reduced further by insulating the back and sides of the collector, as well as the pipes leading to and from the heat-storage vessel. The plate is mounted in such a direction that the glass surface is at the same angle as the sun's path across the sky. Efficiencies of flat-plate collectors may be as high as 70% when operating at close to the ambient (surrounding air) temperature. As they get hot, their efficiency may drop to less than 30%. An average home may require from 3 to 10 m$^2$ of collector area for heating domestic hot water.

# Prevention of heat loss

The effective insulation of hot water pipes and storage vessels is important in reducing fuel running costs. The basic theory regarding insulation is quite simple. It consists of covering the pipes and vessel with a layer of material that traps many tiny air pockets and has a low rate of heat transfer or conductivity. Many materials are used for insulation and a good insulator will have the following properties:

● it should be fire resistant;
● it should not attract vermin;
● if installed in potentially damp situations it must be impervious to moisture so as not to become waterlogged;
● it should not be so fragile that it is too easily damaged.

Good insulation materials include: foamed rubber, foamed plastics, such as expanded polystyrene, cork, fibreglass and rockwool. Pipe insulation can be obtained preformed and can be sleeved over the tube as it is installed. Alternatively, it is available moulded in two halves that can be clipped around the tube after it has been fitted and tested. Fibreglass and rockwool insulation are usually formed in this manner and are sometimes covered with a cotton cloth; this covers the joints between the sides and ends of the halves and fixes the insulation by means of a paste glue. It is a good idea to insulate all circulating pipework, both primary and secondary, because it will be hot for considerable periods of time. Depending on the diameter, short dead-legs of hot water distribution pipe can be left uninsulated. The smaller the diameter, the lower the amount of total heat loss. So, for example, pipes up to 20 mm bore might be left uninsulated if they are less than 12 m long and pipes of 25 mm bore might be left uninsulated if they are under 3 m long.

Insulation is essential on all hot water storage vessels because of their relatively large surface area. Sections of fibreglass quilt can be covered in plastic or cloth and secured around cylindrical storage vessels. Expanded polystyrene sheets can be cut to fit the sides of rectangular storage tanks and cisterns.

It would be possible to save up to 50% of the fuel running costs of an uninsulated hot water system if the system was thoroughly insulated using good quality materials. This might well be very cost effective and pay for itself in two or three years.

## Limitations of storage-based hot water systems

All the hot water systems covered so far have been of the storage type. In these systems, a relatively low power boiler or heater is used to put heat energy into the stored water in the system over a period of time. This hot water is then available for draw-off at the taps as the demand dictates. Provided sufficient stored hot water is available, many hot taps and high flow rates of hot water can be supplied simultaneously. However, once all the stored hot water has been used there will be a delay until the storage vessel has recovered its temperature. An accurate assessment of likely maximum demand is therefore important if the users of the system are not to be inconvenienced by having no hot water available from time to time.

# Instantaneous water heaters

Instantaneous water heaters can be powered by either gas or electricity. They do not store hot water but heat the water as it passes through the heat exchanger when the user opens a tap. Because they only heat the water when it is required, they can be very fuel efficient. Also, provided the water flow-rate is within the capacity of the heater, they can supply hot water continuously. The main disadvantage and limiting factor with any type of instantaneous water heater stems from the fact that water has a very large specific heat capacity. The rate of flow of hot water, the temperature rise required and the power consumption and efficiency of the heater are all related. The following formula will give the flow-rate that can be expected from a given heater:

$$F = 0.238 \times E \times P/T$$

where:
F is the flow-rate in l/s;
T is the temperature rise required in °C;
P is the input power rating in kW;
E is the efficiency of the heater – the ratio of heat output to heat input.

If the manufacturer's efficiency figure is not available, a typical instantaneous gas water heater might be expected to have an efficiency of 0.75 (75%), and an electric instantaneous water heater's efficiency will be about 0.9 (90%).

For example: a gas-fired instantaneous water heater with a heat input power of 27 kW and an efficiency of 75% is required to heat up a flow of water from 15°C to 35°C for a range of showers. The flow rate that the heater can supply is therefore:

$$F = 0.238 \times 0.75 \times 27/20$$
$$F = 0.24 \; l/s$$

As the recommended flow-rate for a shower is 0.1 l/s, the heater would be able to supply two showers and have a little spare capacity in reserve.

Compare this with an electric instantaneous water heater. These can have power inputs of from 3 to about 8 kW and are generally about 90% efficient. So, the flow rate from an 8 kW electric heater with 20°C temperature increase might be expected to be:

$$F = 0.238 \times 0.9 \times 8/20$$
$$F = 0.08 \; l/s$$

This is slightly below the recommended flow-rate for a single shower.

The examples show that instantaneous water heaters have to be provided with an adequate electricity or gas supply if they are to supply their rated heat output into the water. When used in the correct circumstances, such as the supply of hot water to an isolated sink, they can provide a very effective and economical solution.

## Electric instantaneous water heater

This type of heater includes a heating element, which is coiled to occupy a small space, and fitted inside a small copper cylinder. The water flow to the heater is controlled by means of a valve on the inlet pipe. When this is opened, a pressure switch detects the flow and turns on the electric current. The water is heated directly by the element as it flows past. Temperature control is provided by a thermostat fitted to the copper cylinder. Figure 7.40 shows the internal details of a typical instantaneous electric water heater. This type of heater is used to supply a single sink tap or shower rose. It is important to ensure that the water supply is turned on and the heater filled and flushed thoroughly before the electricity is turned on when the unit is being commissioned, or the element could burn out very quickly. Also, it is important to make sure that the electrical work to the heater is correctly done so that the danger of electrocution due to faulty wiring is reduced to the minimum.

## Gas-fired instantaneous water heaters

Because gas can supply greater quantities of power than a typical electrical system it is possible to have both single and multi-point instantaneous gas water heaters.

### Single-point heaters
The single-point heater is usually inlet controlled with a swivel outlet pipe. The heater contains a finned copper tube heat exchanger with a gas burner unit below it. A differential

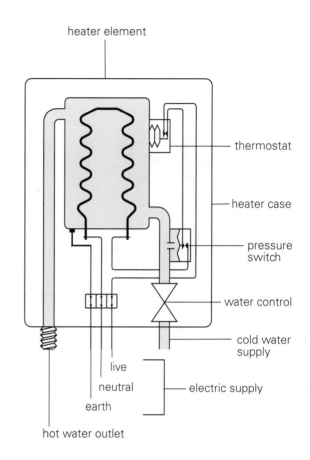

**Figure 7.40** Electric instantaneous water heater

pressure valve is connected between the cold water inlet and the gas supply. The heater has a permanent pilot and thermocouple as the ignition and flame failure device. When the cold supply into the heater is opened, the differential valve diaphragm opens the gas supply in sympathy and the main burner is ignited. Water outlet temperature control is achieved by a combination of increasing or decreasing the flow rate through the heat exchanger and opening a bypass that allows cold water to mix with the hot water stream after it has been through the heat exchanger. Single-point heaters can be supplied without a flue. Provided they are used in a room that is well ventilated and are not used for long periods, such as to fill a bath, they are relatively safe appliances. However, they are also available with a flue and this makes the appliance much safer in use (Figure 7.41).

### Multi-point water heaters
The multi-point heater has its flow controlled by the taps at the discharge points. It is basically a more powerful version of the previously described single-point heater, with a larger burner and heat exchanger. Because they consume more gas, they are fitted with a flue. If the flue is an open type, the heater will

Single point heater
flue outlet

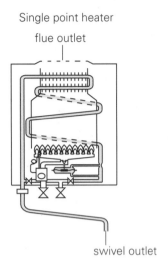

swivel outlet

Multi-point heater

flue outlet

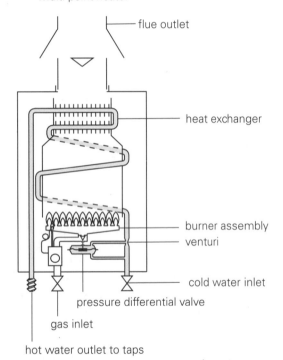

heat exchanger

burner assembly
venturi

cold water inlet

pressure differential valve

gas inlet

hot water outlet to taps

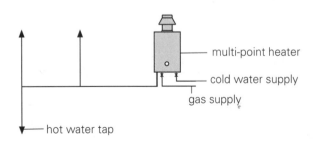

multi-point heater

cold water supply

gas supply

hot water tap

*Figure 7.41* **Single and multi-point instantaneous gas water heater**

require ventilation to allow air for combustion into the room. Figure 7.41 shows typical single and multi-point gas water heaters.

# Commissioning hot water systems

Once the system has been installed it needs to be inspected and tested to ensure that it is safe and will operate in accordance with the manufacturer's instructions and specifications.

A visual inspection should be carried out to see that all the pipework and equipment is correctly supported and fixed and that everything complies with local water regulations. The feed cistern should also be checked to see that no debris or metal fragments can be flushed into the system on filling. All valves should be closed so that the system can be filled in stages.

The system can then be slowly filled with cold water in stages allowing all air to vent off through draw off points on the section being filled. A thorough check must be made for leaks at each stage of the filling process. Float-operated valves should also be checked to make sure that the water level in the cistern is correctly set.

If the specification calls for pressure tests on the pipework it is important to check that the test pressure is not sufficient to cause any damage to the boiler, cylinder or any pump that is fitted. If so, the items in question must be removed and short make-up pipes fitted to bridge across the gaps. Alternatively, blanks or plugs can be fitted or the equipment can be valved off. Usually, where hydraulic tests are required, the test pressure will be 1.5 to 2 times the working pressure of the system.

Once the system is full and any leaks have been located, the system should be thoroughly flushed with cold water to remove any debris or jointing materials from inside the pipe bore. The system can then be refilled. Once the boiler fuel and any electrical supplies are available, any thermostats fitted can be set and the boiler can be run to check the circulation and storage vessel heat up time.

It is possible that leaks might develop as the hot water flows through the pipe for the first time so another visual check for leaks should be carried out.

Once the storage vessel is hot, taps can be checked for satisfactory performance. In a small installation, this might simply be by a visual check of flow rate and feeling for temperature. Where this is in doubt, a flow meter and thermometer can be used to check more accurately.

Once any problems have been overcome, cistern lids can be secured and insulation can be fitted. On large jobs, valve identification labels can be attached. The site drawings can be marked up with any pertinent information. The user can then be instructed in the safe operation of the system and any operating or servicing instructions can be left by the boiler or with a responsible person.

## Maintenance and servicing

The life expectancy of the hot water system can be maximised if faults can be spotted before they cause damage or inconvenience. Regular maintenance of the boiler can also save money by maintaining the efficiency of the system. It is good policy to draw up a maintenance schedule that lists the tasks that should be carried out, probably on an annual basis.

The boiler or water heater should be cleaned and checked for safe operation in accordance with the manufacturer's instructions. Any thermostats fitted should be checked to see that they operate at the correct temperature. Cistern covers should be removed and the float-operated valve checked for correct operation; overflow pipes should also be checked to ensure they are still in good condition and have not become blocked. If necessary, the cistern should be drained and cleaned. Any control valves fitted to the pipework should be checked for easy and correct operation and the pipes should be checked for leaks, corrosion, support and loose fittings. Taps on sanitary fittings should also be checked for correct operation. Finally, any defects or potentially dangerous faults should be brought to the attention of a responsible person.

## Problems in hot water systems

**Undersized distribution pipes** These will result in poor supply of hot water, especially in cistern fed systems with a low head pressure. In mains-fed systems, they can result in noisy operation. If the circulation pipes are too small in diameter, the time required to heat the storage vessel can be excessive because of sluggish circulation.

**Oversized distribution pipes** These will result in the waste of water and fuel due to dead-leg run-off before hot water reaches the taps.

**Airlocks** These are usually caused by badly installed pipework. If the pipe is installed so that it forms an unventilated arch shape it will then trap air. If this occurs on gravity circulation pipes, the very small circulation pressure will not be able to overcome the problem and the cylinder will not get hot. Similarly, if horizontal runs of pipe sag because of inadequate support, or are installed with a back-fall, an airlock can result. Airlocks can cause noises in the system, either in the pipework or from the boiler due to lack of water circulation (Figure 7.42).

**Boiler explosions** Fortunately these are rare. However, an explosion can occur due to blockages in the cold feed and open vent pipe due to scale formation. In larger installations, it is often the case that boilers are fitted with isolation valves for maintenance purposes. These must be operated with care by experienced personnel who understand the operation of the system. Where boilers are fitted with pressure relief valves, it is good practice to check their operation periodically.

**Cylinder collapse** This can result if the open vent and cold feed pipes become blocked. If a hot tap at a lower level in the system is opened, siphonage can result in sub-atmospheric pressures inside the system. If the storage vessel is made from copper, it will have quite a thin wall thickness. Air pressure acting on the outside of the vessel can then crush it.

**Boiler noises** Where scale forms inside the boiler heat exchanger, it can have the effect of an insulator; this can make the boiler less efficient. It can also reduce the water flow and this can lead to the boiler becoming noisy in operation. One type of noise is 'kettling'; this sounds rather like a continuous

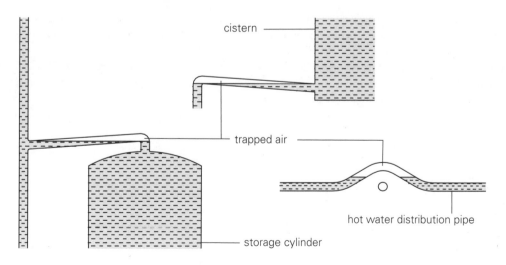

*Figure 7.42* Airlocks in hot water systems

hissing or sizzling. The boiler can also suffer from very loud banging noises. These occur where steam bubbles form momentarily inside the boiler on the boiler plate. As they become detached, they implode causing the noise. Descaling the boiler heat exchanger and increasing the water flow rate can cure both types of noise.

**Corrosion**  Because the system operates hot, the rate of corrosion will be increased compared to a cold water system in the same building. Therefore it is important to select materials for pipes and fittings that are able to stand up to the service conditions required if a long trouble-free life is to be provided by the system.

### CHECK YOUR UNDERSTANDING

● Because water has a relatively high specific heat capacity it requires a lot of energy to heat it up; if a relatively low-powered heater or boiler is used then a storage vessel is required to provide the supply of hot water.

● Heat moves from a hot to a cooler place by either conduction through solid objects, by convection currents that cause liquids or gases to circulate, or by radiation where heat is transmitted from the surface of a hot object or a flame to a cooler surface by infrared rays.

● In areas where the water is temporary hard, the indirect storage system is better than the direct because the water in the boiler and circulation pipes does not change when taps are discharged.

● Preventing oxygen from entering the system will prolong its life by reducing corrosion.

● When installing very long runs of straight tube be careful to allow for the expansion that will occur when the system heats up.

● Try to group sanitary fittings close to the hot water storage vessel to prevent waste of water and fuel due to cold water run-off.

● When choosing the type of hot water system to install consider using small storage or instantaneous water heaters to supply any isolated sinks.

● Install storage cylinders with their longest side vertical wherever possible to encourage stratification.

● Always insulate the hot water storage vessel to save fuel costs.

● Arrange to have the outlet from the storage cistern at the opposite end from the inlet to prevent stagnation of water in the cistern.

● Never fit a valve or block off the open vent(s) on a hot water system; use only lock-shield full-way valves on the primary cold feed pipe to the boiler.

● Remember to adjust the water level in the feed and expansion cistern to allow for the expansion that takes place when the system is heated up.

● Take care to install pipework correctly to avoid airlocks.

● Take time to read the manufacturer's instructions before installing unfamiliar boilers or other pieces of equipment.

● Check that the system complies will all local water regulations, and make sure that the system is safe for further use before handing over to the customer on completion of work or after any maintenance is carried out.

### REVISION EXERCISES AND QUESTIONS

1  Why would an indirect system of hot water supply be better than a direct system in a temporary hard water area?
2  Make a labelled drawing to show the typical arrangement of an indirect hot water storage system.
3  Name the three types of heat transfer and explain how they occur in a hot water system.
4  How are airlocks caused in hot water circulation and distribution pipes. What effects can they have on the operation of the system?
5  Why might secondary circulation pipework be fitted to a hot water system?
6  If a storage vessel containing 250 l of water has to be heated from 18°C to 60°C in a time of 2 hours, how many kW of boiler power would be required?
7  Explain how corrosion can be minimised in a typical hot water system.
8  What are the requirements of good insulation materials?
9  By how many mm would a steel pipe 20 m long expand if it was heated from 20°C to 85°C?
10  Why is it better to install cylindrical hot water storage vessels with their longest side vertical?

# Hot water heating

## Introduction

In regions where the climate is cool and variable, particularly at high altitudes and in high northern or southern latitudes, the hot water system can be extended to provide central heating for the building and its occupants. This is achieved by the installation of a larger boiler, together with a system of flow and return circulation pipes feeding heat emitters installed in the rooms.

In this chapter we shall show how to determine and control the amount of heat energy needed to be added to rooms to maintain **comfort conditions** in domestic-type buildings, with a total heating and hot water load of up to 60 kW. We will illustrate the various layouts of **small-bore pipework** that can be employed to distribute the heat around the building and the types of heat emitters that can be used.

## Comfort conditions

The factors that affect the thermal comfort conditions in the rooms of a building comprise:

- air temperature;
- the temperature of the surfaces in the room;
- the air velocity in the room due to ventilation draughts;
- extremes of humidity (above 70% or below 35% relative humidity);
- the amount of clothing worn by the occupants;
- the level of activity of the occupants.

These factors are illustrated in Figure 8.1. Bear in mind, however, that a central heating system cannot control the air velocity or humidity levels in the building.

People vary in the way that they react to a given thermal environment; conditions that feel comfortable to one person will not necessarily be satisfactory for another. Indeed, people are not consistent in their perceptions over a period of time and conditions that are comfortable one day

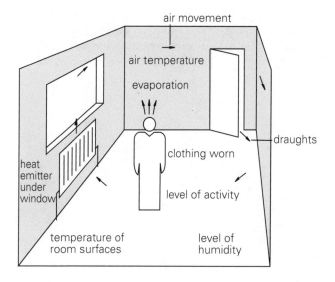

*Figure 8.1* Factors affecting thermal comfort conditions

may be uncomfortable on another. This could be because of apparently imperceptible changes to some of the previously mentioned factors. Because of this, the heating system must be capable of satisfying the needs of occupants who require the highest temperatures with an adequate control system to cater for people who prefer lower temperatures.

### Room usage and temperature levels

Throughout the day, people's levels of activity vary and so a constant room temperature is not usually needed. While work is being carried out, lower temperatures can be tolerated compared to evenings and weekends when people are relaxing. The living room will usually be the most important room to heat so the system should be able to achieve and maintain a temperature of between 21°C and 25°C in that room. In bedrooms, a lower temperature of about 16°C to 18°C is usually acceptable.

## Draughts and ventilation

Air movement can have an important effect on the level of thermal comfort; this is due to its cooling effect. Draughts of under 0.25 m/s will not be noticed at head level but are felt around the feet. Some ventilation is required in all rooms to remove unwanted odours, water vapour and exhaled carbon dioxide. Cold draughts due to convection currents dropping below windows can often cause localised discomfort. To overcome this, it is usual to site heat emitters under the window to counteract the draught (Figure 8.1).

## Determination of heat losses

To determine the heating requirements for the rooms in a building, we must take account of the type of construction, the level of insulation (see Figure 8.2 for suggested methods of insulation to reduce heat losses), the number of likely air changes per hour and the difference in temperature on either side of the surfaces.

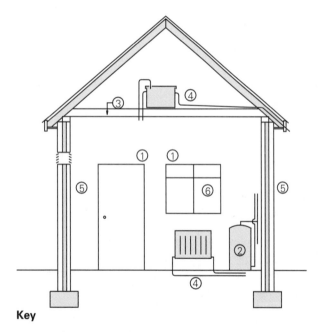

**Key**

1. Fit draft excluder strips to windows and external doors

2. Insulate the hot water storage vessel

3. Lay mineral fibre between ceilings but do not block roof space ventilation

4. Insulate all hot water pipes that are outside the heated rooms of the building

5. Install insulation in cavity walls

6. Fit double glazing to windows

*Figure 8.2*　Methods of insulation to reduce heat losses

## Fabric heat losses

To determine the heat lost through the building fabric a series of calculations are carried out that will give the amount of heat energy lost through the various parts of the structure. The rate of heat loss through the building fabric is found by multiplying the surface area of each different part of the room by the temperature difference between the two sides and a specific heat loss coefficient called the **U value**, as in the formula:

fabric heat loss (W) = surface area (m$^2$)× temperature difference (°C) × U value (W/m$^2$ °C)

U values have been calculated for different types of building construction and a few are given in Table 8.1.

*Table 8.1* Typical U values

| Typical U values for various types of building fabric | W/m°C |
|---|---|
| External solid wall plastered on inside | 2.10 |
| External cavity wall plastered on inside | 1.00 |
| External cavity wall plastered and insulated | 0.50 |
| External timber-framed wall with 60 mm insulation | 0.44 |
| External timber-framed wall with 100 mm insulation | 0.32 |
| Internal partition wall | 1.90 |
| Solid ground floor | 0.45 |
| Timber ground floor ventilated underneath | 0.61 |
| Intermediate floor, heat flow up | 1.60 |
| Intermediate floor, heat flow down | 1.40 |
| Pitched roof with 100 mm insulation on ceiling | 0.36 |
| Pitched roof with no insulation | 2.20 |
| Single glazing to timber frames | 5.00 |
| Double glazing to timber frames | 2.90 |

Note: U values for most other types of construction are available from design guides

## Ventilation heat losses

As air flows through the building and escapes, heat is carried away. Ventilation rates are often quoted in terms of air changes per hour; this is a ratio between the volume of ventilation air and the room volume. If cold, the air has to be heated and the energy required can be found by multiplying together the room volume, the air change rate, the temperature increase required, and a 'ventilation factor' based on the specific heat capacity of air of 0.33W/m$^3$ °C thus:

Ventilation heat loss (W) = room volume ($m^3$) × air change rate per hour × temperature increase × ventilation factor ($0.33 W/m^3 °C$).

## Design room temperatures

Room temperatures should be chosen to give comfort conditions, similar to those quoted in Table 8.2; this suggests suitable temperatures and typical air change rates for a variety of different room uses. External design temperature should be chosen to reflect the typical winter conditions, but not the most extreme expected. In temperate latitudes, an external design temperature of −1°C is often used.

*Table 8.2* Design room temperature and typical air change rates

| Type of room | Design temperature °C | Typical air changes per hour |
|---|---|---|
| Living/dining rooms | 21 | 1 to 2 |
| Hall | 18 | 2 |
| Bedrooms | 16 | 1 to 2 |
| Bedsitting room | 21 | 1 to 2 |
| Kitchen | 18 | 2 |
| Bathroom | 22 | 2 |

### Other allowances

Where the heating system is subject to on/off intermittent operation, it is usual to add 10% to the room heat loss requirements before selecting heat emitters. This is to speed up the initial heat up time. Where the control system allows the boiler to heat both heat emitters and hot water simultaneously, it is usual to add 2 kW (or more, depending on the hot water storage vessel power requirement) to the heating load. Where the building is situated on a very exposed site, a further 10% can be added to give the total boiler power required.

## Heat loss calculation method

There are basically four stages required to determine the heat loss requirements for a system design:

1. For each room, calculate and total the fabric and ventilation heat loss, then add any allowances required.
2. Select suitable heat emitters with outputs equal to or slightly above the room heat losses.
3. Sum the heat losses for each room and add the hot water heat load to obtain the total heat requirement.
4. Select a boiler that has an output as close as possible to, but not below, the total heat requirement.

### Example

A bungalow is shown in Figure 8.3; the calculations to determine the heat losses and boiler power required are shown in Table 8.3.

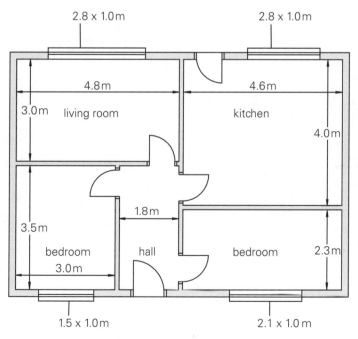

**Construction details**

External walls: 200 concrete block plastered one side

Partition walls: 100 block plastered both sides

Windows: single glazed in timber frames

Solid floor, room heights 2.4 m

Pitched roof with 100 insulation

*Figure 8.3* Plan of bungalow

*Table 8.3* Example heat loss calculation

| Example heat loss calculation for bungalow in Figure 8.3 | | | | | External design temperature –1°C | |
|---|---|---|---|---|---|---|
| **Living room** | Area m² | Temperature difference °C | U value W/m°C | Design heat loss W | | |
| External wall | 15.92 | 22 | 2.1 | 735.5 | | |
| Window | 2.80 | 22 | 5.0 | 308.0 | | |
| Internal wall 1 | 7.20 | 3 | 1.9 | 41.0 | | |
| Internal wall 2 | 4.32 | 3 | 1.9 | 24.6 | | |
| Floor | 14.40 | 22 | 0.45 | 142.5 | | |
| Ceiling/roof | 14.40 | 22 | 0.36 | 114.0 | | |
| | Volume m³ | Temperature difference °C | Air change rate | Ventilation factor | | |
| Ventilation | 34.56 | 22 | 1 | 0.33 | 250.9 | Heat emitter output |
| Total room heat losses | | | | | 1616.5 | Required         Actual |
| Add 10% for initial heat up and select available heat emitter size | | | | | | 1778.1         1792.0 |
| **Bedroom** | Area m² | Temperature difference °C | U value W/m °C | Design heat low W | | |
| External wall | 14.46 | 22 | 2.1 | 668.0 | | |
| Window | 2.10 | 22 | 5.0 | 231.0 | | |
| Internal wall 1 | 5.52 | 2 | 1.9 | 20.9 | Subtract as gain from hall | |
| Internal wall 2 | 11.0 | 2 | 1.9 | 41.8 | Subtract as gain from kitchen | |
| Floor | 10.5 | 22 | 0.45 | 103.9 | | |
| Ceiling/roof | 10.5 | 22 | 0.36 | 83.1 | | |
| | Volume m³ | Temperature difference °C | Air change rate | Ventilation factor | | |
| Ventilation | 25.39 | 22 | 1 | 0.33 | 184.3 | Heat emitter output |
| Total room heat losses | | | | | 1207.6 | Required         Actual |
| Add 10% for initial heat up and select available heat emitter size | | | | | | 1328.3         1356.0 |

| **Total heat losses and boiler size** | | | Design heat losses | Heat emitter output Required          Actual |
|---|---|---|---|---|
| | | Living room | 1616.5 | 1778.1          1792.0 |
| | | Kitchen | 1505.8 | 1656.4          1702.0 |
| | | Bedroom | 1207.6 | 1328.3          1356.0 |
| | | Bathroom | 1138.6 | 1252.5          1247.0 |
| | | Hall | 164.6 | 181.1          205.0 |
| Total heat losses for the bungalow | | | 5633.1 | |
| Total heat requirement of heat emitters | | | | 6196.4          6302 |
| Heat requirement for hot water | | | | 2000 |
| Boiler power required | | (say 8.5 kW) | | 8302 |

# Heat emitters

There are many different designs of heat emitters but they generally fall into two types: radiators or convectors.

## Radiators

A selection of patterns of radiators are illustrated in Figure 8.4. **Panel radiators** are made from pressed mild steel welded together to create a large surface area. They are available in single and double panel types. Heat is given off by both radiation and convection currents (created by heating the air in contact with the surface of the radiator). **Convector radiators** have thin pressed steel plates welded to the rear surface. These increase the amount of heat that a given size of radiator can emit by encouraging convection in the formed channels. Cast iron **column radiators** are used in larger systems; for their overall size they have a large surface area and so can give off heat efficiently, mainly by convection. Whenever possible, the radiator should be installed under a window in the room (Figure 8.1). This is the best position because the hot convection currents will counteract the cold down flow of air from the glass. If the radiator cannot be fitted under the window it should be on an adjacent wall. The worst position is opposite the window as the convection currents will encourage the cold down flow of air.

## Convectors

Convector heat emitters consist of a relatively compact finned tube heating element enclosed in a pressed steel case (Figure 8.5). The case is shaped so that it causes air to flow through the heating element either by natural convection or by the use of a fan to increase the air flow. Convectors have one safety advantage over radiators – they generally have a low surface temperature; this means that the chance of injury through people being burnt by touching the heat emitter is reduced.

## Heat emitter control valves and mountings

Radiators are supplied with female threaded connections at the four corners. One of the top connections is used to fit an **air release valve**; this is to enable the radiator to fill with water when the system is commissioned. The other top connection can be fitted with a **threaded plug** or used to connect the flow

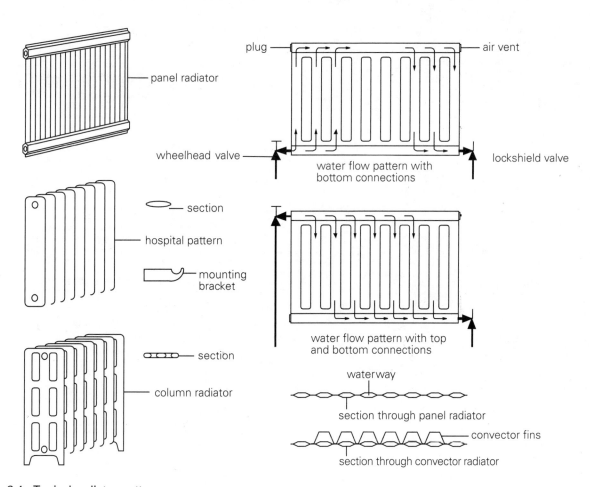

*Figure 8.4* Typical radiator patterns

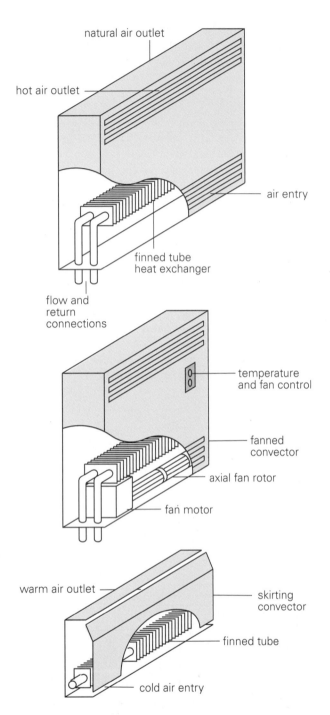

*Figure 8.5* Convector heaters

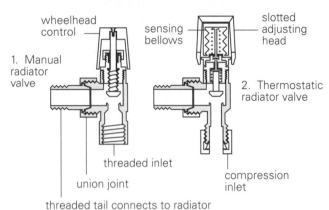

*Figure 8.6* Sections through radiator valves

pipe. Generally though, the flow and return connections are made at opposite ends using the two bottom connections (Figure 8.4). A **lockshield-valve** is used on the return; this enables the water flow through the radiator to be set. A **wheelhead-valve** or a **thermostatic-valve** is fitted to the flowside to enable the user to turn the radiator on and off or control its temperature. Sections through these valves are shown in Figure 8.6.

Most convectors come complete with an air release valve. They should also be fitted with quarter-turn ball-valves on the flow and return connections (Figure 8.5). These valves are for isolation during maintenance. In natural draught convectors, control of heat output is by a manual damper plate in the convector; this can close off the air louvres. A thermostat is usually fitted in fanned convectors; this controls the operation of the booster fan.

# Heating system pipework layouts

The earliest type of wet heating system used natural convection to carry heat energy in the water from the boiler to the heat emitters. The pipes had to be of large diameter and tended to look unsightly. The actual run of pipe had to be carefully considered to prevent airlocks and encourage circulation of the water. The basic principles of natural convection are discussed in Chapter 7 and a schematic layout of a typical system is shown in Figure 8.7.

## Forced circulation heating systems

In modern heating systems, the water is circulated by means of an electrically powered pump. A variety of pipework layouts are possible, including:

- one-pipe;
- two-pipe;
- two-pipe reversed return;
- micro-bore.

### One-pipe system

The one-pipe system comprises a single pumped loop flow and return main. Individual heat emitters are connected into the loop and water circulates through them by natural

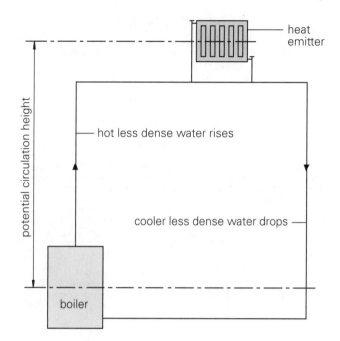

*Figure 8.7* Schematic layout of gravity flow heating system

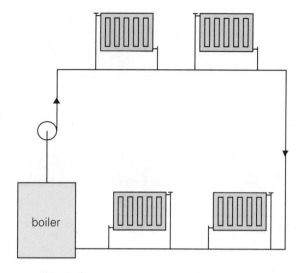

*Figure 8.8*  One-pipe system

convection. One-pipe systems are suitable for small single story buildings where the emitters can be positioned around the perimeter walls (Figure 8.8).

**Two-pipe systems**

In two-pipe systems a series of branching flow pipes carry hot water to the heat emitters. Once the water has passed through the emitters, it is collected and carried back to the boiler for reheating by a series of return pipes that branch together as they approach the boiler. This branching layout has the advantage that the water is pumped through each heat emitter. Effectively, in the two-pipe system, each heat emitter has its own separate circuit (Figure 8.9). The disadvantage of this is that emitters sited close to the boiler have relatively low resistance to water flow. This can allow the water to short circuit and so bypass the more distant emitters. To counteract this the lockshield valves can be adjusted to balance the system. Alternatively, the two-pipe reversed return system can be used (Figure 8.10). This system creates flow and return pipes of about equal length to each heat emitter; as a result, balancing the system is simplified.

**Micro-bore system**

The micro-bore system is basically a two-pipe arrangement of pipes. The individual flow and return loops to each heat emitter are run in very small diameter (8 or 10 mm) soft copper or plastic tubes from a pair of distribution manifolds (Figure 8.11). The small diameter flexible tubes can be easily run and concealed within the building structure or in small surface-mounted ducts.

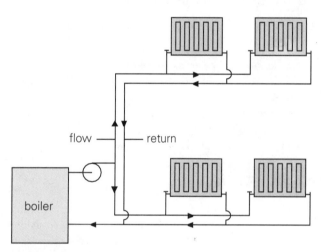

*Figure 8.9*  Two-pipe system

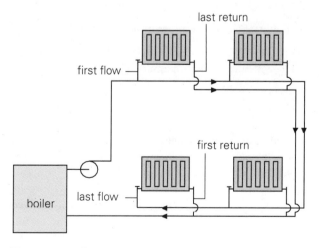

*Figure 8.10*  Two-pipe reversed return system

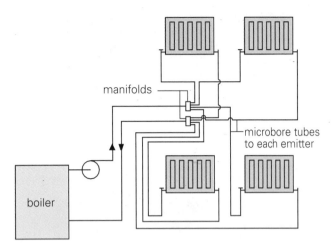

*Figure 8.11*   Micro-bore system layout

## Advantages of pumped systems

The advantages of forced circulation heating systems can be summarised as follows:

- smaller tube diameters can be used;
- freedom to route pipework to follow the building structure;
- neater installation;
- quicker system heat up;
- better control of room temperatures.

## Design mass flow rate

If the heat emitters are to give their correct output, they must be supplied with water at the design temperature (usually a flow temperature of 82 °C) and at the correct **mass flow rate**. This can be found for a particular emitter by dividing the heat output required (W) by the temperature drop around the circuit (usually 11 °C) multiplied by the specific heat capacity of the water (4182 J/kg/°C) as in the formula:

mass flow rate (kg/s) = emitter heat output/46 000

For example: if the emitter output required is 1792 W, the mass flow rate will need to be a minimum of:

1792/46 000
= 0.039 kg/s

### Flow and return tube diameters

For many installers and designers, choosing tube diameters is based on experience, custom and practice. The full procedure for calculating diameters from flow rate, lengths of run, resistance of bends and fittings, and surface roughness of the tube is beyond the scope of this book. However, based on a maximum water velocity of 1.5 m/s (so as not to create flow noise in the system) the total heat emitter

output that can be delivered using small-bore tube is given in Table 8.4. The measurements given will give acceptable results provided they are only used to choose diameters for small systems.

Take the previous example of a bungalow (Figure 8.3). If the heat emitters (sized in Table 8.3) are to be connected using a two-pipe layout as illustrated in Figure 8.12, then suitable tube diameters could be as shown in Table 8.5.

*Table 8.4* Tube diameter and heat carrying capacity

| Heat carrying capacity of small bore heating pipes (water velocity of 1.5 m/s) | | |
|---|---|---|
| Nominal tube diameter | Maximum flow rate kg/s | Heat carrying capacity W |
| 10 | 0.06 | 2700 |
| 12 | 0.09 | 4000 |
| 15 | 0.16 | 7000 |
| 20 | 0.32 | 14 000 |
| 25 | 0.56 | 25 000 |

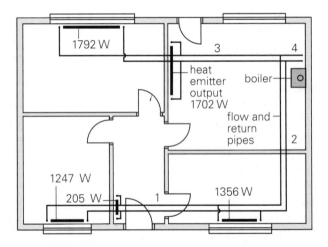

*Figure 8.12*   Plan of typical two-pipe heating circuit layout

## Pump head and capacity

Small single-stage heating pumps can circulate up to about 0.8 kg/s of water at a head pressure of up to 4.5 m, depending on the rate of flow required and resistance of the pipework circuit. Provided that the pump pressure can satisfy the **index circuit** (the pipe loop with the greatest total resistance, usually the longest run of tube), the system will work satisfactorily. Most small heating pumps have adjustable ratings (a typical performance graph is shown in Figure 8.13). By altering the setting point, the amount of pump pressure can be made to match the pressure needed

*Table 8.5* Suggested tube diameters for heating circuit layout

| Tube diameter selection for bungalow in Figure 8.3 | | | |
|---|---|---|---|
| Room | Emitter output W | Tube diameter mm | Note |
| Living room | 1792 | 10 | The diameters indicated are the *minimum* that can be used. Similar systems will often be installed using larger diameters, typically 15 and 20 mm. Knowing the total mass flow rate enables better pump selection and adjustment of the setting point |
| Kitchen | 1702 | 10 | |
| Bedroom | 1356 | 10 | |
| Bathroom | 1247 | 10 | |
| Hall | 205 | 10 | |
| Tube reference number | Total emitter output W | Tube diameter mm | |
| 1 | 1247 + 205 = 1452 | 10 | |
| 2 | 1247 + 205 + 1356 = 2808 | 12 | |
| 3 | 1792 + 1702 = 3492 | 12 | Mass flow rate kg/s |
| 4 | 2808 + 3492 = 6302 | 15 | 0.137 |
| F and R to hot water | 2000 | 12 | 0.043 |

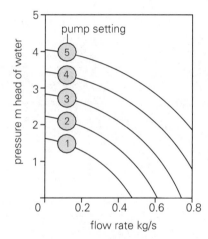

*Figure 8.13* Typical pump performance graph

by the system. In practice, it is best to start with the pump set to its minimum; if all the heat emitters can be balanced to give the correct temperatures, no adjustment is necessary. Otherwise the pump pressure can be turned up in stages until all emitters have the correct temperature drop (11°C).

**Pump position**

It is best to install the circulation pump into the flow pipe after the **neutral point** (the point in an open system where the cold feed connects into the system). The reason for this is that the system pressure is increased by the action of the pump (Figure 8.14). If the pump is connected into the return, before the neutral point, the system pressure is decreased by the action of the pump. Air is then more likely to be drawn into the system, with increased risk of corrosion.

## Balancing the system

When the heating system is first operated, heat emitters that are close to the pump or that have a low heat output will tend to have an excessive flow through them. This will result in reduced flow through the remote or larger emitters. By closing down the lockshield-valves on the small or close emitters and opening up the lockshield-valves on the larger or more remote emitters, the system can be balanced and the pump adjusted to operate effectively.

### Provision for expansion of the system water

It is important to remember that the water in the system will expand in volume by about 4% when heated. The volume of water contained in the heating system must be added to that in the primary hot water circuit when determining the capacity of the feed and expansion cistern or the expansion vessel if the system is sealed (see Chapter 7 for further details).

## Heating system controls

A number of components can be fitted to the heating system to give control over both the times at which the system is to be on or off and the temperatures required in the various parts of the system and the building.

### Simple pumped heating systems

In simple heating systems with gravity circulation for the hot water, the only automatic controls (apart from those fitted to the boiler) are usually a **time switch** and a **room thermostat**.

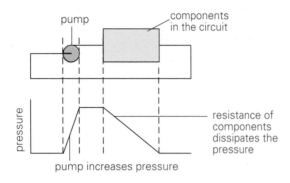

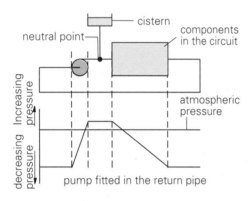

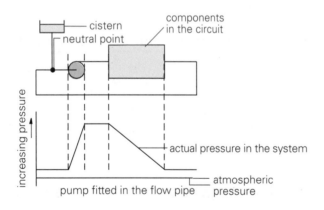

*Figure 8.14* **Effect of pump positioning on system pressures**

The room thermostat works in series with the time switch to turn the pump on and off to give temperature control to the heated spaces in the building. See Figure 8.15 for location of the controls.

By the addition of a cylinder thermostat (wiring shown dotted in Figure 8.15) some control of the hot water

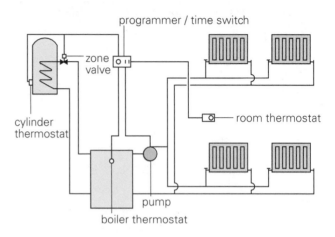

*Figure 8.15* **Controls for simple gravity hot water and pumped heating system**

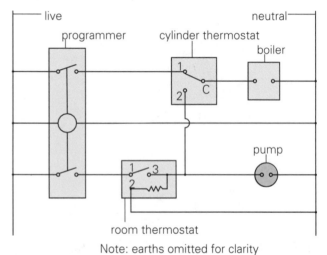

Note: earths omitted for clarity

*Figure 8.16* **Schematic wiring diagram**

temperature can be achieved. Figure 8.16 shows a schematic wiring diagram that will only allow the boiler to fire when either the room or cylinder thermostat calls for heat. However, for full independent control of the stored hot water temperature it is necessary to fit a **zone valve** (a two-port motorised valve) into the circulation pipes near the storage vessel (see Figure 8.15 for location of the valve (shown dotted) and Figure 8.17 for a sectional view).

Control of the system is initially achieved by the time switch or programmer. When this is 'off' no part of the system will operate. During 'on' periods, depending on the demand from the thermostats, the boiler will fire, the pump will run and the hot water zone valve will open and close to maintain and control the temperature of the storage vessel.

## Fully pumped hot water and heating system

In fully pumped systems (see Figure 8.18 for schematic layout) either two-zone valves or a **three-port motorised valve** (see Figure 8.19 for sectional view) can be used to give independent control of the heating and hot water, usually in conjunction with a **programmer**. This is a time controller that has more flexibility in the number of modes of operation than the simple time clock.

In these systems, the boiler and pump both run whenever the thermostats call for heat. In the case of the three-port valve system, the thermostats control the valve spindle position to share heat between the storage vessel and heat emitters or give heat to one when the other is satisfied. Where two-zone valves are used, either both are open, or one or the other depending on the call for heat.

### Benefits of fully pumped systems
The benefits of fully pumped systems can be summarised as follows:

- Faster hot water storage vessel heat up and recovery time.
- Smaller storage vessel and primary circulation pipes.

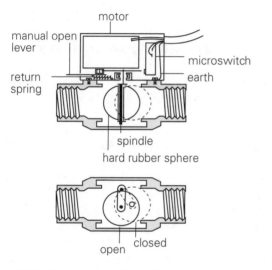

Figure 8.17   Two-port motorised valve

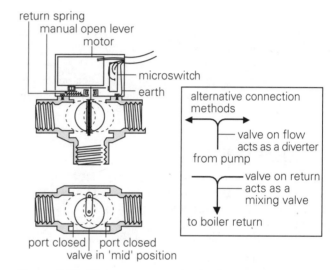

Figure 8.19   Three-port motorised valve

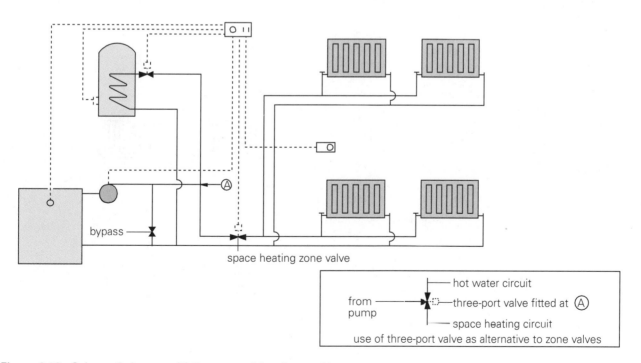

Figure 8.18   Schematic layout of fully pumped heating and hot water system

- Greater flexibility in siting the storage vessel.
- Independent control of both circuits.
- Improved fuel efficiency.

However, care must be taken not to connect the pump into the circuit *between* the primary cold feed and open vent otherwise overpumping is likely (see Figure 8.14 for the effect of pump position on the system pressure).

## Control of solar heat gain

In rooms with relatively large windows that are subjected to high levels of solar radiation through the day, or other forms of heat energy input such as from cooking, **thermostatic radiator valves** can be fitted. They give independent automatic temperature control of the emitter in the room by using the principle of thermal expansion. They use the volume change of a liquid contained in a sealed bellows to open and close the valve washer as the temperature of the room varies (see Figure 8.6 for sectional view).

## Frost protection

In climates where frost protection of the system is necessary, such as in buildings that are left unoccupied for periods of time in winter, a **frost thermostat** can be fitted. This will be connected to override the other controls and bring the system into operation when there is a danger of freezing.

## Compensating control systems

The most modern heating systems use weather compensating controls to provide steady comfort conditions and optimise the use of fuel. These systems make use of an externally mounted temperature sensor, located in a shady position on an outside wall. This feeds a signal that varies with the temperature to a microprocessor control panel. The microprocessor also receives signals from sensors fitted into the heating flow water circuit and hot water storage vessel (Figure 8.20).

The microprocessor has a program that is used to predict the quantity of heat energy that will be required to maintain the temperatures in the rooms and hot water storage vessel based on the rate of change of the signals coming from the sensors. As the conditions vary, the microprocessor causes the boiler to fire and the motorised valve to modulate the temperature of the water flowing around the circuits.

## Combination boilers

These, as their name suggests, combine the functions of a gas fired boiler/instantaneous multi-point hot water heater with a sealed central heating system all into one case (Figure 8.21). They are designed to give priority to the supply of domestic hot water; when there is no demand for hot water the unit circulates heat around the emitters to heat the rooms.

Combination boilers make the installation of much of the system relatively quick and easy (Figure 8.22 shows the schematic system layout) because an expansion vessel is built into the unit. Once the unit has been fitted to the wall and connected to its flue, the only other connections required are a mains cold water feed and distribution pipes for the hot taps, the flow and return pipes to the emitters, the gas supply pipe, a warning pipe from the pressure relief valve to outside and an electrical supply. However, they do have limitations. It is most important that the cold water feed is adequate both in terms of pressure and volume flow rate if

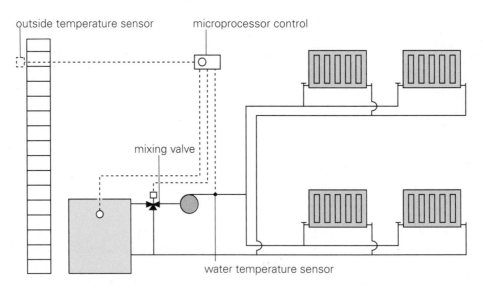

*Figure 8.20*  Compensating control system layout

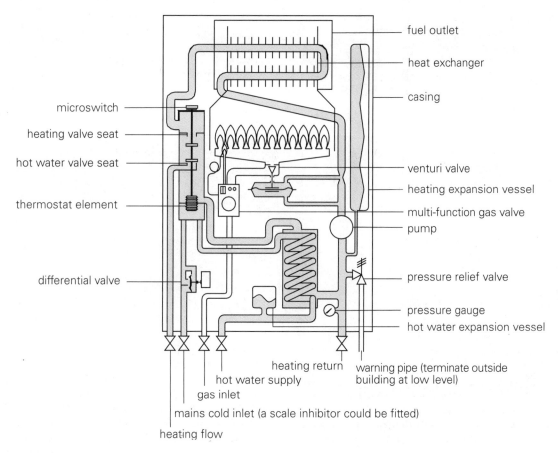

microswitch
heating valve seat
hot water valve seat
thermostat element
differential valve

fuel outlet
heat exchanger
casing
venturi valve
heating expansion vessel
multi-function gas valve
pump
pressure relief valve
pressure gauge
hot water expansion vessel

heating return
warning pipe (terminate outside building at low level)
hot water supply
gas inlet
mains cold inlet (a scale inhibitor could be fitted)
heating flow

*Figure 8.21* Typical combination boiler

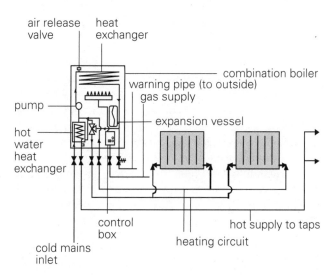

air release valve
heat exchanger
pump
hot water heat exchanger
cold mains inlet
combination boiler
warning pipe (to outside)
gas supply
expansion vessel
control box
heating circuit
hot supply to taps

*Figure 8.22* Schematic layout of combination boiler system

the unit is to perform to its specification. The pressure should be checked with a gauge and the volume flow rate estimated by timing the filling rate of a container of known capacity before deciding to fit a combination boiler. Furthermore,

they are limited in the amount of hot water they can supply. Even the most powerful will be slow to fill a bath and none can supply more than one hot tap at once. Provided the customer understands these facts and the unit is fitted into small dwellings they can give good service.

## Thermal storage systems

This system is designed to minimise boiler on/off cycling and increase system efficiency. Thermal storage systems are comprised of a boiler which is connected to a primary hot water storage vessel, which is in turn connected to the flow and return to the heat emitters; the vessel contains a heat exchanger coil through which mains cold water can pass (see Figure 8.23 for details). When the boiler fires, it runs continuously until the primary storage vessel is heated. When the room thermostat calls for heat, the pump runs and the emitters are heated by the energy in the water of the vessel. When a hot tap is opened, mains water flows through the coil to be heated on demand. The boiler does not fire until sufficient energy has been used to reduce the temperature of the vessel significantly.

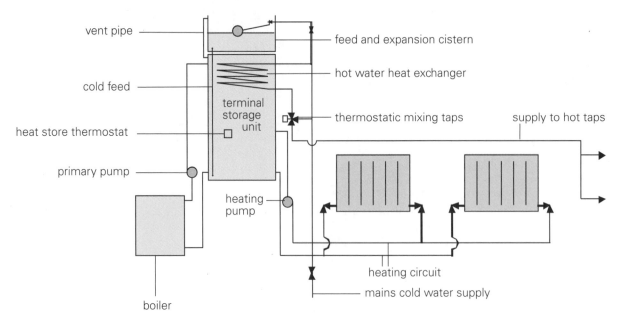

*Figure 8.23* Thermal storage heater and hot water system

# Commissioning the system

It is most important that all parts of the heating/hot water system are checked and left working correctly (in accordance with the manufacturer's instructions and specification) and that the user understands how to operate it correctly before it is handed over on completion of the job.

The basic stages involved are:

1. visual check of the installation;
2. cold flush;
3. refill and commission the boiler;
4. hot flush;
5. refill and balance the system, and set pump operating point;
6. instruct user how to operate the system.

## Cold flush

This is carried out to remove particles of grit or metal or unused flux that could cause corrosion or damage to the pump. Cold flushing is achieved by opening drain valves while allowing the system to remain full by keeping the water feed open. Any manual or automatic valves should be fully open and the pump replaced with a short 'make-up' piece of tube. Once the water runs clear, close off the water supply and allow the system to drain. Repair any leaks discovered and replace the pump. Refill and vent the system and then commission the boiler in accordance with the manufacturer's instructions, ensuring that all statutory requirements have been met.

## Hot flush

Run the boiler and pump until the system is heated, then turn off and drain while still hot. It is possible that leaks will develop as the system is heated, so check again for signs of leaks at joints and repair as required. The system should then be refilled and vented. The boiler and pump should be run to heat up the system. Once hot, the emitters should again be vented and can then be balanced to give the design temperature drop as follows:

1. Open and adjust the bypass if fitted (the bypass must never be left fully closed) in accordance with the manufacturer's instructions. This could require adjusting the system with only the living room emitter open, the bypass being opened until the boiler shuts off due to the thermostat reaching its operating temperature.
2. Before opening the other emitter control valves, check that water is not overpumping from the vent pipe into the feed and expansion cistern.
3. Finally, all the other emitters can be gradually opened and adjusted to obtain the design temperature drop across the flow and return.

## Handing over

Any operating and maintenance instructions should be given to the user. Clear verbal instructions and demonstrations should be given to ensure that the user understands how to operate the boiler and the system controls. Generally the following need to be covered:

**Boiler thermostat setting**  This is usually set to maximum.

**Programmer/time control**  Explain and demonstrate how to set the on and off times and how to operate the manual override.

**Room thermostat**  Explain how to set the thermostat and give guidance on suggested temperatures for comfort conditions based on the type of room, for example 21°C in the living room.

**Cylinder thermostat**  Set this to 60°C.

**Heat emitter control valves**  Explain that the wheelhead valve is for on/off control of the emitter; mention that the lockshield valve has been set to balance the system and should not normally be touched. If thermostatic radiator valves are fitted, demonstrate how to set the temperature and mention that once altered they can take one to two hours for the room temperature to settle.

**Regular maintenance**  Explain the importance of annual servicing for both safety and continued system efficiency.

# Maintenance and servicing

When carrying out annual maintenance, the boiler must be cleaned and tested to see that the safety controls (boiler thermostat, flame failure device and flue) are operating effectively.

In open systems, the water level should be checked in the feed and expansion cistern; momentarily press down the float valve to allow a little water to enter to make sure that the valve has not stuck shut. If sealed, check that the system still contains water at the correct pressure (usually 1 bar cold).

Examine the pipework and heat emitters for signs of corrosion or leaks and vent the emitters to release any trapped air. Note that if the emitters require regular venting, this is a sign of internal corrosion in the system, due possibly to overpumping or galvanic action. Check radiators for even heat up; cold spots at the bottom-centre could be signs of sludge build up necessitating a drain down and flush before the addition of a corrosion inhibitor. Check the heat emitter valves for signs of leakage from the spindle and repack the gland or replace the 'O' ring seals as necessary.

# Problems in heating systems

Poor system design and installation can cause problems in heating systems. Where the heat emitters are too large or too small in the various rooms, problems with over or under heating can result. Furthermore, if the circulation pipework is too small, the emitters will not reach their required temperature and complaints about lack of heat will result.

Poor installation practice can create a noisy system. This is due to thermal movement in the pipework creating clicking noises if the pipes bind where they contact with the building structure.

Poor choice of materials and bad installation practice can cause problems of corrosion resulting in the formation of pinholes in the heat emitters or pipework. Pinholes can also be a problem where the water supply is aggressive; in this case chemical **corrosion inhibitors** can be added to neutralise the effects of the water.

## CHECK YOUR UNDERSTANDING

● Thermal comfort conditions are affected by: air temperature; the temperature of the surfaces in the room; the air velocity in the room due to ventilation draughts; extremes of humidity; the amount of clothing worn by the occupants; the level of activity of the occupants.

● Heat the living room to maintain a temperature of between 21°C and 25°C; in bedrooms a lower temperature of about 16°C to 18°C is usually acceptable.

● Site heat emitters under windows to counteract the effect of cold down-draughts.

● Add 10% to the room heat loss requirements before selecting heat emitters; this is to speed up the initial heat up time in systems that are intermittently operated.

● Choose convector radiators whenever possible. These have thin pressed-steel plates welded to their rear surface to increase the amount of heat that a given size of radiator can emit by encouraging convection in the formed channels.

● Two-pipe systems have the advantage that the water is pumped through each heat emitter, so will tend to be more effective than the one-pipe system.

● Choose and install pipes that will give the required mass flow rate so that the heat emitters will give their rated output.

● Install the pipework so that it does not bind with the building structure and create clicking noises as it heats and cools.

● Balance the system by closing down the lockshield-valves on the small emitters that are close to the pump and opening up the lockshield-valves on the larger or more remote emitters. Adjust the pump setting point so the system operates effectively.

● Remember that the water in the system will expand in volume by about 4% when heated, so make sure that the feed and expansion cistern (or expansion vessel in sealed systems) is large enough to accommodate this.

● Where possible, install fully pumped systems to enable the following benefits: faster hot water storage vessel heat up and recovery time; smaller storage vessel and primary circulation pipes; greater flexibility in siting the storage vessel; independent control of both circuits; and improved fuel efficiency.

● Take care not to connect the pump into the circuit between the primary cold feed and open vent otherwise overpumping is likely.

● In rooms that are subjected to high levels of solar radiation through the day, or other forms of heat energy input such as from cooking, fit thermostatic radiator valves to prevent excessive temperatures.

● Take the time to commission the system thoroughly and make sure the user understands how to operate the system before finally handing the installation over.

## REVISION EXERCISES AND QUESTIONS

1    List the factors that a central heating system can control to maintain thermal comfort conditions in rooms.

2    Name three types of heat emitter.

3    Make a labelled diagram to show an open-vented two-pipe heating system suitable to serve a two-story house with four heat emitters.

4    State the advantages of a fully pumped central heating system.

5    Explain the main differences between small-bore and micro-bore heating systems.

6    What are the minimum controls required to provide full independent control of both heating and hot water in a fully pumped small-bore system?

7    What checks should be carried out on the cold water supply before recommending the installation of a combination boiler?

8    In what type of room should thermostatic radiator valves be fitted to the heat emitters?

9    When commissioning, why is it necessary to balance a heating system?

10    List the stages involved in commissioning and handing over a new heating system.

# Gas supply

## Introduction

It is vital that people who install, maintain or repair gas installations or appliances are competent and carry out their work in a safe and careful manner that does not put people at risk.

To be able to do this effectively an understanding of the properties and characteristics of fuel gases is essential. Also essential is knowledge of how to create the conditions for and how to control safe combustion and afterwards effectively remove the products of combustion. Furthermore, the ability to recognise the kinds of faults that create dangerous or potentially dangerous installations or appliances is needed. To help achieve these aims this chapter covers the basic knowledge and theory necessary to work safely on gas installations in domestic-type buildings.

## Gas escape emergency procedure

Gas escapes are usually discovered by smell. Unfortunately smell does not give any indication of the size and seriousness of the escape so *all gas escapes are dangerous and must be dealt with immediately*! The order of priority is:

- turn off the gas at the emergency control;
- ensure safety of people and evacuate the building if thought necessary;
- ensure safety of property;
- open all doors and windows to allow the gas to disperse;
- remove all possible sources of ignition; do not operate electrical switches; never use a naked light for illumination or for leak location – use soap and water solution only;
- locate and repair the escape, leaving the installation safe.

It may be that the escape is due to an external leak or that the gas escape cannot be stopped by turning off the emergency control; in this case, inform the gas supplier at once!

## Types of fuel gas

Fuel gases used for domestic cooking and heating are members of the **hydrocarbon** family of compounds. **Methane** ($CH_4$), or marsh gas, is a colourless, odourless gas that is the principal component of **natural gas**. With one carbon atom per molecule, methane is the simplest hydrocarbon. The gas is nonpoisonous but inflammable, burning with a pale blue flame.

### Natural gas

Natural gas forms within the Earth's crust; it consists mostly (88 to 95%) of methane; it also contains ethane, 3 to 8%; propane, 0.7 to 2%; and butane, 0.2 to 0.7%. Other constituents include carbon dioxide, 0.6 to 2.0%; nitrogen, 0.3 to 3.0%; and helium, 0.01 to 0.5%. Natural gas is supplied to the consumer by pipeline and is metered as it enters the building for revenue purposes (see Figure 9.1 for typical service entry detail).

### Liquefied petroleum gas

Liquefied petroleum gas (LPG) is formed as a mixture of gases, mainly **propane** ($C_3H_8$) and **butane** ($C_4H_8$), produced from natural gas, or through the fractionation of crude oil. The gases are easily separated and condensed to liquid form. LPG is similar to natural gas in combustion efficiency and controllability. It can be transported and stored in pressure tanks as a liquid, and is subsequently converted to a fuel gas by vaporisation. The liquid turns to gas very easily, and gas fills the space above the liquid in the tank. As gas is drawn off in use, more liquid turns to gas to replace it until no liquid is left. Figure 9.2 shows details of LPG cylinder storage installation.

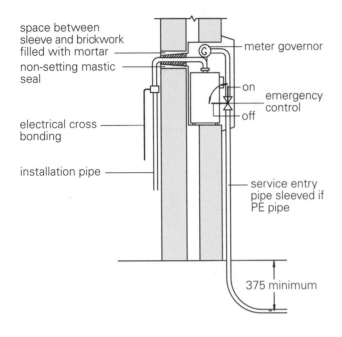

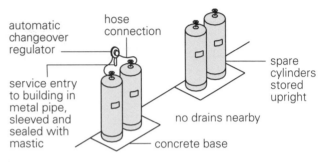

no openings into buildings nearby

Figure 9.2   LPG cylinder storage installation

## Properties of fuel gases

### Gas pressure

A confined gas exerts a pressure on the container that holds it; this can be explained by the **kinetic theory** in terms of moving molecules. Enormous numbers of molecules hit the sides of the container every second giving the effect of a steady push. If more gas is forced into the container, there will be more collisions and the pressure is increased. Similarly, if the gas is forced into a smaller volume, the molecules will hit the sides more often and the pressure increases. Furthermore, heating the gas will impart more energy into the molecules causing them to move more vigorously and so again the pressure will be increased.

### Calorific value

The calorific value of a fuel is the amount of heat energy that is released when a unit mass or volume of the fuel is burnt. Gas volumes can be measured in $m^3$ and the unit of heat energy is the joule. For example, completely burning $1\,m^3$ of natural gas will release about 38.5 MJ of energy.

### Specific gravity

Specific gravity (SG) is a method of comparing the relative densities of substances. In the case of gases, air is taken to have an SG of 1. Any gas that has an SG that is less than 1 will float upwards in the atmosphere, for example natural gas (SG 0.58); on the other hand, LPG (with an SG of about 1.5) will tend to sink and collect in low parts of a building.

### Ignition temperature

This is the temperature at which an inflammable mixture of the fuel gas and air will be ignited. In the case of LPG it can be as low as 480°C; this is only the temperature of 'black hot' steel!

Figure 9.1   Typical natural gas service entry

## Biogas

The decomposition of organic wastes can be used to generate biogas, a mixture of methane and carbon dioxide; this can be an inexpensive source of energy where sufficient waste matter is available.

### Limits of flammability

The **lower explosive limit** (LEL) and the **upper explosive limit** (UEL), quoted as a percentage, indicate the limits of the ratio of fuel gas to air between which ignition and subsequent combustion can occur. For propane, the limits are between 2% and 10.3%.

### Flame speed

The term flame speed relates to the velocity at which the flame can pass through the gas/air mixture. In a well-designed burner, turbulent flow will be created so that the velocity of the gas/air mixture will be below the flame speed, resulting in **flame retention** and a stable flame (Figure 9.3). If the velocity is too high, **flame lift off** can occur. This can result in the flame being extinguished with the consequent danger of explosion due to build up of unburnt gas. If the velocity of the gas/air mixture is too low, **light back** of the flame into the burner can occur with the danger of incomplete combustion. In the case of propane, the maximum flame speed is 0.47 m/s.

### Stoichiometric mixture

The ratio of air to fuel gas required for complete combustion is known as the stoichiometric mixture. In the case of propane, this is 23:1; in other words for each 1 $m^3$ of propane gas burnt 23 $m^3$ of fresh air is required. It is most important that at least this amount of fresh air is available for combustion. The volume of air required might seem large at first sight. However, it must be remembered that fresh air contains only approximately one fifth oxygen (20.9%), the remainder being mainly nitrogen (78%).

Domestic gas appliances are usually fired with excess air to try to ensure that they do not produce **carbon monoxide** (CO), a deadly poisonous gas. However, firing the appliance with excess air will reduce its efficiency.

## Products of combustion

When the conditions for combustion are correct the major products of combustion of hydrocarbon gases in air are water vapour ($H_2O$) and carbon dioxide ($CO_2$).

The chemical reaction for methane ($CH_4$) is:
$$CH_4 + 2O_2 \rightarrow CO_2 + 2H_2O$$

for propane ($C_3H_8$) it is:
$$C_3H_8 + 5O_2 \rightarrow 3CO_2 + 4H_2O$$

and for butane ($C_4H_{10}$) it is:
$$2C_4H_{10} + 13O_2 \rightarrow 8CO_2 + 10H_2O$$

Although adding to the volume of products of combustion, nitrogen from the air for combustion can be ignored in this simple explanation of the combustion process.

It is important that the products of combustion are effectively removed from the appliance and that air used in the combustion process is replaced, otherwise the air will become **vitiated** (depleted in oxygen) and the danger of carbon monoxide poisoning will be created.

### Incomplete combustion

Anything that interferes with the combustion process is dangerous. The two main causes are starving the flame of oxygen and chilling; both will result in the formation of soot in the appliance, and this will exacerbate the problem.

Chilling occurs when the flame touches a cold surface (compared to the flame). Starving the flame of oxygen can result from blockages to the ventilation into the room, by blocking the flue outlet or by dirt, fluff or soot in the burner mixing tube. The flame will become longer in its search for oxygen; this can cause it to impinge or touch the sides of the combustion chamber, again leading to chilling.

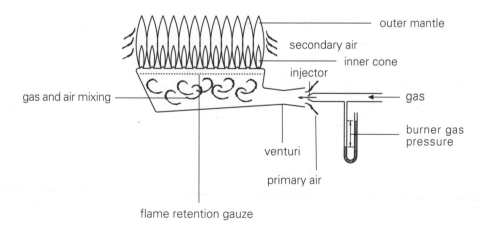

*Figure 9.3*  The effect of burner design on correct combustion

**Effect of carbon monoxide**

If incomplete combustion occurs and the products of combustion enter the room, then people are at great risk of carbon monoxide poisoning! Low concentrations of CO can kill very quickly. Breathing a concentration of only 0.4% CO in air can result in severe headache, dizziness, loss of consciousness and coma, followed by death in a few minutes.

## Physical characteristics of fuel gases

Table 9.1 sets out some of the physical properties of hydrocarbon gases used as fuel; it also outlines the key differences between them. It is important that the gas operative is fully aware of these differences and takes account of them when working on the various types of installation and appliance.

## Burners and combustion

There are two types of burner: the pre-aerated and the post-aerated. In the post-aerated burner all the air for combustion mixes with the gas after it has left the burner jet, creating a luminous flame. This is not very efficient and so, apart from decorative fuel effect appliances, this type of burner is not used in modern appliances.

In the **pre-aerated burner** (Figure 9.3), about 50% of the air required for combustion, called **primary air**, is drawn into the burner and mixed with the gas before it is ignited. This is achieved by the venturi effect of the fuel gas flowing through the specially designed mixing tube after it leaves the **injector** at the correct **burner pressure**. Mixing the gas with some of its combustion air before ignition creates a cleaner, hotter flame. The remainder of the combustion air, the **secondary air**, enters the flame around the outer mantle.

A visual examination of the flame from a correctly set up pre-aerated burner will show that it consists of two parts: an **inner cone** (coloured pale turquoise) and an **outer mantle** (coloured pale blue/purple). The junction between the two is the flame front, inside the inner cone is the reaction zone and the hottest temperatures in the flame are reached in the mantle just beyond the tip of the inner cone. Furthermore, the flame will be stable and will be retained on the burner ports.

For a correctly designed and constructed burner to operate in accordance with the manufacturer's specification it is important that the following are all correct:

- the type of fuel gas used;
- the burner gas pressure;
- the type and size of the injector and its position relative to the burner mixing tube;
- the primary air inlet is free of dirt, so that the supply of primary air will be correct;
- the ventilation to the appliance is adequate, to give the correct secondary air for complete combustion.

Figure 9.4 shows how changing the burner pressure and injector size can alter and affect the flame. The burner

*Table 9.1* Physical characteristics of fuel gases

| Physical property | Type of fuel gas | | | Comments |
|---|---|---|---|---|
| | NG (methane) | Propane | Butane | |
| Calorific value (vapourised) | 38.5 MJ/cubic m | 95 MJ/cubic m | 121.5 MJ/cubic m | LPG has greater energy level than methane, so smaller jets required |
| SG of gas (air = 1) | 0.58 | 2.0 | 1.5 | LPG sinks in air, methane floats |
| SG of liquid (water = 1) | – | 0.51 | 0.57 | |
| Boiling point of LPG | – | –42°C | –10°C | BP at atmospheric pressure |
| Cylinder gauge pressure | – | 7 bar | 2 bar | Pressure at normal temperature |
| Volume of gas/mass of liquid | – | 0.54 cubic m/kg | 0.41 cubic m/kg | |
| Ignition temperature | 704°C | 480°C | 540°C | LPG more easily ignited |
| Lower explosive limit | 5% | 2% | 1.9% | LPG creates explosive mixtures more readily than methane |
| Upper explosive limit | 15% | 10.3% | 8.5% | |
| Air/gas ratio | 9.6:1 | 23:1 | 30:1 | LPG has more energy so needs more air for combustion |
| Operating pressure | 20 mbar | 37 mbar | 28 mbar | |

Note: Appliance type must be correct for type of gas. LPG is very searching so use only approved jointing compounds and greases; also LPG is chemically active and will attack natural rubber and many plastics. There is *no* acceptable level of leak with LPG; installations must be totally gas tight!

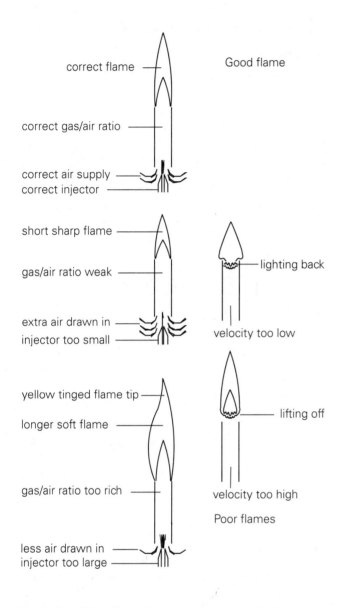

correct flame —————
correct gas/air ratio —————
correct air supply —————
correct injector —————

Good flame

short sharp flame —————
gas/air ratio weak —————
extra air drawn in —————
injector too small —————

——— lighting back

velocity too low

yellow tinged flame tip —————
longer soft flame —————
gas/air ratio too rich —————

——— lifting off

velocity too high

Poor flames

less air drawn in —————
injector too large —————

**Figure 9.4**  The effect of burner pressure and injector size on flame picture

| Appliance type: | | Boiler | |
|---|---|---|---|
| Gas type   NG | Min | Mid | Max |
| Heat intput      kW | 9.5 | 11.0 | 12.5 |
| Heat output     kW | 8.0 | 9.5 | 11.0 |
| Burner pressure    mb | 12 | 14 | 16 |
| Injector size 2.6 mm | | | |
| Appliance serial number | | | 1234567 |

**Figure 9.5**  Typical appliance data plate

- the type of gas it is designed to burn (usually NG or LPG);
- the size and type of injector fitted;
- the heat input and output of the appliance (in kW) at the design burner pressure (in mbar);
- a serial number to enable identification of the exact model of appliance so that correct spare parts can be obtained.

## Burner pressure

This can be checked (and adjusted if the appliance has a governor fitted) by use of a **water gauge** (a u-gauge or manometer). Figure 9.6 shows how to connect the gauge and adjust the governor output pressure so that it matches the figure on the data plate.

The stages involved are:

1. Turn the appliance control tap off.
2. Attach a suitable u-gauge to the burner pressure test point (between the appliance governor and the burner).
3. Turn the appliance full on.
4. Note the gauge reading; if not correct adjust the governor screw.
5. Turn the appliance off, remove the gauge and replace the test screw.
6. Reignite the appliance and test the test screw with leak detection fluid.

## Checking the gas rate/injector size

By observing the meter check digits or test dial (Figure 9.7) on metered gas installations, and timing, in seconds, how long it takes to burn a given volume of gas, it is possible to infer whether the injector size is correct (assuming that the burner pressure has already been checked and has proved satisfactory).

One method of checking the gas rate is to first determine the flow rate required in l/s by dividing the kW of heat input of the appliance by the calorific value of the gas being burnt. For example, a gas appliance designed to burn NG with a calorific value of 38.5 MJ/m$^3$ has a heat input of 10 kW, the flow rate is therefore:

$$10/38.5 = 0.26 \text{ l/s}.$$

pressure must be checked (and adjusted if necessary) whenever an appliance is commissioned or serviced. Whether the injector size is correct or not can be inferred by checking the gas rate of the appliance.

## Appliance data plate

As well as supplying installation, operating and maintenance instructions, manufacturers of gas appliances attach a data plate to the appliance (Figure 9.5). This gives the information required to set up or check that the appliance is functioning correctly even if the servicing instructions are not available. The data plate will show:

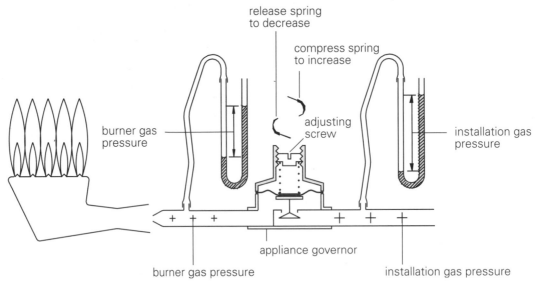

*Figure 9.6*  Checking and adjusting the burner pressure

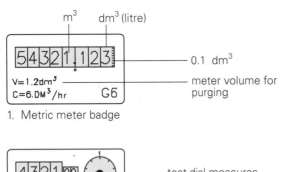

1. Metric meter badge

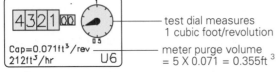

2. Older type meter badge

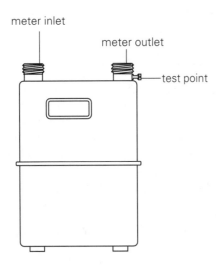

*Figure 9.7*  Meter test dial

In order to give greater accuracy, we can multiply up the flow rate, say by a factor of 100 for this example, to give a predicted 100 seconds to burn 26 l of gas.

Now, ignite the appliance and determine the actual time to burn the 26 l by observing the meter dial. If the time taken is a reasonable match, bearing in mind the likelihood of small differences due to human error in timing or adjusting the burner pressure, we can assume that the injector is correct and is allowing the correct volume flow rate of gas through the burner.

If the figures differ significantly, the percentage difference can be found by dividing the calculated flow rate by the actual flow rate and multiplying the result by 100. For example, if the appliance actually took 80 seconds to burn the 26 l then:

$(100/80) \times 100 = 125\%$, in other words the appliance is burning 25% more gas than the data plate value.

If results like this are found, whether over-gassed or under-gassed they should be investigated to determine the cause – possibly an over-sized or under-sized injector.

Where the meter reads in ft$^3$ and has a test dial, it is easier to check the gas rate by:

1.  timing in seconds how long the appliance takes to burn    1 ft$^3$ of gas;
2.  dividing the seconds in one hour by the time taken, to obtain a flow rate in ft$^3$/hr;
3.  multiplying the flow rate by the calorific value of the gas (for NG this is about 1035 btu/ft$^3$).

For example, observing a meter test dial shows that an appliance takes 80 seconds to burn 1 ft$^3$ of NG. The gas rate is:

$3600/80 \times 1035 = 46\,575$ btu/hr

## Pressure regulation

Gas flows along the pipes from the gas main or storage cylinder to the appliance due to its pressure. As the number of appliances in use changes, the pressure in the pipelines will vary. For a particular appliance burner to function correctly the pressure at the burner must be maintained at a constant level, so most gas appliances are fitted with a **governor**. Constant outlet pressure governors or **regulators** are also used to reduce and control the pressure at various points in the installation.

### Governor operation

Governors all operate in a similar way; they consist of a flexible rubber diaphragm that has a relatively large surface area on which the gas pressure can act. This is connected to and moves a washer to open and close a valve. The gas pressure is resisted by a spring whose tension can be adjusted by turning a screw (Figure 9.8).

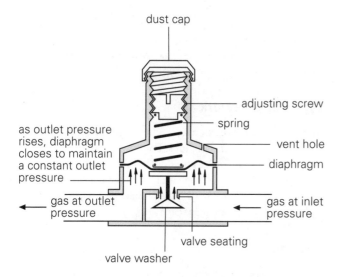

*Figure 9.8* Simple constant pressure governor

When there is no flow of gas, the pressure on the outlet side will build up until the governor locks-up (closes); this limits the outlet pressure to a preset value. When an appliance is ignited and gas begins to flow, the outlet pressure will fall slightly and this enables the spring pressure to open the valve against the pressure of the gas in proportion to the flow rate to maintain a constant outlet pressure whilst the appliance is lit.

On mains natural gas installations, the meter and installation pipework are protected against over pressurisation by the meter governor; this is a compensated constant outlet pressure governor (see Figure 9.1). It will be adjusted to give an installation **standing pressure** of 20 to 25 mbar and sealed by the gas supplier to prevent alteration.

On LPG cylinder installations, a regulator (Figure 9.9) is attached to the cylinder to limit the installation pipework to the pressure (28 or 37 mbar) required by the appliance. On LPG bulk tank installations (Figure 9.10) the tank is fitted with a first stage regulator to limit the external service pipe to 0.75 bar pressure. A second stage regulator (similar in operation to that shown in Figure 9.8) is fitted at the point of entry to reduce the pressure to that required by the appliance(s).

## Planning and pipe sizing

When planning a gas installation it is important to ensure that the tube diameters chosen are able to supply the volume of gas required by the appliances without excessive pressure loss as this can lead to dangerous incomplete combustion. Gas appliance manufacturer's installation instructions will give guidance on the appropriate diameter tube to be used to supply their appliance.

Where more than one appliance is to be installed, it is necessary to determine suitable tube diameters that can satisfy the maximum likely demand without excessive pressure drop. Similarly, before adding another appliance to an existing installation it is necessary to consider whether the system has any spare capacity available. For mains natural gas installations the pressure drop along the pipeline at periods of

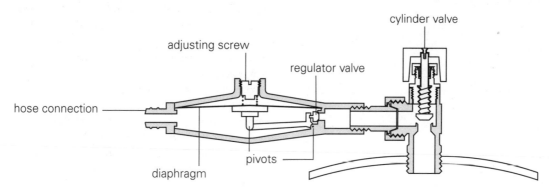

*Figure 9.9* Section through LPG cylinder regulator

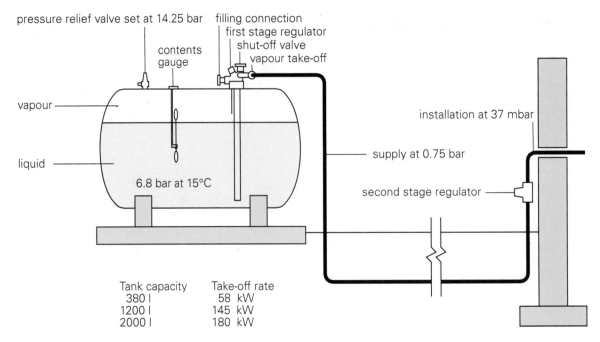

*Figure 9.10* Bulk LPG storage tank installation

maximum demand should be no more than 1 mbar. For LPG installations the pressure drop should be no more than 2.5 mbar at maximum demand.

If undersized pipes are installed, the pressure at the burner could become so low that dangerous incomplete combustion occurs. This will result in the production of carbon monoxide. Table 9.2 suggests tube diameters for connecting individual domestic gas appliances with pipes up to 3 or 6 m in length. The usual diameter for the main runs will be 20 and

*Table 9.2* Suggested tube diameters for connections to gas appliances

| Suggested tube diameters in mm for individual domestic gas appliances | | |
|---|---|---|
| Type of appliance | Up to 3 m run | 3 to 6 m run |
| Central heating boiler | 15 | 20 |
| Cooker | 10 | 15 |
| Fires and convector heaters | 10 | 15 |
| Single-point instantaneous water heater | 10 | 15 |
| Multi-point instantaneous water heater | 15 | 22 |
| Over sink storage water heater | 8 | 10 |
| Circulators | 8 | 10 |

The diameters indicated are for the final run of tube to the appliance

15 mm bore tube. Where the runs are longer or higher rates of flow are required, pipe flow charts should be consulted to determine tube diameters that will satisfy the demand without excessive pressure drop.

## Types of pipework

Medium-grade low-carbon steel tube or light gauge copper tube can be used for gas installations. Polyethylene tube can be used for external buried service pipes only; if above ground it must be protected against ultraviolet light and mechanical damage by fitting a sleeve. Only metal tube should be used to enter the building and for internal gas pipework.

## Jointing

Use only approved jointing compound on threads or the thicker type (0.2 mm) of approved PTFE tape wrapped with a 50% overlap. It is important that all joints are carefully made because gas, particularly propane, is very searching. Pipe threads should be carefully cut, preferably with a block die to ensure consistent tight fit. Never use two parallel threads together; the male thread must be tapered both on bought fittings and pipe.

When using a blow torch to solder capillary fittings, always have a $CO_2$ fire extinguisher available. It is important to examine visually every completed capillary joint to ensure that the solder has run. The flux used must only be corrosive during heating and any residue should be removed after making the joint. Apply a thin coating of flux to the outside of the cleaned tube only, not into the mouth of the fitting. Twist the tube as it is assembled into the cleaned fitting to spread the flux and then wipe off any excess before completing the joint.

Compression fittings should only be used where they are readily accessible for tightening and inspection. This means that they cannot be buried underground, buried in the structure or used in ducts or under floors.

# Installation

During installation, prevent dirt and water entering the tube by the use of adhesive tape over the ends. Remove burrs left by tube cutters to minimise any pressure drop due to turbulent flow.

If work has to be done on pipes already connected to a meter or LPG storage, they must be temporarily disconnected. Dust caps should be fitted and the pipework purged to remove any fuel gas before using a blow lamp. Any open ends of pipework must be sealed before the work is left unattended. If is also important to fit temporary earth continuity bonding on metal pipes before cutting through to install tees. This is to reduce the risk to you of possibly fatal shocks from stray electric currents and to prevent a spark igniting any gas present!

## Installing tube in walls and floors

When tube is to be buried in solid floors or walls the number of joints should be kept to a minimum. Ideally the tube should be run in a preformed duct with a suitable protective cover. Where tube is to be laid on top of the base concrete, it must be protected against corrosion (by use of plastic coated tube, or wrapping with petroleum jelly impregnated or PVC tape) and soundness tested before wrapping any joints and covering by a suitable screed. Try to run vertical pipes in walls in ducts with access if possible, never inside the cavity of a cavity wall. If the wall is thick enough to provide proper cover, the pipe can be run in a chase. Always sleeve the pipe where it passes through solid walls or floors and seal the gap with flexible fire resistant compound at each end as in Figure 9.11.

If tube is to be laid in timber floors, the joists should be notched and the tube supported in accordance with Figure 9.12. Care should be taken to mark floor boards so that nails and screws do not damage the tube. Maximum spacings for tube supports are set out in Chapter 5. Tubes installed between joists should be properly supported (Figure 9.12).

In a timber-framed construction, run vertical tube through purpose-designed ducts which are sealed to prevent the passage of gas into the cavity as in Figure 9.13. If the duct has a cross-sectional area of more than 0.1 m² it should be vented (at high level for NG and low level for LPG) to allow any escape of gas to dissipate into the rooms. Use the minimum number of joints and cover the duct with a metal plate to minimise the risk from nail punctures.

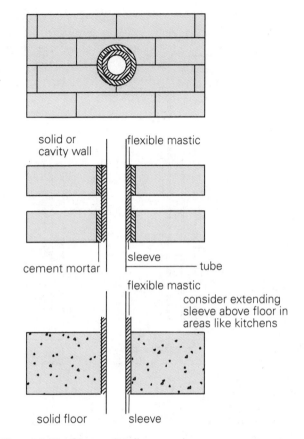

**Figure 9.11**  Sleeve details

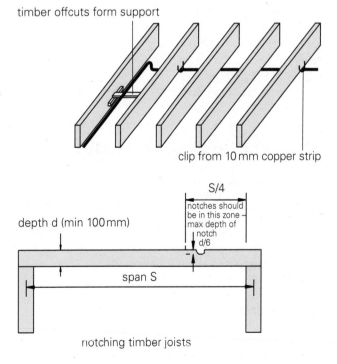

**Figure 9.12**  Notching and support of tube in timber floors

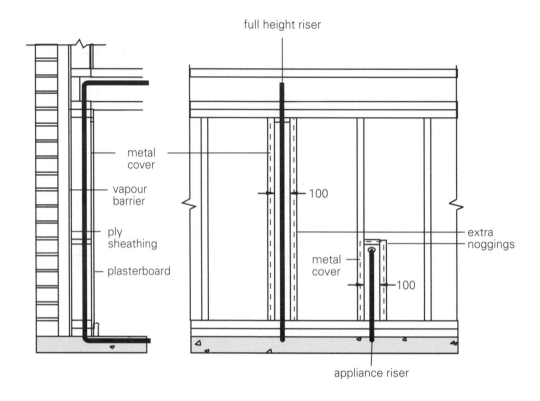

*Figure 9.13*  Gas pipes in a timber-framed construction

## Other services

Keep a gap of at least 25 mm between gas lines and other services and at least 150 mm away from electricity meters and fuse boxes. Where electrical cross-bonding is necessary, a clamp is used to connect the protective conductor near (ideally within 600 mm) the outlet side of the meter or service entry point (see Figure 9.1).

## Testing gas installations

Gas safety requires that new installations be tested before the meter or storage vessel is connected. If work is to be carried out on an existing installation, it must be tested before starting and any faults traced and rectified or the installation made safe. On completion of the work, another test must be carried out and the installation purged.

The testing and purging of domestic installations must be carried out in accordance with any local regulations. Testing will be required:

● whenever a smell of gas or gas escape is suspected;
● when work is done on a gas fitting (including pipework, meters and connections or appliances) that might affect its gas soundness;

● on installation pipework prior to fitting a gas meter or connection to the gas supply;
● on the original installation before connecting any extension;
● on completion of the extension.

## Testing mains natural gas installations

These test procedures are suitable for low pressure pipework up to 25 mm bore for domestic premises.

**Testing new installations with no meter fitted using air**
1. Visually inspect the installation for compliance with safety regulations to see that it is safe to test.
2. Check that all appliance isolating valves are open and that pilots and burner controls are turned off.
3. Connect a u-gauge to the installation using one branch of a test tee; the other branch being valved is used to pump air into the installation (Figure 9.14).
4. Slowly raise the pressure to a minimum of 20 mbar.
5. Turn off the valved branch.
6. Wait one minute for temperature stabilisation (for the temperature of the pipes to balance the temperature of the air pumped in).
7. Take a reading of the gauge.
8. Wait two minutes, then take another reading.

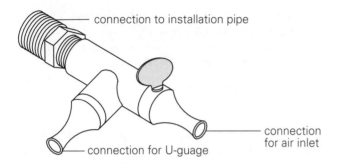

*Figure 9.14* **Test tee detail**

9. If the test is successful, remove the gauge and reseal the test connection point. If the test is not successful, trace leaks with leak detection fluid and repair.

For a successful test there must be no pressure drop over the two minutes.

### Testing natural gas installations with appliances fitted

1. Visually inspect the installation for compliance with safety regulations to see that it is safe to test.
2. Check that all appliance isolating valves are open and that pilots and burner controls are turned off.
3. Connect a u-gauge to the installation using the meter test point (Figure 9.15) and observe the gauge to see if the water level starts to creep up. Note: if this occurs, it indicates **let-by** of the emergency control valve; this must be corrected before proceeding.
4. Gradually raise the pressure to a minimum of 20 mbar by slowly opening the emergency control valve.
5. Turn off the valve making sure that the pressure does not exceed 25 mbar (if it does the meter governor could be faulty).
6. Wait one minute for temperature stabilisation.
7. Take a reading of the gauge.
8. Wait two minutes, then take another reading.
9. If the test is successful, remove the gauge, replace the test screw, turn the gas on slowly and test screw with leak detection fluid. If test is not successful, trace leaks with leak detection fluid and repair.

For a successful test, if natural gas burning appliances are fitted, there must be no more than 4 mbar pressure drop over the two minutes (for an installation with a meter that can pass up to 6 m$^3$/hour).

### Purging natural gas installations

Purging is carried out to clear the pipework, meter and appliances of air or an air/gas mixture that may be explosive! Purging must be carried out:

- after a successful test for gas soundness on any newly connected or altered installation;

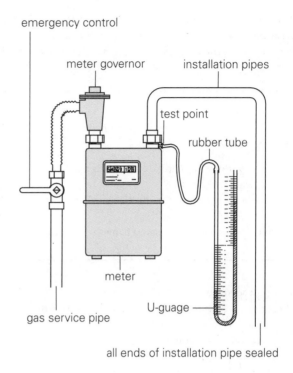

all ends of installation pipe sealed

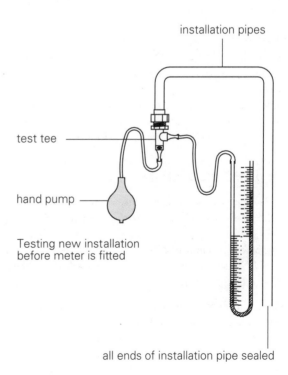

Testing new installation before meter is fitted

all ends of installation pipe sealed

*Figure 9.15* **Testing natural gas installations**

● after any work has been done on an installation that may have allowed air to enter the gas ways, or on an installation that is to be turned on after a long period of being turned off.

> **⚠ Safety precautions**
> Purging is a dangerous procedure so before purging ensure that:
>
> ● there is adequate ventilation by opening windows and doors;
> ● people are informed that no electrical switches are to be operated;
> ● smoking or the use of naked flames is banned.

### Purging procedure

1. Determine the purge volume – not less than 5 times the capacity per revolution of the gas meter mechanism as marked on the meter index (Figure 9.7).
2. Purge the pipework and appliances starting from the furthest point away from the meter by opening a control tap or slightly opening a pipe union. Allow the air to vent until gas is smelt, then close the tap or tighten the union and test the joint with leak detection fluid to ensure gas tightness.
3. Purge any other branches working back to the meter.
4. Check that the correct purge volume has passed through the meter and then light any installed appliances and continue to operate them until the flame picture is normal (Figure 9.4).
5. Fully commission any new appliance(s) in accordance with the manufacturer's instructions and gas safety regulations ensuring that the installation is safe for further use.

## Testing LPG installations

No pressure drop is to be permitted when soundness testing on LPG installations, even if appliances are connected.

### Testing before gas is connected

Testing LPG installations can be carried out before appliances are connected, using air.

1. Visually inspect the installation for compliance with safety regulations to see that it is safe to test.
2. Cap or plug all open ends of the system.
3. Connect a suitable 60 mbar u-gauge to the installation using one branch of a test tee; the other branch being valved is used to pump air into the installation (Figure 9.14).
4. Slowly raise the pressure to a minimum of 45 mbar and turn off the valved branch.

5. Wait five minutes for temperature stabilisation.
7. Take a reading from the gauge.
8. Wait another five minutes, then take another reading.
9. If the test is successful, remove the gauge and reseal the test connection test point. If the test is not successful, examine the whole of the installation to trace leaks with leak detection fluid, and repair.

For a successful test there must be no pressure drop over the five minutes of the test.

### Testing with gas connected

Testing the LPG installation can be carried out from the low pressure side of the regulator with the gas connected and appliances fitted.

Pre-requisite – establish the correct gas soundness of the pipework then:

1. Check that all appliance taps are closed.
2. Connect a suitable u-gauge to the installation.
3. Turn the gas on slowly.
4. Purge each appliance separately, closing each tap off in turn on completion.
5. Check the regulator is operating correctly and if necessary adjust while an appliance is in use (37 mbar for propane, 28 mbar for butane).
6. Make a note of the actual working pressure.
7. Turn off the appliances and the gas supply.
8. Open an appliance tap until a pressure of 2 mbar below the actual working pressure is achieved. Note: due to the high pressure gas trapped between the cylinder valve and the regulator, this operation can take a number of attempts, but the reduced pressure must be achieved before proceeding.
9. Allow five minutes for temperature stabilisation.
10. Note the u-gauge reading and observe the gauge to see if the water level starts to creep up. Note: if this occurs it indicates let-by of the cylinder control valve; this must be corrected before proceeding.
11. Wait a further five minutes, then take another reading; there must be no pressure drop or smell of gas.
12. If the test is successful, remove the gauge, replace the test screw, turn the gas on slowly and test screw with leak detection fluid. If the test is not successful, trace leaks with leak detection fluid and repair. Remember: the installation must not be commissioned until all gas escapes are found and repaired.

### Purging LPG installations

Purging is achieved by turning on each appliance in turn while applying an ignition source close to the issuing gas/air mixture to ignite it when it becomes rich enough. Continue to operate the appliance until the flame picture is normal, then fully commission the appliance in accordance with the manufacturer's instructions.

## Bulk LPG tanks

Any pipework or controls fitted to the bulk tank installation and subject to the full tank pressure must be tested. A suitable dial gauge (reading 0 to 10 bar with a face at least 100 mm in diameter) would have to be fitted into the pipework to enable the test, no drop being allowed for the five minutes of the test. If the first stage regulator is fitted directly to the tank valve, it is acceptable to test this short section with leak detection fluid alone.

> ⚠ Never leave any installation or appliance connected unless the soundness test, purge and commissioning are successfully completed. The installation must not be used unless it is confirmed that it can be used safely. If purging and testing cannot be completed, seal off all ends with an appropriate fitting.

## Dynamic performance testing

Once the installation has been tested and purged, the working pressure at the meter should be checked; this can be done in the following way:

1. Connect u-guage to meter test point.
2. Ignite appliances in accordance with Table 9.3.
3. Check the pressure on the gauge; it should read 21 mbar ± 1 mbar.
4. Remove guage, seal and test the test point with leak detection fluid.

*Table 9.3* Operation of appliances for gas installation performance testing

| Type of appliance | Appliance operation |
|---|---|
| Central heating or hot water boiler | Main burner on |
| Gas fire or space heater | Full gas rate |
| Cooker | Three hotplate burners on |
| Other appliances | Full gas rate |

If the working pressure is not correct, the gas supplier should be informed: too high a pressure indicates a faulty service governor; if the pressure is too low the service pipe, meter or governor could be at fault.

### Problem with low burner pressure

In cases where the correct burner pressure or gas rate cannot be achieved, taking pressure readings at the meter and the inlet pressure test points on the appliances can identify the likely source of the problem.

## Installation performance

Once the meter outlet working pressure is known (or LPG standing pressure after the second stage regulator), the installation pipes can be checked for pressure drop. Attach a manometer to the inlet pressure test point before the appliance governor, and with the appliances lit take a reading. If this is more than 1 mbar below the meter outlet working pressure, the pipework is either too small in diameter for its length, or it may have been crushed or partially blocked by debris. Whatever the cause, the problem lies within the installation. If the installation pressure drop is 1 mbar or less (2.5 mbar for LPG) and the burner pressure cannot be achieved, the problem lies within the appliance, possibly in the appliance governor.

# Flame failure devices

As their name implies, flame failure devices are sensors that detect whether a flame is present or not. Depending on this information, they will shut down the appliance in a fail-safe way or allow it to operate. Flame failure devices have been made that use a number of principles including:

- differential expansion of metals;
- expansion of fluids;
- thermoelectric effect;
- flame rectification.

## Bi-metal flame failure device

The bi-metal flame failure device was the first to be developed and is still used on small over-sink water heaters. It consists of a bonded brass and steel strip that is heated by the pilot light. Because the metals have different rates of expansion, when the bi-metal is heated it curves and this movement can be used to open and close a valve (see Figure 9.16 for details). Although very reliable, the bi-metal device suffers from two disadvantages: it is slow to react and it cannot shut off the gas feed to the pilot.

## Mercury vapour flame failure device

Used mainly to protect oven burners, the mercury vapour flame failure device consists of a hollow sensor probe that is heated by the burner pilot flame. The sensor is connected to a bellows by means of a capillary tube. Inside this arrangement is a small quantity of mercury (a metal that is liquid at room temperature and has a low boiling point). When the pilot flame is ignited, the mercury in the sensor probe boils, resulting in a pressure increase that expands the bellows. This then opens a valve that allows full flow of gas to the burner (Figure 9.17).

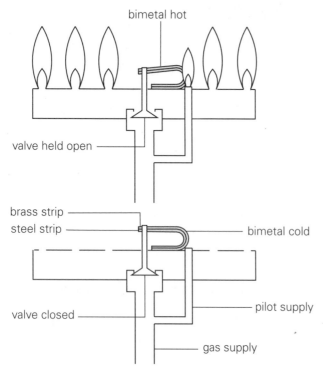

*Figure 9.16*   Bi-metal flame failure device

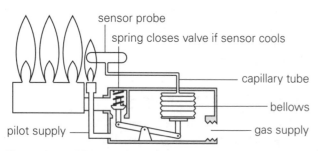

*Figure 9.17*   Mercury vapour flame failure device

## Thermoelectric flame failure device

**Thermoelectric effect**   If two different metals are joined to form a **thermocouple** and the joint is heated, a small amount of electricity is produced (see Figure 9.18); the current can be used to hold a solenoid valve open.

This is usually incorporated into a multifunction-gas-valve (see Figure 9.19). The device consists of a user-operated button to initiate the pilot flame by means of an **interrupter valve**; this is followed by a constant outlet pressure governor for burner pressure adjustment and a mains-powered **solenoid valve** to turn the burner on and off when the appliance thermostat calls for heat.

### Valve operation

When the user button is pressed, it operates the interrupter valve. This temporarily closes the gas-way to the main burner solenoid valve, opens a gas-way to the pilot and opens the

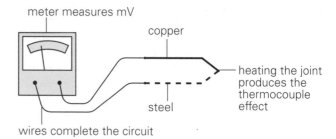

*Figure 9.18*   Thermoelectric effect

thermocouple solenoid valve causing the valve keeper to be held in contact with its coil. The user must hold the button down while the pilot is ignited; it can then heat up the thermocouple. After about 30 seconds, the thermocouple will have been heated sufficiently to produce enough current to energise the electromagnet, holding the keeper against the solenoid coil. When the user releases the button, the gas-way to the main burner solenoid valve is opened. If the pilot is extinguished, the thermocouple will cool, the electro-magnetism will die away and the valve and gas supply to the pilot will be cut off; the valve will be 'fail-safe' in operation.

Assuming the pilot remains lit, when the appliance thermostat calls for heat the main burner solenoid valve will be energised; this is strong enough to open the valve allowing gas to flow and the burner to ignite.

### Testing thermoelectric flame failure devices

Once the appliance is fitted and working it is important to test the flame failure device to see that it correctly shuts off the gas supply if the pilot is extinguished. To do this, light the pilot, then turn off the gas supply at the appliance shut-off valve and listen carefully for the click that signals that the interrupter valve has closed. Then turn on the gas at the appliance shut-off valve and listen; gas should not issue from the pilot nozzle. If all is well, reignite the pilot, otherwise investigate the cause.

## Oxygen depletion sensor

Although not a flame failure device, an oxygen depletion sensor (or oxy-pilot assembly, see Figure 9.19) gives automatic safety shut-down of the appliance when predetermined levels of $CO/CO_2$ are exceeded. This is achieved because the thermocouple pilot is starved of oxygen when the levels are exceeded, causing it to lift off the thermocouple, which cools, resulting in the gas valve shutting down the supply and so becoming safe.

## Flame rectification

Used in appliances that have full automatic ignition, flame rectification is a fast-acting method of flame failure detection. It uses the flame to carry a small flow of ions from

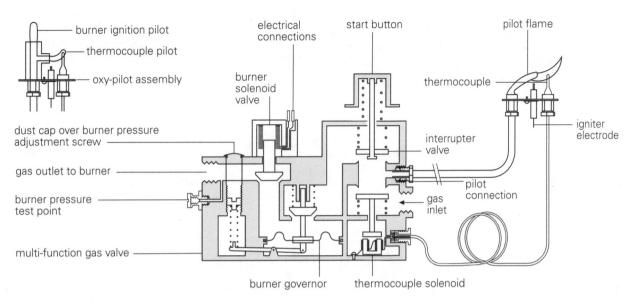

*Figure 9.19* Thermocouple and multifunction-gas-valve

a probe to the metal of the burner. The flame in effect completes an electrical circuit. The small current flow is amplified in a control box; this increases the current flow to energise a solenoid valve allowing the burner to fire at full rate (Figure 9.20).

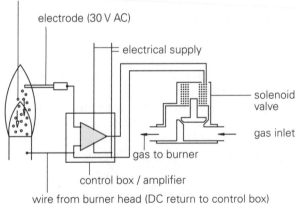

*Figure 9.20* Flame rectification principle

# Flues and ventilation of gas appliances

Gas appliances are available with a number of different types of flue; some are made that discharge the products of combustion into the room in which they are fitted. Whatever the type, it is most important that they are correctly installed and tested to ensure that they operate safely in accordance with the manufacturer's instructions and any local regulations.

## Open-flued appliances

These have a flue pipe (Figure 9.21) that consists of four parts, each with its own function:

- primary flue;
- draught diverter;
- secondary flue;
- terminal.

### Primary flue

This is usually a part of the appliance; it creates the initial flue draught and enables the burner to function correctly during short periods of down blow.

### Draught diverter

The draught diverter, again usually part of the appliance, performs three functions:

- it allows air to enter the secondary flue to dilute the products of combustion;
- it breaks, and so controls, the amount of pull that the secondary flue can exert over the appliance;
- it allows down blow to escape from the flue into the room, preventing it interfering with combustion.

### Secondary flue

This is the run of flue pipe between the draught diverter and the terminal. It is a channel for the products of combustion. In it the hot gases rise due to natural convection. The route of the flue should be as upright and direct as possible and there

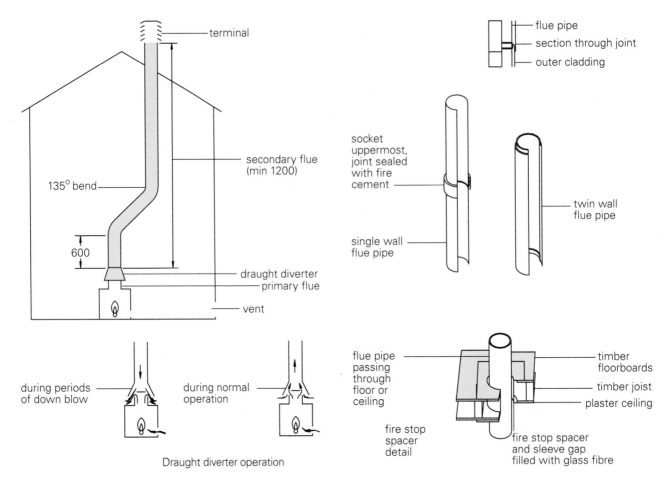

*Figure 9.21*   An open-flued appliance

*Figure 9.22*   Construction of secondary flues

should be at least 600 mm of vertical pipe after the draught diverter before any bends are fitted. Bends should be at least 135° in angle; horizontal runs of flue pipe should not be fitted as they create resistance and reduce the flue pull. The flue pipe should be kept at least 25 mm away from combustible materials and a **fire-stop spacer** (Figure 9.22) should be fitted where the flue passes through timber floors and ceilings.

Because the products of combustion contain carbon dioxide and water vapour, they are slightly acidic. Consequently the flue must be made from materials that are corrosion resistant, such as aluminium, galvanised steel, stainless steel, acid resistant concrete or ceramic pipes. Any socket and spigot joints used must be installed with the sockets uppermost to keep condensation inside the flue. This is so that it can run down inside and be re-evaporated as the flue warms with use. To encourage flue pull by keeping the flue warm, twin-wall flue pipe (see Figure 9.22) should be used where possible. The flue pipe must also be properly supported with brackets to carry the load. It must be at least 1.2 m in height to create sufficient draught, and must not be too tall (say 12 m for domestic

appliances) otherwise, when heat is lost as the flue gases pass up the flue, there will be more resistance than uplift and the flue will not function.

If a gas appliance is to be fitted into a masonry chimney, it should be lined with concrete or ceramic when it is constructed, or retro-fitted with a flexible stainless steel liner to prevent condensation damaging the masonry.

**Terminal**

A terminal is fitted on the top of the secondary flue; it performs three essential functions:

● it prevents the entry of rain, leaves and debris or birds nests from blocking the flue;
● it assists in the release of flue products from the secondary flue;
● by being sited in the correct position, it minimises down blow effects.

The terminal should have openings that are in total equal to twice the cross-sectional area of the flue. The openings should be positioned all round the terminal and not too small, say 16 mm across the narrowest part; neither should they be too large, otherwise small birds could enter. The terminal must be sited in a position where it will not be affected by turbulence, creating down blow due to high pressure (Figure 9.23).

The best position for the terminal is at or above the ridge of a pitched roof. If the roof pitch is less than 45°, the terminal must be at least 600 mm above the surface of the roof. If the pitch is 45° or greater, the terminal must be at least 1 m above it (Figure 9.24 shows details of terminal locations for pitched roofs). Where the terminal is located above a flat roof, it should be at least 600 mm high above the parapet level, or roof surface if close to the edge. If there are no obstructions and no parapet then the terminal height could be reduced to 250 mm (Figure 9.25).

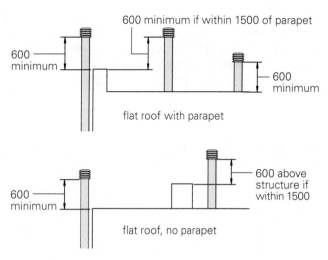

Figure 9.25  Terminal position for flat roofs

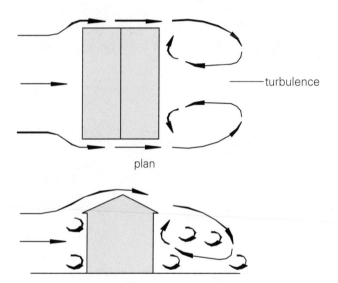

Figure 9.23  Wind effects around buildings

## Testing open flues

Before connecting an open-flued gas appliance to an existing chimney or flue, a **flue flow test** or flue pull test should be carried out. This is to determine that the flue is not blocked and is of good sound construction without leaks. To carry out the test, the flue should be warmed for five minutes, using a blow torch. Then a **smoke pellet** is ignited at the base of the flue or in the fireplace opening. This will create copious amounts of smoke. If the smoke is drawn up the flue without leaking from any joints or the brickwork, and discharges from one terminal or chimney, the flue should be satisfactory. If, on the other-hand, the smoke comes out from the opening and fills the room or leaks out of joints into the room or discharges from more than one chimney pot, this indicates that the flue is not sound and the problem should be investigated and corrected before the flue is used.

### Spillage test

Once the appliance has been installed, one of the commissioning tasks will be to carry out a spillage test. This test uses a **smoke match** to determine whether all the products of combustion are being drawn up the flue when the appliance is operating.

To carry out a spillage test, the appliance should be lit and allowed to operate for five minutes. All doors and windows should be closed and if the room contains an extractor fan, it should be running during the test. Next, a lit smoke match should be introduced just inside the draught diverter while the appliance is firing (Figure 9.26). The match should be moved to test all round the diverter; if all the smoke is drawn away, the test is passed. If the smoke is blown down into the room, it indicates that the flue is not carrying away the products of combustion. This may be due to the flue not

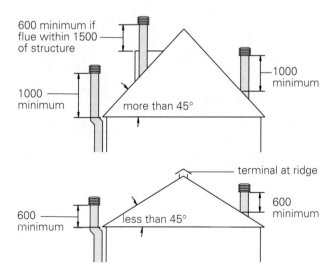

Figure 9.24  Terminal position for pitched roofs

yet being warm enough, so allow it to be heated for a further five minutes before retesting. If the test is still unsatisfactory, the cause must be investigated. This is potentially very dangerous; if the appliance is producing carbon monoxide, people will be at great risk! The appliance must not be allowed to be used; it must be disconnected, the gas pipe capped and a warning label attached.

## Room-sealed appliances

These are safer than open-flued appliances because they do not take the air for combustion from the room in which they are fitted. To do this, they have a duct that allows air to enter the appliance directly from outside. There are two types of room-sealed appliance:

- balanced flue;
- fanned flue.

### Room-sealed balanced flue appliance

The balanced flue gets its name from the fact that the combustion air inlet and flue outlet are both at one point; the air pressure acting on both is therefore 'balanced'. The small amount of updraught created by the heat of the combustion is sufficient to cause air to circulate in the appliance (Figure 9.27) and, provided the flue is correctly sited, it will not be affected by the action of the wind.

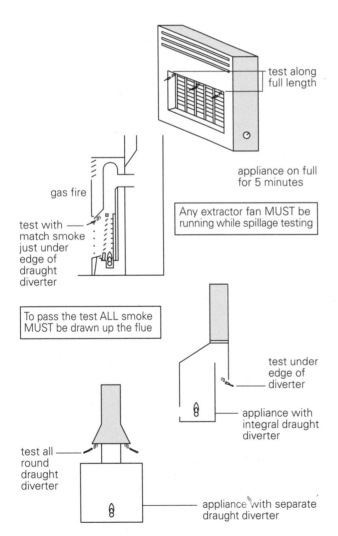

Figure 9.26  Spillage testing of open-flued appliances

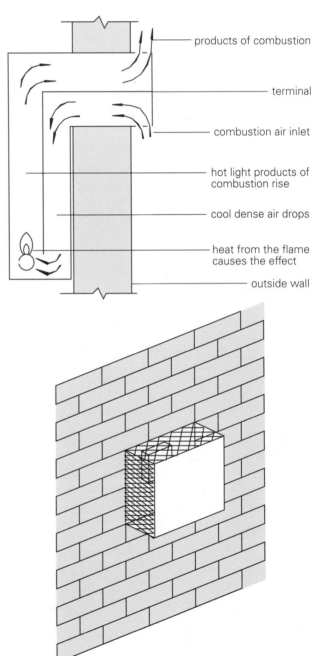

Figure 9.27  Balanced flue appliance

The balanced flue terminal must not be sited in a position that will allow products of combustion to re-enter the building. It must not be less than 300 mm below any ventilator or opening window. It must also not be closer than 600 mm to any corner or projection (see Figure 9.28 for recommended minimum distances from obstructions to terminals).

### Fanned flue room-sealed appliances

These appliances use a small fan to force air through the appliance for combustion. The flue and air inlet ducts can therefore be much smaller in area. Also, the appliance can be positioned away from an outside wall making it more flexible in terms of its siting. The appliance will only be safe to operate if the fan is circulating air correctly and so the appliance has an air pressure switch built in that will not allow the burner to fire unless the air is moving through the ducts, and the casing is properly fitted (see Figure 9.29 for details).

## Flued gas appliances in rooms

Open-flued gas appliances of over 7 kW heat input installed in rooms require **permanent ventilation**. However, research has shown that it is virtually impossible to completely seal the cracks and other openings into a room so that some

adventitious ventilation will be present (equal to about 35 cm$^2$ and sufficient for 7 kW of appliance heat input). To take account of this, the vent should be sized so that there is 4.5 cm$^2$ of free area for each kW of appliance with a maximum rated input over 7 kW. For example, an open-flued boiler with a maximum heat input of 15 kW requires a vent of:

$$(15 - 7) \times 4.5 = 36 \text{ cm}^2$$

The ventilator is best fitted so that it goes directly to the outside. However, ventilators can be fitted in series so that the air goes through an adjacent room if necessary (see Figure 9.30 for methods of installing the vent).

Room-sealed appliances installed in rooms do not need a permanent ventilator to be fitted; this is because they have their own built in air supply duct.

## Flued gas appliances in compartments

A compartment is a part of a building that is designed to hold a gas appliance; it could be a specially built cupboard or a kitchen unit, for example. The compartment must be ventilated at both high and low levels to keep it cool and, if the appliance is open-flued, the low-level vent needs to be larger to provide air for combustion and so will pass through the flue to leave the compartment. The vents can go directly outside (this is best for an open-flued appliance) or be fitted so that they communicate with the room (satisfactory for a room-sealed appliance). The vent sizes are

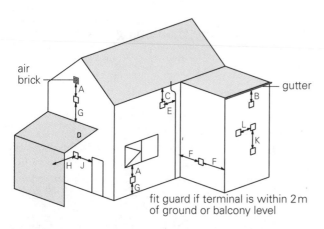

fit guard if terminal is within 2 m of ground or balcony level

Suggested minimum distances (mm) from obstructions to balanced flue terminals

| Terminal location | | Natural draught | Fanned draught |
|---|---|---|---|
| A | Directly below opening windows or air bricks | 300 | 300 |
| B | Below gutters, soil or drain pipes | 300 | 75 |
| C | Below roof eaves | 300 | 200 |
| D | Below balconies or car-port roof | 600 | 200 |
| E | From vertical drain and soil pipes | 75 | 75 |
| F | From internal and external corners | 600 | 300 |
| G | Above ground, roof or balcony level | 300 | 300 |
| H | From a surface facing a terminal | 600 | 600 |
|   | From a terminal facing a terminal | 300 | 300 |
| J | From an opening in the car-port | 1200 | 1200 |
| K | Vertically from a terminal on the same wall | 1500 | 1500 |
| L | Horizontally from a terminal on the same wall | 300 | 300 |

*Figure 9.28* Minimum distances from obstructions to terminals

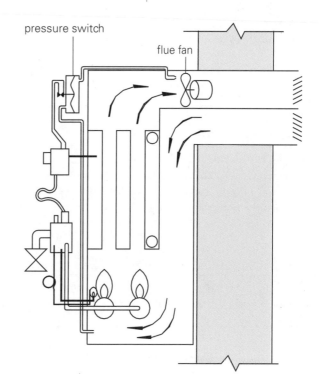

*Figure 9.29* Room-sealed fanned flue

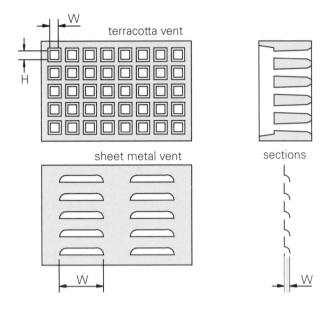

*Figure 9.30* Assessing the free area in an air vent

determined by the maximum heat input of the appliance, the type of flue and the position of the vent (in accordance with Table 9.4).

To use Table 9.4, first determine the maximum heat input of the appliance, its type of flue and whether the vents are to go directly outside or into the room. Then select the appropriate multiplication factors from the table and use them to size the vents. For example, an open-flued appliance with a maximum heat input of 10 kW in a compartment with vents directly to the outside will require vents sized as follows:

high-level       $10 \times 4.5 = 45\,cm^2$
low-level        $10 \times 9.0 = 90\,cm^2$

## Flueless appliances

Flueless appliances, such as cookers and over-sink instantaneous water heaters, discharge their products of combustion into the room in which they are installed. This gives them the potential to be very dangerous if they are not installed to take account of the following factors:

- the need for sufficient permanent ventilation to enable the appliance to operate without causing the air to become vitiated;
- the heat input of the appliance – if it burns gas at a relatively fast rate it will require more ventilation;
- the size of the room – if the room is small the air will quickly become vitiated.

Because of these factors, a room containing a flueless appliance requires a permanent vent directly to the outside, plus an openable window. Depending on the type of appliance and the volume of the room, the vent should have a free area as shown in Table 9.5.

To use the table the following facts need to be known:

- the type of appliance and whether it is within the maximum suggested heat input rating limit;
- the volume of the room;
- the availability of an opening window, if required.

For example: a gas cooker fitted in a small room 1.9 m by 1.6 m by 2.2 m high. The room volume is $1.9 \times 1.5 \times 2.2 = 6.27\,m^3$ so, by reference to Table 9.5, there is no limit to the power of the cooker; the vent size required is 50 cm² free area and an opening window is required.

## Vent size for more than one gas appliance

Where rooms have more than one gas appliance fitted, it is necessary to categorise the appliances to determine an adequate vent size as follows:

- if there are any flueless space heaters, work out the vent size required in accordance with Table 9.5;
- if there are one or more open-flued space heaters, work out the total vent size based on 4.5 cm² for each kW over 7 kW;
- for all other appliances, work out their vent size requirement and note whichever is the largest.

The vent size to be fitted is the largest requirement from the three categories above.

*Table 9.4* Suggested minimum free area of vent for compartment installation of flued gas appliances

| Minimum air vent free areas for compartments (sq cm per kW of appliance maximum rated heat input) | | | |
|---|---|---|---|
| Appliance flue type | Compartment vent route | High level vent sizing factor | Low level vent sizing factor |
| Room-sealed | Into room or internal space | 9 | 9 |
| | Direct outside | 4.5 | 4.5 |
| Open-flued | Into room or internal space | 9 | 18 |
| | Direct outside | 4.5 | 9 |

*Table 9.5* Suggested sizes of vents for flueless appliances

| Minimum permanent vent free area (sq cm) for flueless gas appliances | | | | | | |
|---|---|---|---|---|---|---|
| Type of appliances | Maximum appliance rated input limit | Room volume (cubic m) | | | | Openable window also required |
| | | Up to 5 | 5 to 10 | 11 to 20 | Over 20 | |
| Domestic oven, hotplate, grill or any combination of these | None | 100 | 50 | Nil | Nil | Yes |
| Instantaneous water heater | 12 kW | Installation not permitted | 100 | 50 | Nil | Yes |
| Flueless space heater installed in room | 50 W/cubic m of heated space | 100 plus 50 for every kW over 3 kW | | | | Yes |
| Flueless space heater installed in an internal space | 100 W/cubic m of heated space | 100 plus 25 for every kW over 6 kW | | | | Yes |
| Refrigerator | None | Nil | | | | No |
| Single boiling ring | None | Nil | | | | No |

## Assessing vents for free area

When assessing whether a particular vent is adequate to serve a gas appliance, the important factor is the free area of the openings not the overall length or height of the vent. So, to work out a vent's free area, measure the length and height or projection of a slot in cm and multiply these by the number of slots (see Figure 9.30). For example, a vent with 8 slots each 5 cm by 0.7 cm will have a free area of:

$$5 \times 0.7 \times 8 = 28\,\text{cm}^2$$

Other factors to note are that the vent should not be fitted with an insect screen because this will become blocked in time. Also, permanent ventilation is required so vents with movable shutters that can be closed are not suitable.

## Installing domestic gas appliances

When fitting appliances it is important to make sure that the appliance is installed in accordance with the manufacturer's instructions and any local gas safety regulations. The proposed location of the appliance should be checked for suitability. If the appliance has a flue, the route and terminal location will be one of the most important features to consider, as will the ventilation requirements for open-flued and flueless appliances installed in rooms. If the appliance needs a fireproof hearth, this will have to be provided and care must be taken to see that combustible materials are not affected by the appliance.

### Cookers

When connecting cookers, use an approved flexible connecting pipe that has a bayonet valve to allow disconnection when the cooker is moved for cleaning. If the cooker supply pipe is fed with a fixed pipe, fit an appliance shut-off valve in the pipe immediately before the cooker. Fit a stability bracket or chain restraint to prevent the cooker from toppling over if someone presses down on the open oven door, and site the cooker so that there is clearance around the hot-plate and grill combustible materials will not come into contact with naked flames (Figure 9.31).

### Gas fires

Gas fires, designed to be fitted into pre-cast concrete gas fire flues and chimney fireplace openings, come in three types:

- traditional radiant convector fires;
- inset live fuel-effect fires;
- decorative fuel-effect fires.

The installation of gas fires is shown in Figure 9.32. The flue must be checked before a fire is installed by means of a flue flow or pull test. Also, if the flue has been used before, it must be swept to clear any soot or debris. A **closure plate** must be fitted and sealed around the edges to control the amount of draught and seal off the opening behind the fire. The space behind the closure plate must be sufficient in volume to allow for the build up of debris between annual service visits and should be at least 250 mm high to the bottom of the fire flue spigot. Also, there must be a space of at least 50 mm horizontally from the flue spigot to the fire back (Figure 9.32). Use a **restrictor floor plate elbow** to

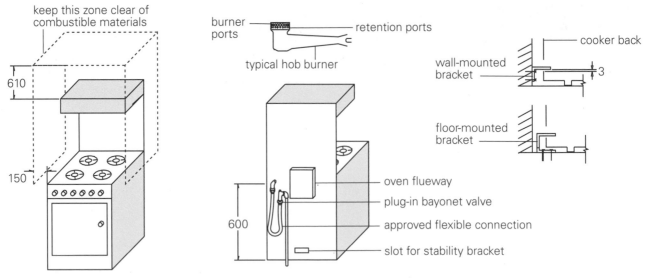

*Figure 9.31* Cooker installation details

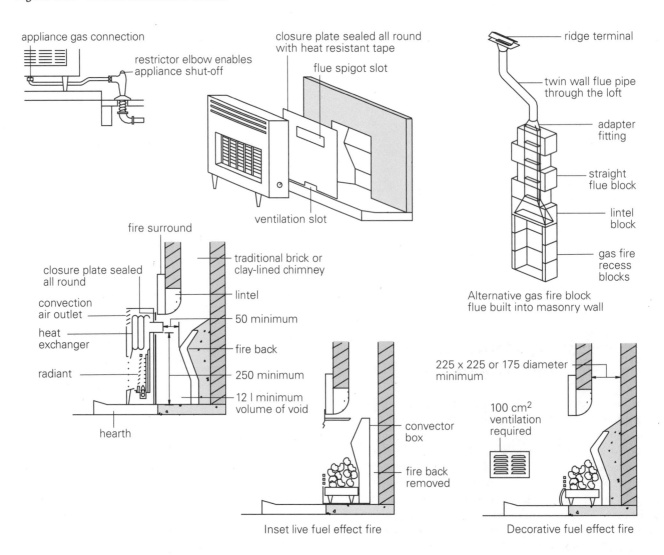

*Figure 9.32* Gas fire installation details

enable shut-off for maintenance, or fit an appliance shut-off valve in the pipe under the fire if the pipe is concealed. Once the fire has been installed, it is vital to carry out a satisfactory test for spillage at the draught diverter in accordance with the manufacturer's instructions, before leaving the fire in use.

# Ignition devices

Many gas appliances use a permanent pilot for ignition. Spark ignition, created by means of a high tension transformer, either battery or mains powered, is also sometimes used but the most common modern ignition device is based on the **piezo-electric effect**.

### Piezo-electric ignition device

Compressing piezo crystals using a lever and then suddenly releasing the pressure creates sufficient voltage (over 5000 V) to cause a spark to jump across a gap of 3 mm (Figure 9.33). As with all types of spark ignition, it is important to ensure that the electrode is clean and in the correct position relative to the pilot gas supply otherwise the spark will not work. Also, the insulation around the electrode lead must be in good condition and not dirty or the electricity can 'track' and escape to earth without sparking across the gap.

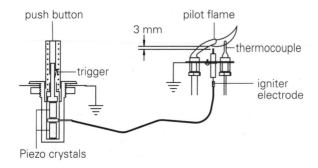

*Figure 9.33*  Piezo-electric ignition device

# Gas appliance thermostats

The purpose of a thermostat is to regulate and control the appliance burner when it reaches a preset temperature. Thermostats use the principle of expansion due to temperature to open and close a valve and so control the burner (Figure 9.34). On appliances that have pilot ignition, the thermostat can simply turn the burner on and off to achieve control. Other appliances, such as cooker ovens and gas fires, cannot be turned off completely because the burner would not be relit. In cases like these, the thermostat has a 'weep' bypass that enables the burner to continue firing at a very low rate when the thermostat is satisfied.

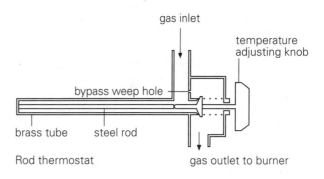

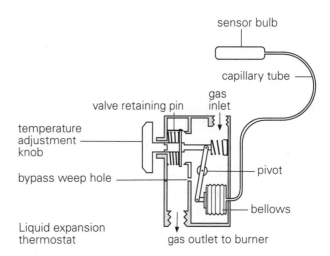

*Figure 9.34*  Gas appliance thermostats

### Rod thermostat

This consists of a steel rod inside, connected to the end of a brass tube; at the other end of this assembly, a valve washer is connected to the end of the rod while the valve body and seating is connected to the brass tube. Because the steel rod and brass tube expand at different rates, the valve will open and close as the temperature varies.

### Liquid expansion type thermostat

This comprises a flexible metal bellows connected to a hollow probe by means of a capillary tube. The bellows and probe are full of liquid (usually ether), so when the probe is heated, the bellows expands causing the thermostat valve to close.

# Commissioning and hand-over

When the installation is complete, it is important to check all parts of it carefully, to see that they conform to local safety regulations and the appliance and component manufacturer's instructions before testing the pipework for soundness and purging using the previously described procedures (Figure 9.35). If the appliances use other services

Job/Client:

Location:

Gas installer:

Date:

| Appliance type and location | General condition of installation pipes and meter, satisfactory (Y/N) | Inspected and tested | | Burner pressure (mbar) | Heat input (kW) | Soundness test and purge result (Pass/fail) | Flame picture correct (Y/N) | Pilot flame correct (Y/N) | FFD working correct (Y/N) | Thermostat working correct (Y/N) | Purge volume (1) | Ventilator grille(s) | | Flue pull Correct (Y/N) | Spillage test Correct (Y/N) | Standing pressure (mbar) | Electrical supply | | | Working pressure (mbar) | Water services Correct (Y/N) | Notes |
|---|---|---|---|---|---|---|---|---|---|---|---|---|---|---|---|---|---|---|---|---|---|---|
| | | Yes | No | | | | | | | | | Required size (sq cm) | Correct (Y/N) | | | | Polarity correct (Y/N) | Earthing correct (Y/N) | Fuse rating (Amps) | | | |
| | | | | | | | | | | | | | | | | | | | | | | |
| | | | | | | | | | | | | | | | | | | | | | | |
| | | | | | | | | | | | | | | | | | | | | | | |
| | | | | | | | | | | | | | | | | | | | | | | |
| | | | | | | | | | | | | | | | | | | | | | | |

Recommendations or warning notices issued:

Gas installer signature:

Client signature:

*Figure 9.35* Installation check-list for gas appliances

(water or electricity), these must also be tested and available. Once the gas supply is tested and purged, depending on the range and types of appliances fitted, the following tests should be carried out:

- testing the burner gas pressure and heat input;
- a visual check for correct flame picture;
- testing the operation of the flame failure device;
- testing the operation of any thermostats or other controls;
- a check for spillage on open-flued appliances;
- a check for correct ventilation.

If all tests are satisfactory, demonstrate how to operate the appliance and explain how to turn off the gas in an emergency. Explain the importance of regular annual maintenance and hand over the operating instructions, service and maintenance instructions to the user.

## Maintenance and servicing

It is vital for the long-term safety and efficiency of the installation that regular annual maintenance is carried out on all gas appliances. This should be done following the manufacturer's guidelines and will usually include:

- a visual check of the installation pipes and meter for signs of damage or corrosion; if leakage is suspected a soundness test must be carried out;
- stripping down the appliances to enable cleaning of the heat exchanger, the burner and any anti-lint gauzes fitted;
- reassembly and checking for correct combustion;
- checking the flame failure device and other controls;
- checking any ventilation to make sure that the grilles are still clear and unobstructed;
- checking open flues for spillage.

Only if everything is working safely should the appliance and installation be used. Never leave a leaking gas installation or unsafe appliance connected to the gas supply. Any dangerous or potentially dangerous faults found must be reported to the person responsible for the building and then repaired at once, or the appliance or installation should be shut-off and warning labels attached informing people not to use the installation.

### CHECK YOUR UNDERSTANDING

- Anyone who works with gas must be competent to do so.
- Know the emergency gas escape procedures and be ready to carry them out if necessary.
- A leak in an LPG installation has an extra danger because LPG has a specific gravity of about 1.5 so it will tend to sink and collect in low parts of the building.
- The lower explosive limit and the upper explosive limit indicate the ratio of fuel gas to air between which ignition and subsequent combustion can occur. For propane the limits are between 2% and 10.3%.
- It is most important that the correct amount of fresh air is available for combustion at the point of combustion, in the case of propane 23 $m^3$ of air are required for each 1 $m^3$ of gas.
- The major products of combustion of hydrocarbon gases in air are water vapour and carbon dioxide.
- Anything that interferes with the combustion process is dangerous. The two main causes are starving the flame of oxygen and chilling; both will result in the formation of soot in the appliance, and this will exacerbate the problem leading to dangerous incomplete combustion and the formation of carbon monoxide.
- The flame on a correctly set up pre-aerated burner will show two parts; an inner cone (coloured pale turquoise) and an outer mantle (coloured pale blue).
- Altering the burner gas pressure and size of the injector will determine the heat input of the burner.
- Use the information on the appliance data plate to set up or check that the appliance is functioning correctly if the servicing instructions are not available.
- Constant outlet pressure governors or regulators are used to reduce and control the pressure at various points in the installation.
- Gas pipes should be large enough in diameter to supply all the appliances without an excessive pressure drop (1 mbar maximum for NG and 2.5 mbar for LPG installations).
- Only metal tube should be used to enter the building and for internal gas pipework; it is important to check that all joints are carefully made because gas is very searching.
- Any open ends of pipework must be sealed before the work is left unattended.
- Never run gas pipes inside the cavity of a cavity wall.
- Always sleeve the pipe where it passes through solid walls or floors and seal the gap with flexible fire-resistant compound at each end.
- New installations must be tested before the meter or storage vessel is connected. If work is to be carried out on an existing installation, it must be tested before starting and any faults traced and rectified or the installation made safe. On completion of the work, another test must be carried out and the installation purged.
- Never leave any installation or appliance connected unless the soundness test, purge and commissioning are successfully completed. The installation must not be used unless it is confirmed that it can be used safely.
- If purging and testing cannot be completed, seal off all ends with an appropriate fitting.
- Always check that the flue and ventilation required by the appliance are correct before leaving it in service.
- Always take notice of the manufacturer's installation and servicing instructions when working on a gas appliance.
- Demonstrate how to operate appliances and explain how to

turn off the gas in an emergency. Explain the importance of regular annual maintenance and hand over the operating, service and maintenance instructions to the user on completion of the work.

## REVISION EXERCISES AND QUESTIONS

1  List the procedure to follow on discovering a gas escape.
2  State the three inflammable constituents and percentages of natural gas.
3  i)   Name the two principal products of combustion.
   ii)  What gas is produced when a flame is starved of oxygen?
4  State four items of information that can be found on a gas appliance data plate.
5  List the procedure to be followed, including the pressure and times, when testing and purging a metered natural gas installation that has appliances fitted.
6  What is the purpose of a gas governor; explain how it operates.
7  Make a labelled drawing to show the operation of a natural draught balanced flue.
8  Describe the procedure necessary to carry out a spillage test on an open-flued appliance.
9  What ventilation is required for the following situations:
   i)   A 21 kW open-flued gas boiler fitted in a room?
   ii)  A gas cooker fitted in a room that is 1.8 m × 1.3 m × 2.1 m high?
   iii) A 12 kW room-sealed water heater fitted in a compartment and vented into a room?
10 Name the four parts of an open flue and list their functions.

# Sanitary appliances

## Introduction

Sanitary appliances are fitments or receptacles that are designed to receive foul or waste water then discharge it through a system of sanitary pipework or directly to a drainage system where it will be disposed of. This chapter will describe all the main details associated with the common appliances found in the home and in public buildings.

Appliances are classified as either soil appliances, which receive and dispose of human excreta, or waste appliances, which are used for general washing purposes or food preparation.

**Soil appliances** include: bed pan washers, slop sinks, urinals and water closets.

**Waste appliances** include: basins, baths, bidets, drinking fountains, sinks and showers.

Because of the function of sanitary appliances, they must as far as possible be strong and durable, resistant to corrosion, smooth and impervious to water, easily cleaned and 'self-cleansing' in operation. The materials that best suit this purpose include ceramics, and in particular vitreous china, stainless steel and certain kinds of plastics. Soil appliances are fitted with flushing cisterns to flush the contents into the drains. Waste appliances have both hot and cold water supplies which must discharge their water into the appliance above the flood level of the appliance, or be piped up or fitted with some device to prevent back siphonage of waste water into the water main. To prevent smells from the connecting drain entering the room where the appliance is fitted, all appliances should be fitted with a trap.

## Soil appliances

### Bed pan washer

These appliances are only usually found in hospitals, hospices and large hotels. They are used for emptying and washing bed pans and usually include a 'Mackintosh' drainer and connecting sink for washing soiled waterproof bed sheets (Figure 10.1). The bed pan washer or sluice is like a heavy duty low-level sink with a trap built integrally as part of the appliance. It is available as a pedestal type, floor-mounted, or corbel type, fitted on the wall with a clear floor area beneath for easy cleaning. A flushing cistern connects to the appliance for cleansing and disposal of contents. Hot and cold water taps discharging above the drainers and sinks are usually elbow controlled. Traditionally, heavy duty ceramics such as glazed earthenware or fireclay were used, but stainless steel is now increasingly popular. Modern installations include steam cleaning and sterilisation equipment.

### Slop sink

Similar to a bed pan washer but without the associated sink and drainer. Sometimes called a slop-hopper. They are fitted in any building that is likely to require cleaning up slops, such as hospitals, schools and hotels. They can be pedestal or corbel mounted with an integral trap, hot and cold taps, and a high-level cistern (Figure 10.2). They are usually made of glazed earthenware or fireclay with a hardwood front insert to prevent damage from buckets. They have a brass-hinged grating to stand buckets on with a lower domed grating over the outlet to prevent cleaning brushes etc. falling into the trap.

### Urinals

These appliances are fixed in public places like cinemas, bars, restaurants, hotels, schools and factories. They are designed for use by males. There are three types: stall, slab and bowl.

**Stall urinals** are made in single units complete with a floor channel and have sides which provide some privacy. They can be built up into ranges by bedding them together and covering the joints with a capping piece. They are usually made from glazed fireclay or stoneware (Figure 10.3).

**Slab urinals** can also be built up to any required length but they do not generally have the side pieces except at the ends of the range. Traditional materials are glazed fireclay or

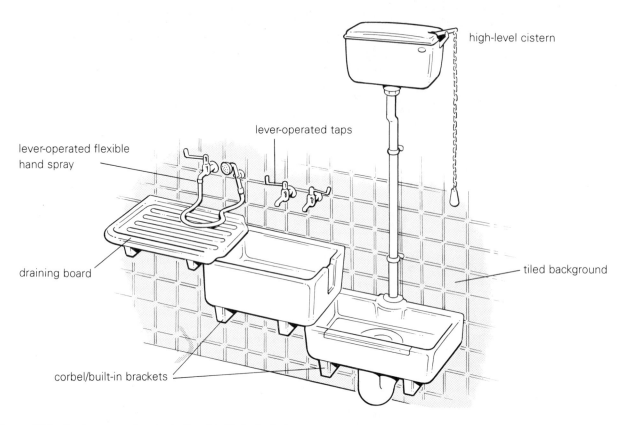

*Figure 10.1*   Bed pan washer including Makintosh drainer

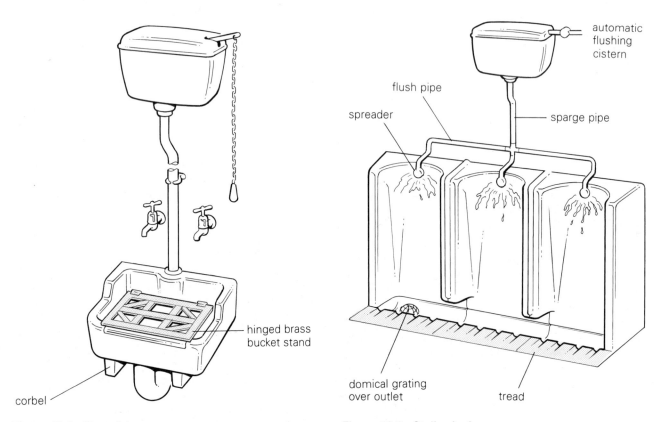

*Figure 10.2*   Slop sink

*Figure 10.3*   Stall urinal

stoneware. The floor channel is built up separately and must be made first by laying each piece perfectly level; the fall is in the channel itself so each piece is numbered in sequence at the factory (Figure 10.4). Once positioned, a weak grout of sand and cement must be poured behind the slabs.

> Great care must be taken to make sure all joints on slab and stall urinals are watertight. Special mastics are available that can provide a good seal. Sheet lead trays can also be laid on the ground and against the wall prior to installation to give added protection. The traps on slab and stall urinals must be securely connected because access may be difficult, particularly on ground floors.

Stainless steel urinals are becoming more popular because they are available as one-piece ranges, therefore there are no joints to leak. At 80% lighter than fireclay, they are easier to install and will not crack or stain.

**Bowl urinals** are the easiest type of urinal to install, consisting of a wall-mounted bowl with optional separate screens if fitted in ranges. They are available in glazed fireclay, stoneware, vitreous china or stainless steel (Figure 10.5).

Another type of urinal, even cheaper and easier to install than a range of bowl urinals, is the stainless steel trough urinal. Fitted at the same height as bowl urinals, these are available in 4 m long one-piece sections (Figure 10.6).

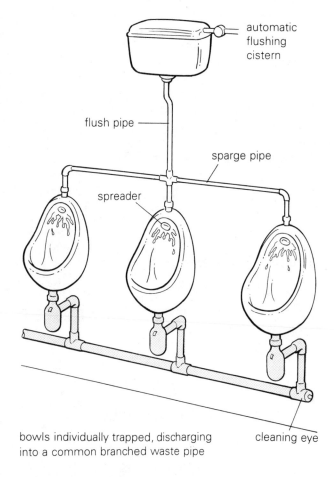

bowls individually trapped, discharging into a common branched waste pipe

*Figure 10.5*  Bowl urinal

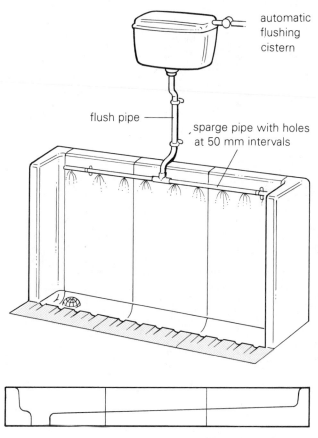

this view of the channel shows the fall to the outlet

*Figure 10.4*  Slab urinal

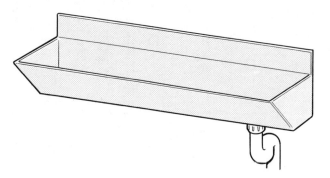

*Figure 10.6*  Stainless steel trough urinal

Urinals must be designed so that they are easily cleaned and with no sharp edges or corners to harbour dirt. All urinal outlets must be fitted with a domical grating to help prevent blockages.

## Automatic flushing cisterns

Urinals must be cleaned regularly and are usually flushed from a high-level automatic flushing cistern, which should deliver approximately 4 litres of water per 600 mm of slab or per bowl at 20 minute intervals when the building is occupied. The water supply to automatic flushing cisterns is fed through a pet or drip cock, which should be regulated to fill the cistern to the top of the siphon in 20 minutes (Figure 10.7).

The inside of the cistern contains a siphon arrangement with a domed top which includes a water trap, the outlet side connecting to a flush pipe.

### How the automatic flushing cistern works

As the water level rises in the cistern and inside the siphon, it compresses the air under the dome which creates pressure to prevent the water rising any further inside the siphon. As the level continues to rise outside the siphon, the pressure will eventually build up under the dome and force the level of water in the trap down on the siphon side and up on the outlet side, causing water to trickle down the flush pipe. The water trickling down the flush pipe will absorb some of the air inside the siphon which will reduce the pressure, causing the greater atmospheric pressure acting on the water in the cistern to force it through the siphon and down the flush pipe.

The flush pipe connects to a perforated **sparge pipe** which should run the length of the slab, or to spreader outlets in individual stalls or bowls to fully cleanse all soiled surfaces.

Special automatic control valves to regulate water flow to pet cocks are now popular as control of water resources becomes more important. They are sensitive to water pressure in the building and when the building is not in use, such as at night or during holiday periods in a factory, the water pressure will be higher, which stops the flow to the cistern and stops it flushing automatically every 20 minutes, thus saving water. Another alternative is to use a spring-controlled flush valve (see the section on flushing valves later in this chapter).

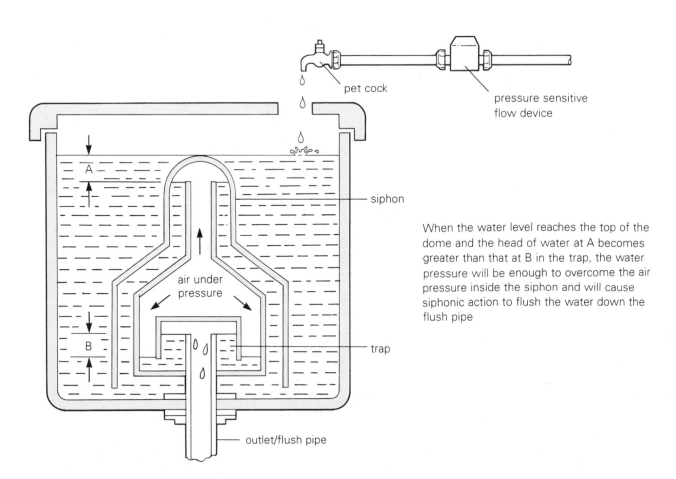

When the water level reaches the top of the dome and the head of water at A becomes greater than that at B in the trap, the water pressure will be enough to overcome the air pressure inside the siphon and will cause siphonic action to flush the water down the flush pipe

*Figure 10.7*  Simple automatic flushing cistern

# Water closets

These are designed to receive excreta and to flush it into a drainage system. There are several types but all must have smooth and easily cleaned surfaces and be made in one-piece wherever possible, with an integral water trap with a 50 mm minimum seal. They are made from glazed fireclay, vitreous china or stainless steel and must be connected to a manual flushing cistern which may be fitted at low or high-level or be close-coupled depending on the type of water closet (WC). Flushing cisterns can be made from ceramic materials or plastics.

Hardwood or plastic seats to make WC use more comfortable are usually fitted, with rear brass or chromed pillar hinges. Open-fronted seats are available to reduce soiling in public buildings such as schools.

## Wash-down closets

The contents of the pan are washed out by the action of the flushing water, which must be directed all around the pan by a flushing rim. The back of the pan should be vertical to reduce soiling. The trap seal is normally 50 mm and can be either an S- or P-outlet, which can be straight, left or right-handed and 100 mm diameter. The outlet joint depends on the type of soil pipe. Simple rubber push-fit connectors are available to suit most materials but putty and hemp joints to brass collars for lead and cast iron, and sand and cement with tarred gasket for clayware drains, are also acceptable (Figure 10.8).

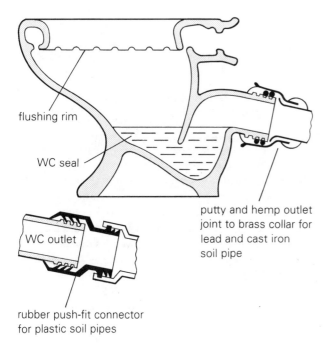

*Figure 10.8* Wash-down water closet

The pans can be corbel type, which are wall-mounted, making cleaning the floor easy, or floor-mounted. Floor-mounted ceramic pans should be bedded with non-setting mastic and brass screws on timber floors and with a weak sand and cement grout on concrete or solid floors. The 38 mm flush pipe usually connects to the back of the pan with an internal or external rubber cone or adaptor. The external ones are sometimes secured with copper wire (Figure 10.9).

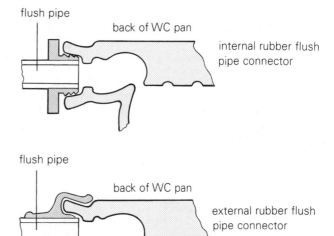

*Figure 10.9* Flush pipe connectors

## Siphonic closets

These rely on siphonic action to empty the contents of the pan; the flushing water is used to clean the pan and refill the trap seal. They are quieter in operation than wash-down pans but can block more easily with constant and rough use. There are two main types, the double-trap or the single-trap reduced outlet.

### How siphonic water closets work

**Single-trap** As the water is flushed, it completely fills the reduced outlet and cuts off the air from the drain side of the trap, which creates a partial vacuum in the wider chamber or bulb. As soon as this happens, the greater atmospheric pressure acting on the surface of the water in the pan starts up the siphonic action and empties the contents. The outlet diameter is between 65 and 70 mm, with the internal diameter of the chamber 100 mm (Figure 10.10).

**Double-trap** As the water is flushed, a small pipe connected to the flush pipe, or a special device known as a 'bomb' fixed where the flush pipe connects to the pan, draws air out of the chamber between the traps creating a partial vacuum. As soon as this happens, siphonic action is created and the contents of the pan are carried away before the flush water enters the pan. The second trap prevents foul air from the drains entering the building when the first water seal is broken during siphonic action. The flush water then cleans the pan and reseals the first trap. The outlet is usually 75 mm diameter (Figure 10.11).

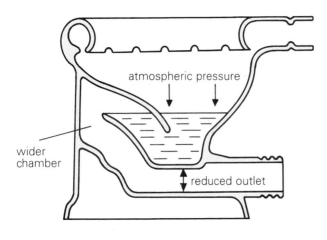

*Figure 10.10*  Single-trap restricted out-go siphonic WC pan

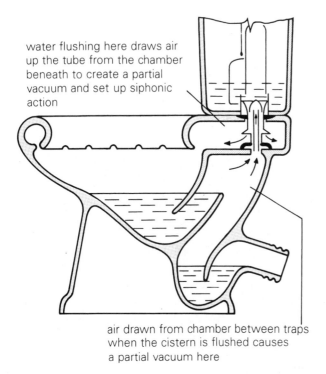

*Figure 10.11*  Double-trap siphonic WC pan

## Eastern or squatting closet

This floor-mounted closet is unlike other closets in that you do not sit on it but crouch or squat. It is a square receptacle similar in size to a shower tray with raised foot plinths positioned to allow the user to squat over a hole positioned near the back which forms the outlet trap (Figure 10.12).

It is usually connected to a high-level flushing cistern with a spreader outlet to direct water around the closet. Because it is floor-mounted it can be connected directly to the drains. As with other appliances with restricted access traps, special care must be taken when jointing traps and outlets. This type of closet is easier to clean than other types and many people claim the squatting position to be healthier than sitting.

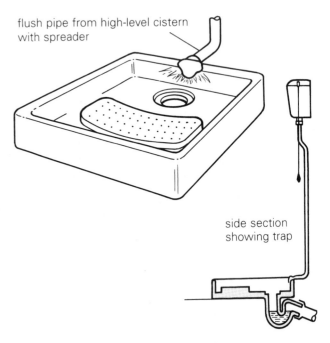

*Figure 10.12*  Eastern or squatting closet

## Flushing cisterns

These are used to contain and discharge water manually into soil appliances such as WC pans to flush out the contents and clean the soiled surfaces. For urinals it is usual to use the automatic type. Most modern flushing cisterns are siphonic and can only discharge when a lever is operated. They were originally designed as waste water preventers to replace valve cisterns which would continually leak water into the pan, often unnoticed, when the valve seating became worn.

There are basically two types, the bell type and the plunger type (Figure 10.13). Both rely on mechanical means to set up siphonic action to empty the contents. All siphons have a long leg and a short leg in the form of an inverted 'J'. When water begins to fall down the long leg it creates a partial vacuum

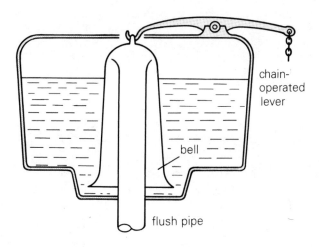

1.   Bell type flushing cistern (ball valve and overflow
     not shown)

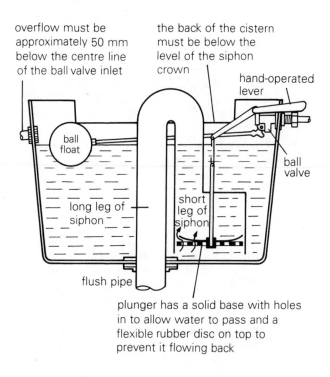

overflow must be
approximately 50 mm
below the centre line
of the ball valve inlet

the back of the cistern
must be below the
level of the siphon
crown

hand-operated
lever

ball
float

long leg of
siphon

short
leg of
siphon

ball
valve

flush pipe

plunger has a solid base with holes
in to allow water to pass and a
flexible rubber disc on top to
prevent it flowing back

2.   Plunger type flushing cistern

*Figure 10.13* **Flushing cisterns**

inside the crown of the siphon; atmospheric pressure acting
on the surface of the water outside the siphon will then force
the water up the short leg until the level drops below the short
leg and allows air into the tube to equalise the pressure inside
and outside, and stop the flush.

To set up the action in a bell type cistern, the bell is raised
then lowered, forcing water over into the flush pipe which acts
as the long leg of the siphon. In a plunger type, a lever arm is
pulled down which raises a plunger inside the short leg of the
siphon, which in turn lifts water over into the long leg or flush
pipe creating siphonic action.

The bell type cistern is simpler but the plunger type more
efficient and quieter in operation. Bell cisterns are also an
older design with both cistern and bell made from cast iron.
Plunger type cisterns are made from ceramics or plastics. Most
moving parts in modern cisterns are now made from plastics.

Plunger and lever arm arrangements require occasional
maintenance when parts become loose or damaged. For
example, the seal between the plunger arm and the siphon
tube may become displaced, which prevents siphonic action
taking place.

Flushing cisterns should be fitted with a ball valve to
control the flow of water into the cistern, and an overflow
pipe set approximately 50 mm below the inlet level of the
ball valve. For domestic use, the ball valve should be 15 mm
diameter, with the overflow 22 mm diameter. They can be
mounted to the side of the cistern or with stand pipes to the
bottom. The overflow should discharge where it will be
noticed so that the ball valve can be adjusted or fixed. In the
unlikely event of the overflow becoming blocked and the ball
valve not closing, the crown of the siphon should always stand
above the flood level of the cistern to prevent it flushing like
an automatic flushing cistern.

Flushing cisterns can be fitted at high or low level or can be
close-coupled to the WC. High level cisterns should have a  32
mm diameter flush pipe and those fitted at low level should
have a 38 mm diameter flush pipe. The lever arm for high
level cisterns is operated by a hanging chain.

## Dual-flush cisterns

To prevent undue wastage of water, dual-flush cisterns are also
available which can give a full flush of 9 litres, the contents of a
standard cistern, or half a flush of 4.5 litres (Figure 10.14). To
give a full flush, the lever arm must be held in position until
the flush is finished. For half a flush, the lever is operated then
left; when the water level gets half way down the cistern, air
enters the short leg of the siphon tube through a hole or small
pipe to break siphonic action. With the lever arm held, it keeps
the plunger valve tight against the hole, preventing air from
entering the siphon. Some countries now specify a maximum
7.5 litre or even 6 litre flush.

## Flushing trough

These can be fixed in buildings where ranges of WCs are
heavily used, such as in factories or schools (Figure 10.15). A
long trough made of metal, plastics or timber, and lined with
non-ferrous metal, is fixed at high level over the top of a

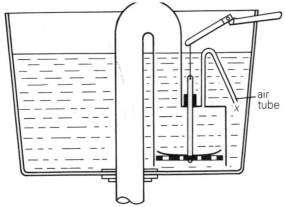

If the lever is held down, the plunger will be held against the air inlet tube preventing air from entering the siphon and allowing a full flush. If released, air will enter the siphon when the water level falls to *x*, giving a reduced flush

*Figure 10.14*  Typical dual-flush cistern

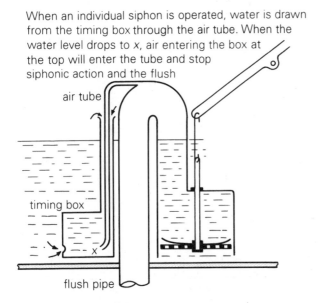

When an individual siphon is operated, water is drawn from the timing box through the air tube. When the water level drops to *x*, air entering the box at the top will enter the tube and stop siphonic action and the flush

*Figure 10.15*  Flushing trough siphon

number of WCs. Each WC has its own flush pipe connected to its own siphon and lever arm fixed to the trough, which is full of water. When an individual siphon is operated it will flush until a pre-set amount of water is discharged, at which point air will enter the siphon from an individual chamber or timing box and stop the flush. It is similar in operation to a dual-flush siphon, but the air inlet pipe connects to a measuring and filling chamber which allows a set quantity of water into the siphon without affecting the rest of the water in the trough. The siphon is ready to flush again almost immediately.

Flushing troughs are useful where periods of constant heavy use are anticipated. They can save on pipework and materials but during periods of maintenance all the WCs will be out of action.

## Flushing valves

These are used as an alternative to a flushing cistern and have the advantage of saving on pipework and components. They are common in marine plumbing systems where open flushing cisterns could spill over in rough weather. Due to the possibility of back-siphonage and wastage of water, some countries restrict their use.

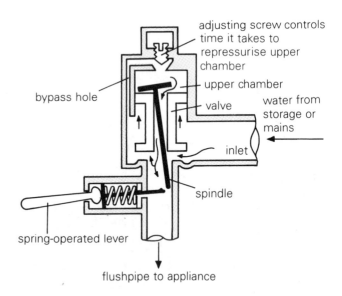

The valve is shown opening after the lever has tilted the spindle and allowed the pressure in the upper chamber to be reduced. The water from the inlet side will force the valve up off the seating to allow a full flush which is governed by the time it takes the pressure to build up in the upper chamber again, through the bypass.

*Figure 10.16*  Flushing valve

They consist of a hand-operated valve which controls water from a remote storage cistern into the appliance via a flush pipe.

### How a flushing valve works

A spring lever or handle is operated which tilts a spindle that allows water from a chamber to pass through a valve held in place by water pressure in the upper chamber of the valve. This allows water to pass down the flush pipe, which reduces the pressure in the upper chamber and increases the pressure under the valve, causing it to open fully and allow a full-bore flush. As the water flushes, it also passes through a small hole into the upper chamber, which eventually fills with water and equalises the pressure above and below the valve, allowing it to fall back on to its seating and stopping the flush. The length of time it takes water to refill the upper chamber through the small by-pass hole is governed by a small adjustment screw.

Sometimes simple spring return valves similar to the taps that are often used in public places to prevent wastage of water are used as an alternative to flushing valves. They are found more in urinal installations as an alternative to an automatic flushing cistern and are fed directly off the main. As with the flushing valve described above, some countries either restrict or do not allow their use.

## Waste appliances

### Ablution fountains and drinking fountains

Ablution or wash fountains are normally only installed in factories and mines where heavy peak-time washing of hands is needed and a range of wash basins would not be sufficient. Made of glazed fireclay or stainless steel, they are usually manufactured as large circular bowls with a central pillar through which several nozzles issue sprays of water into the bowl (Figure 10.17). They are fixed away from walls so that all round use is possible and the spray may be hand or foot controlled.

Drinking fountains are found in many public buildings, schools and factories and as the name suggests they are used to supply drinking water in a spray form to be drunk by the user without the mouth coming into contact with the nozzle outlet. For this reason the jet is shielded. They can be wall mounted or free-standing on a pedestal. They are available in glazed fireclay or stainless steel and are similar to a very small wash basin. The water is controlled by a self-closing tap to prevent wastage of water and the waste fitting is 28 mm minimum diameter (Figure 10.18).

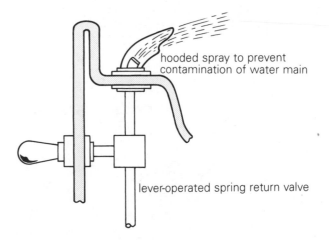

*Figure 10.18* Drinking fountain

### Lavatory or wash basin

These are used for hand and face washing (Figure 10.19). Domestic basins are usually fixed in a bathroom with other sanitary appliances or in a bedroom. In public places such as toilets, several basins may be fitted in ranges. They are available in various sizes but the commonest are between 600 and 685 mm wide and between 400 and 560 mm deep to

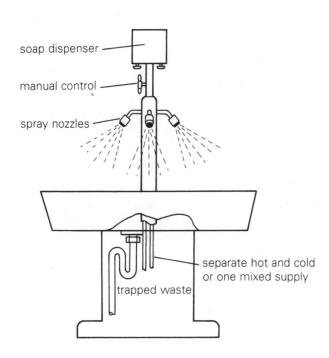

*Figure 10.17* Ablution fountain

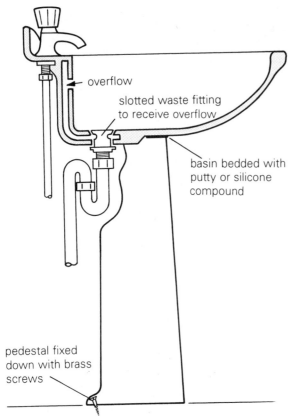

overflow

slotted waste fitting
to receive overflow

basin bedded with
putty or silicone
compound

pedestal fixed
down with brass
screws

1.    Basin fixed on pedestal showing piping and fixing
      arrangements

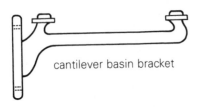

cantilever basin bracket

one-hole basin mixer with pop-up waste

pop-up waste lever

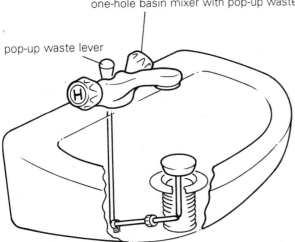

2.    Basin cut away showing pop-up waste lever action

*Figure 10.19*  Wash basin

the back, with a bowl approximately 240 mm deep.
Domestic basins are usually made of vitreous china and
supported on pedestals of the same material. Basins in
public places need to be more robust with glazed fireclay
or stainless steel more common. Public wash basins are
normally supported on iron cantilever brackets but may
have additional supporting legs fixed to the end of the
brackets. Ranges of washbasins may be built into special
acrylic-covered timber units.

The height from the front edge of the basin to the floor
should be between 760 and 860 mm. The height of pedestal-
mounted basins will be fixed by the pedestal itself. Hot and
cold taps are fitted into holes built into the top of basins
suitable for a 15 mm diameter supply, and a waste fitting is
fitted into a hole in the bottom of the bowl which connects to
an integral overflow. Waste fittings are usually 32 mm diameter,
and made of chrome-coated brass with a slot to line up with the
integral overflow. They may also be the pop-up type with a lever
for operation fixed into a third hole in the top of the basin or
they may have a simple plug and chain stopper. Some mixer
taps are available with a built-in pop-up waste control,
needing only one fixing hole in the middle.

---

**Points to remember**:
- When ordering you must specify whether you need 1,
  2 or 3 holes in the top of the basin.
- All fixing screws for brackets and pedestals should
  be non-ferrous. Basins can be bedded on to brackets
  and pedestals with putty, plaster or mastic sealant.
- P-traps should be used with basins, which may be
  tubular or bottle type. The material will depend on
  the waste pipe itself but polypropylene or polythene
  is usual.
- Holes in the underside of the back of ceramic basins
  allow additional fixing to the wall but care must be
  taken not to overtighten the screws or you could
  crack the basin. You can use leather or lead washers
  to act as a cushion.

---

## Baths

These are used for whole body washing and are usually
rectangular or tub shaped, with sizes ranging from 1.68–1.83
m long, 0.71–0.74 m wide and 0.43–0.45 m deep. They are
available in a range of materials including porcelain
enamelled cast iron or steel, acrylic or glass reinforced
plastics (Figure 10.20). They are supported on adjustable legs.
Legs for cast iron baths should be placed on timber bearers to
spread the load on timber floors. Baths made from other
materials are usually supported in a steel cradle fixed to the
floor (Figure 10.21). Internal safety handles and ribbed bases
are available to prevent slipping.

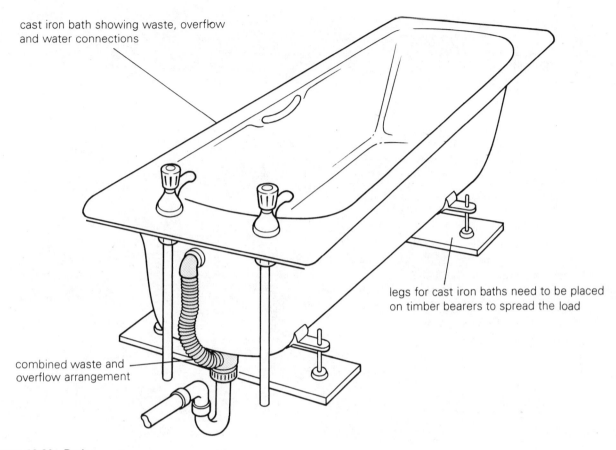

cast iron bath showing waste, overflow and water connections

legs for cast iron baths need to be placed on timber bearers to spread the load

combined waste and overflow arrangement

*Figure 10.20* Bath

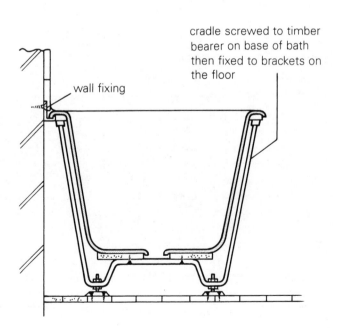

cradle screwed to timber bearer on base of bath then fixed to brackets on the floor

wall fixing

*Figure 10.21* Cradle fixing for acrylic and glass-reinforced plastic baths

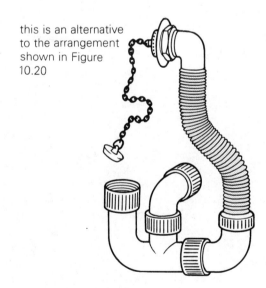

this is an alternative to the arrangement shown in Figure 10.20

*Figure 10.22* Combined bath trap and flexible overflow

Hot and cold taps are fitted into holes in the top of the bath suitable for a 22 mm diameter supply. The taps may be separate or a mixer type with a pop-up waste attachment. Some mixers include a shower pipe attachment. The waste fitting should be 38 mm diameter and may be chromed brass or plastic depending on the material the bath is made of. Baths do not have integral overflows; an overflow fitting fits into the side of the bath which connects to a tubular trap with a flexible pipe. Bath traps are available with shallow seals but deep seals of 75 mm are preferable (Figure 10.22).

Special baths are available for elderly or infirm people; these have an integral seat built in so the user can bathe in the seated position. Some even have sealed side doors for access.

---

**Points to remember:**
- Baths should be adjusted until they are level across both length and width, with the distance from the underside of the edge of the bath to the floor being recommended by the manufacturer or suitable for the height of the bath panel, usually a minimum of 0.48 m; the fall is built into the bath itself.
- Mixer taps for the baths with shower attachments where the water mixes in the fitting should be fed with cold water from a cistern to prevent the possibility of back-siphonage.
- Baths made from plastic materials are subject to more thermal movement than cast iron baths so a good non-setting sealant should be used all around the edges near the wall. Wall fixing brackets can also be used.

---

## Showers

A shower can be installed to discharge into a bath or into a ceramic or plastic shower tray inside a waterproof cubicle (Figure 10.23). Showers are used for whole body washing and are more hygienic than baths because you are not actually immersed in dirty water. They are also more economical because they use less water.

Shower trays are available in ceramics or plastics, with a 38 mm diameter waste pipe which should not be fitted with a plug. Ceramic trays sometimes have integral overflows but trays made from plastics usually do not have an overflow at all (Figure 10.23). Those that do, have a similar waste and overflow arrangement to a bath. Sizes of trays vary from 600–920 mm square, and they are 180 mm deep. Large public shower trays are often built *in situ* out of concrete and are tiled.

The water supply to showers may be either cold water only, directly from the main and heated up in an electrically powered mixer unit, or it may be hot and cold water from a storage system at low pressure, in which both the hot and cold water are fed to a thermostatic mixer at the same pressure. The mixer may also be supplied by both hot and cold water at mains pressure, the hot water being heated in an instantaneous gas heater.

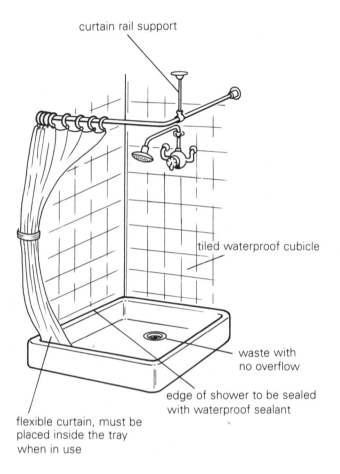

curtain rail support

tiled waterproof cubicle

waste with no overflow

edge of shower to be sealed with waterproof sealant

flexible curtain, must be placed inside the tray when in use

*Figure 10.23*  Typical shower tray arrangement

---

**Points to remember:**
- Due to the very important safety electrical requirements associated with electric showers, only qualified and experienced electricians should connect them up so that they will operate safely.
- When both hot and cold supplies are fed directly off the main and a simple non-thermostatic mixer is used, cold water drawn off at other taps may cut the supply to the shower causing scalding.
- The cold water feed to a shower fed with hot water from storage must also be fed from storage otherwise back-siphonage may occur. If different feed cisterns are used for hot and cold they must be at the same level and must provide a minimum head of 900 mm from the underside of the cistern to the spray head outlet.

The shower fitting itself is made of non-ferrous metal although it may be housed in a plastic cover. It consists of a chamber in which the hot and cold water mix together and is then fed to a spray head at the desired temperature. Thermostatically controlled mixer valves are better because they prevent accidental scalding, but are more expensive than manual mixer valves (Figure 10.24). In a thermostatic mixer, once set, if the temperature of the water rises, a copper or brass device inside the mixer will expand and thus close down the hot water inlet to the mixer, at the same time as opening up the cold water inlet to maintain the set temperature.

The spray heads for showers can be the fixed 'rose' type sprays or adjustable 'umbrella' type which can also be hand held.

## Sinks

These are usually fitted in kitchens and used for general household work, including washing and preparing food, and washing up cutlery and crockery after use. The traditional types are made of ceramics such as glazed fireclay, and range in size from 450–1200 mm long,      380–600 mm wide and 200–300 mm deep (Figure 10.25). The 'Belfast' model is deepest and contains an integral weir type overflow; the 'London' model is shallower with no overflow. A hardwood draining board is usually fitted next to these sinks. Some combination models have an integral drainer. Cast iron legs and brackets are used to support these sinks although because of their weight they are sometimes supported by glazed masonry piers at each end. A finished minimum height of 800 mm to the top edge of the sink is usual. For industrial and commercial uses, larger models are available in different formats.

Materials like stainless steel, enamelled steel and plastics are more popular these days and can be manufactured in a variety of shapes and sizes with 1, 2 or more bowls and drainers possible.

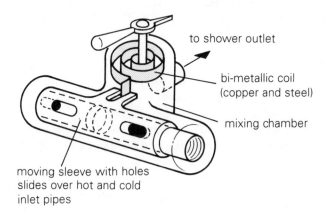

to shower outlet

bi-metallic coil (copper and steel)

mixing chamber

moving sleeve with holes slides over hot and cold inlet pipes

Once the temperature is set, if there are any temperature or pressure changes, the water in the mixing chamber will cause the coil to move the sleeve, either letting in more hot or more cold water to balance the temperature.

*Figure 10.24* Simple thermostatic shower mixing valve

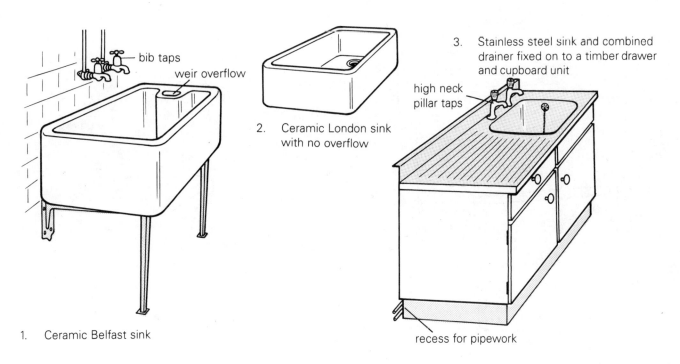

bib taps

weir overflow

1. Ceramic Belfast sink

2. Ceramic London sink with no overflow

3. Stainless steel sink and combined drainer fixed on to a timber drawer and cupboard unit

high neck pillar taps

recess for pipework

*Figure 10.25* Typical sinks

Modern household models are fitted into resin coated working surfaces fixed in with clips underneath and sealed with mastic, or fitted into timber base units that are screwed back to a wall. Industrial and commercial models are usually fitted into stainless steel cradles with open shelves for storage.

Hot and cold water supplies to sinks can be through bib taps fixed at a suitable height above the sink to enable buckets to be filled or by high-necked pillar taps fitted to holes in the top of the unit. Mixer taps can be used on sinks but should only be the dual-flow type that do not mix water in the fitting, thus preventing back-siphonage (see Chapter 4, Figure 4.27).

Waste fittings should be 38 mm diameter and fitted with a 75 mm deep seal P-trap. Special cleaner's sinks or bucket sinks are sometimes fitted in large buildings; these are similar to the Belfast model but are fitted at a low level and with a hardwood insert on the front edge to support a hinged brass grate. Bib taps are fitted at a suitable height above the sink (Figure 10.26).

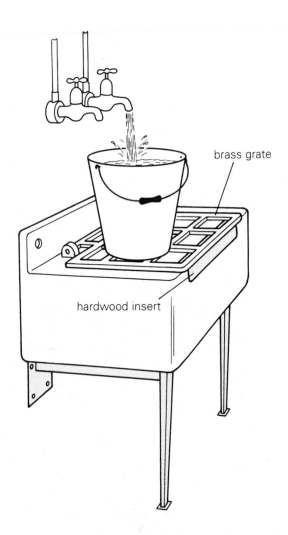

*Figure 10.26*  Cleaner's bucket sink

## Bidets

Bidets are similar in appearance to small WCs but should not be confused because they are a waste appliance used for washing the excretory organs not for soil purposes. They are more common in some countries than others, and are found particularly in the home or in hotel bedrooms (Figure 10.27).

This low-level appliance may have water supply and waste arrangements the same as wash basins or it may have separate hot and cold controls and a diverter valve, which can supply water around the rim to heat it and fill the bowl or divert it to an ascending spray. Because the spray is submersible, back-siphonage and contamination are possible so hot and cold supplies should be from storage or arranged in a manner that will not allow back-siphonage. Pop-up waste fittings are usual with this arrangement (Figure 10.28).

The water supplies to bidets are usually 15 mm diameter, with waste fittings 32 mm diameter connecting to a 75 mm deep seal trap.

Some countries allow WC pans to be used as a bidet for washing purposes and have a 8–12 mm diameter copper cold water supply pipe passing under the seat and looped to provide a seal, positioned to form an ascending spray in the pan. The pipe is branched into the cold water supply to the

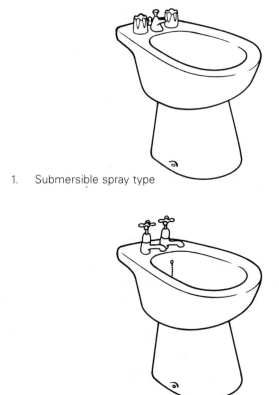

1.   Submersible spray type

2.   Over the rim 'traditional' type

*Figure 10.27*  Bidet details

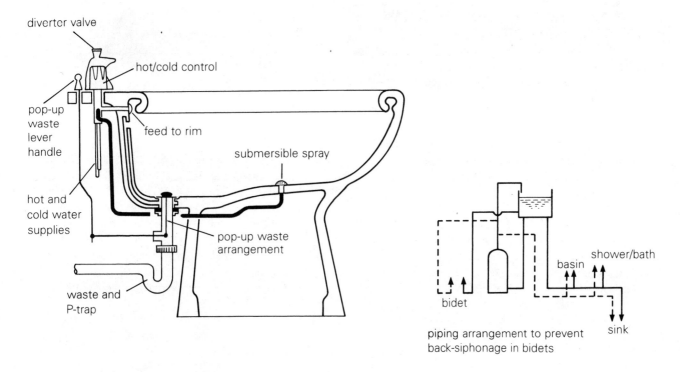

**Figure 10.28**  Submersible spray, pop-up waste and piping arrangements

WC flushing cistern and controlled with a stop tap. This type of installation should only be considered if the cold water supply to the sanitary fittings is from storage and even then some form of additional protection against back-siphonage, such as a non-return valve, should be fitted because of the possibility of contamination (Figure 10.29).

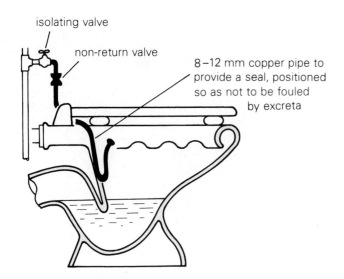

**Figure 10.29**  Special arrangements for ascending spray in WCs

## CHECK YOUR UNDERSTANDING

● Sanitary appliances are categorised as either soil appliances or waste appliances.

● Soil appliances receive and dispose of human excreta and include urinals, water closets, bed-pan washers and slop sinks.

● Waste appliances are used for general washing purposes and include baths, washbasins, bidets, sinks and showers.

● All sanitary appliances should have a trap to prevent foul smells from the drains entering the building.

● Sanitary appliances should be made from materials impervious to water and be designed so as to be smooth, easy to clean and with a self-cleansing action.

● Ranges of urinals should be regularly flushed by either an automatic flushing cistern fed with water through a regulated control valve or by a flushing valve.

● All water closets should be flushed with water from a flushing cistern fitted at either high or low level or close-coupled to the closet or pan.

● The overflow to a flushing cistern should always be positioned below the inlet level of the ball-valve to prevent back-siphonage.

● The taps on washbasins, sinks and baths should always discharge above the flood-level of the appliance to prevent back-siphonage.

● Cold water supplies to mixer taps on baths, showers and bidets should always be fed from storage to prevent back-siphonage.

## REVISION EXERCISES AND QUESTIONS

Answer questions 1 to 5 by selecting one of the four options given.

1   Which of the following is a soil appliance?
    i)    bidet
    ii)   bath
    iii)  basin
    iv)   slop sink

2   Which of the following is a waste appliance?
    i)    WC
    ii)   urinal
    iii)  bidet
    iv)   slop sink

3   Materials used for the manufacture of sanitary appliances should be:
    i)    absorbent
    ii)   impervious
    iii)  rough
    iv)   permeable

4   Siphonic action in a flushing cistern is assisted by:
    i)    surface tension
    ii)   capillarity
    iii)  atmospheric pressure
    iv)   friction

5   The hot and cold water flowing through a dual-flow mixer tap mixes:
    i)    as it leaves the spout
    ii)   in the feed cistern
    iii)  inside the tap body
    iv)   in the feed pipes

6   Describe *two* possible results if a ball-valve fails to shut off the water to a flushing cistern with a blocked overflow pipe and a sealed cover.

7   Draw a section through a plunger action siphon in a flushing cistern and describe in simple terms how it works.

8   List *three* materials from which domestic sinks can be made.

9   Why is it necessary to fix acrylic/glass-fibre baths inside a supporting cradle?

10  Describe with the aid of a sketch how a bidet with a submersible spray should be connected to the water supply, and explain why.

# Above ground drainage

## Introduction

**Sanitary pipework** is the system of pipework which conveys soil and waste matter from the sanitary appliances to the drainage system. It includes **soil pipes** and **waste pipes**, either separate or combined, and also ventilation or **vent pipes** which may be separate to the main soil and waste pipes or part of them. The main vertical pipes are also known as **stacks**. There are a number of different systems that can be used; the type chosen will depend on local bye-laws and regulations and the type of drainage system in use in the area. There are basically three different systems: the one-pipe system; the two-pipe system; and the single stack system. Regardless of the actual system, there are certain basic principles that are common to all sanitary pipework.

### General principles
- All soil and waste pipework should be big enough to take the discharge from all appliances connected to it and should in no case be less than the diameter of any appliance outlet or branch pipe connecting to it.
- The material for sanitary pipework should be strong and durable and securely fixed to the building structure, while at the same time allowing for thermal movement.
- All sanitary pipework should be fixed in an accessible position for maintenance.
- The internal surface of all pipes and fittings should be smooth and self-cleansing during use.
- Foul gases from the drainage system must be prevented from entering the building through the appliance; this is achieved by fitting a trap with a water seal to the appliance unless it has an integral trap.
- Ranges of waste appliances can discharge into a common waste pipe, with the waste pipe itself trapped (instead of the appliances) before it enters the main discharge stack.

Suitable materials for sanitary pipework
**Main stacks**: cast iron, galvanised steel and UPVC.
**Branch waste and vent pipes**: ABS plastic, copper, galvanised steel, lead, polypropylene.

## Traps and loss of trap seal

A trap is a U-tube containing water that is either integral, forming part of the outlet of an appliance such as a WC, or separate and fitted to the outlet of a sanitary appliance (Figure 11.1). The water seal must remain in the trap both during and after use to prevent foul smells from the drains entering the room where the appliance is fixed. The depth of water seal depends on the type of discharge system, but between 38 and 75 mm is usual with a 75 mm deep seal being preferable. As far as possible traps should have a self-cleansing action and should be smooth inside.

Traps come in all shapes and sizes including **P**, **S** and **Q traps**, named after the angle of their outlets, and **bottle**, **bag** and **running traps**, named after their appearance. They are made from a variety of materials including brass, chrome, copper, lead and more commonly these days polythene or polypropylene. Most are designed to fit directly to the waste outlet of the appliance and have a large threaded connecting nut to screw on to the waste fitting (Figure 11.2).

In some circumstances, ranges of certain appliances do not need to be individually trapped but can drain directly into an open channel which must be trapped, or into a common branch pipe which must be trapped before connecting into the main discharge stack (Figure 11.3).

The outlet of the trap is designed to connect directly to the waste pipe; in the case of plastics this is usually done with a push-fit O-ring or compression nut and ring. All traps should have a cleaning eye or some other means of access for cleaning.

Take care not to overtighten nuts made from plastic because the threads may cross and damage. Hand-tight plus a quarter turn with a wrench should be enough.

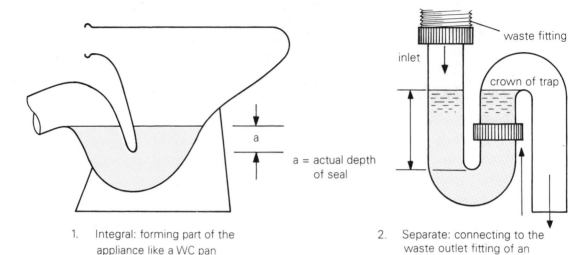

1.  Integral: forming part of the appliance like a WC pan

2.  Separate: connecting to the waste outlet fitting of an appliance like a sink ('S' trap shown)

*Figure 11.1*  Integral and separate traps

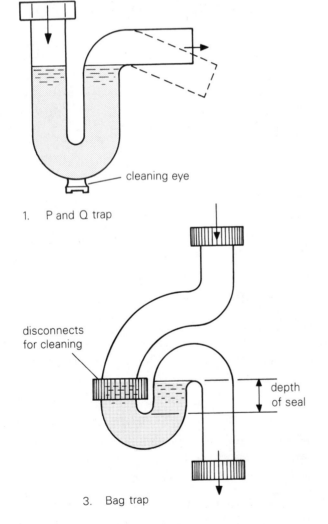

1.  P and Q trap

3.  Bag trap

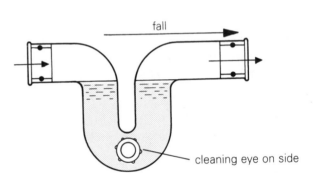

2.  Running trap with push-fit connections (usually fitted away from appliance)

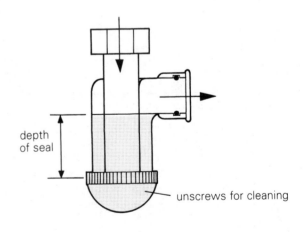

4.  Bottle trap with dip-tube

*Figure 11.2*  Selection of different types of traps

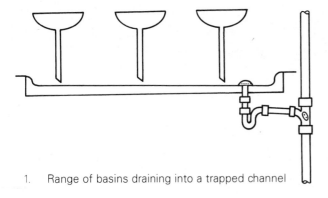

1.   Range of basins draining into a trapped channel

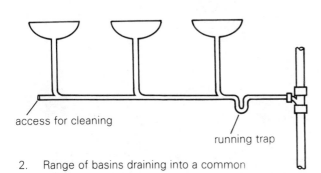

access for cleaning

running trap

2.   Range of basins draining into a common
     trapped branch pipe

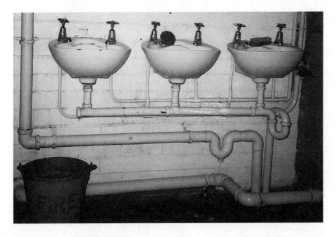

*Figure 11.3* Alternative trapping arrangements for
ranges of appliances

In some circumstances, it is possible for the trap seal to be
lost; the good design of soil and waste discharge systems or
sanitary pipework should help to reduce this possibility but
you must first of all have a basic understanding of the
various methods of trap seal loss (Figure 11.4).

The water seal in traps can be lost by:

**Capillarity**   This is where fibrous material such as strands of
hair, cotton or rags are lodged over the crown and outlet of
the trap and soak up water from the seal. This happens mostly
with S-traps and often in hairdressers salons.

**Compression**   If the pressure builds up inside the waste pipe
it will cause the seal to 'blow-out' into the appliance. This can
happen to traps fitted to appliances connected near the
bottom of vertical discharge stacks in buildings with
appliances on several floors, all discharging into the same
stack and creating a build up of pressure at the bottom of the
stack.

**Evaporation**   This is where the water in the trap evaporates
because the appliance or building is not in use for long
periods.

**Leakage or mechanical damage**   Traps connected to
appliances that are heavily used, such as those in schools,
factories and hotels, sometimes get knocked and bumped
causing them to work loose or break, resulting in loss of water.

**Momentum**   This is usually caused by the quick discharge of
water through the trap, causing the water seal to 'follow' the
discharged water. You can see this easily if you empty a bucket
full of water down a WC pan – the seal will usually drop.

**Siphonage**   This is caused by a reduction in pressure inside
the main discharge stack causing the greater pressure of the
atmosphere in the room acting on the seal on the inlet side
of the trap to force the seal through to the outlet side. This
can be induced siphonage where water flowing down a main
stack draws air out of a connecting waste pipe creating a drop
in pressure, or it can be self-siphonage where water
discharging through the appliance causes full-bore flow in
the waste pipe, reducing the pressure on the outlet side of
the trap itself and causing the seal to be drawn out with the
main flow. This is similar to the loss of seal caused by
momentum.

**Wavering out**   In windy conditions, changing air pressure
inside the main stack can create wave motion in the trap
water seal causing some of the water to be lost over the
crown of the trap. Apart from mechanical damage, the main
cause of loss of trap seal is due to siphonage and the effects of
differences in pressure on either side of the seal. The most
effective way of keeping the pressures equal on both sides of
the seal is to provide anti-siphonage pipes or branch
ventilation pipes which are connected to a main ventilation
stack (Figure 11.5).

Anti-siphon pipes should connect to the top of the waste
pipe within 300 mm of the crown of the trap but not nearer
than 75 mm to the crown. They should also connect in the
direction of the flow so that water does not actually flow
into them. The diameter of the pipe is usually not less than
two-thirds the diameter of the waste pipe and never less
than 32 mm. If there are a number of appliances grouped
together they can be **loop vented** together before
connecting to the main ventilation stack (Figure 11.6). Once
above the highest appliances, the ventilation stack can
connect into the main discharge stack, which at that point
will have no discharge and will be acting as a vent pipe itself.

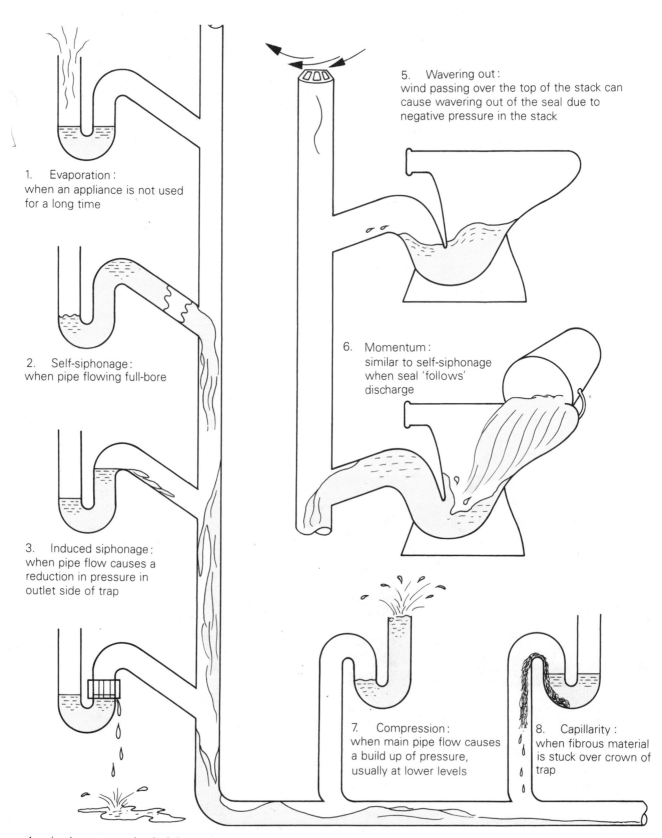

1.   Evaporation :
when an appliance is not used
for a long time

2.   Self-siphonage :
when pipe flowing full-bore

3.   Induced siphonage :
when pipe flow causes a
reduction in pressure in
outlet side of trap

4.   Leakage or mechanical damage

5.   Wavering out :
wind passing over the top of the stack can
cause wavering out of the seal due to
negative pressure in the stack

6.   Momentum :
similar to self-siphonage
when seal 'follows'
discharge

7.   Compression :
when main pipe flow causes
a build up of pressure,
usually at lower levels

8.   Capillarity :
when fibrous material
is stuck over crown of
trap

*Figure 11.4*  Unsealing of traps

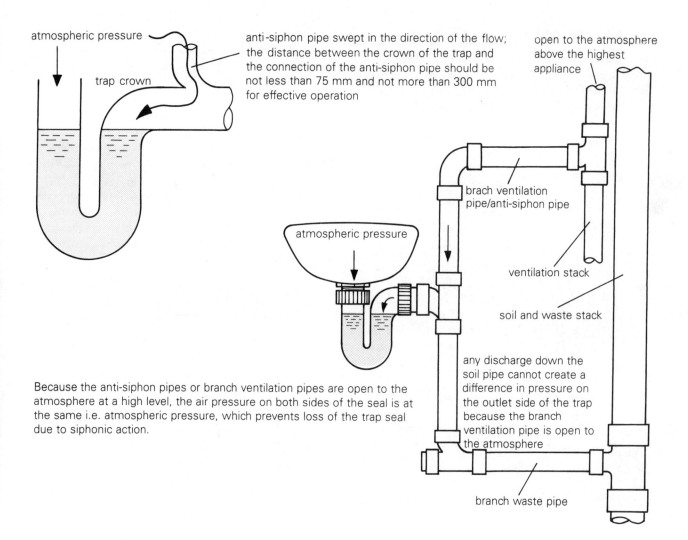

atmospheric pressure

trap crown

anti-siphon pipe swept in the direction of the flow; the distance between the crown of the trap and the connection of the anti-siphon pipe should be not less than 75 mm and not more than 300 mm for effective operation

open to the atmosphere above the highest appliance

atmospheric pressure

brach ventilation pipe/anti-siphon pipe

ventilation stack

soil and waste stack

Because the anti-siphon pipes or branch ventilation pipes are open to the atmosphere at a high level, the air pressure on both sides of the seal is at the same i.e. atmospheric pressure, which prevents loss of the trap seal due to siphonic action.

any discharge down the soil pipe cannot create a difference in pressure on the outlet side of the trap because the branch ventilation pipe is open to the atmosphere

branch waste pipe

*Figure 11.5* Anti-siphon pipe

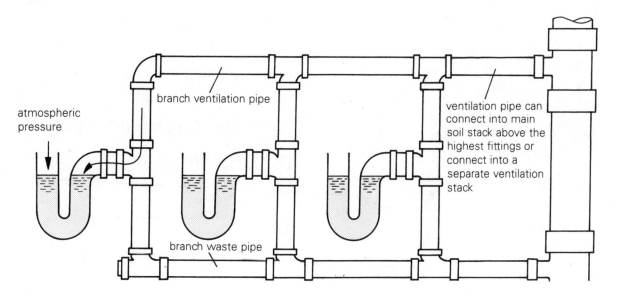

branch ventilation pipe

atmospheric pressure

ventilation pipe can connect into main soil stack above the highest fittings or connect into a separate ventilation stack

branch waste pipe

*Figure 11.6* Ventilation details for ranges of appliances

## Anti-siphonage and resealing traps

The installation of ventilation pipework can be time-consuming and costly. One cheaper and proven alternative is to install either anti-siphonage or anti-vac traps or resealing traps, which automatically reseal if the water starts to siphon out. The first resealing traps to be successfully developed were the McAlpine and Grevack traps (Figure 11.7). The McAlpine contains a resealing chamber, which is a wider section of the

outlet side of the U-tube. As the water level drops below the lower seal level, air is allowed up into the resealing chamber to equalise the pressure. The water flowing around the walls of the chamber falls back down to reseal the trap. The Grevack trap has an in-built anti-siphon tube which goes from near the crown of the trap to just above the lower seal level of the inlet side of the U-tube. As the water level drops to this lower level it allows air to pass through the tube to equalise the pressure on the outlet side. Water at this 'reserve' position falls back to reseal the trap.

More modern anti-vac traps are designed to prevent siphonic action before it happens by balancing the differences in pressure as soon as they are set up. These traps have an air bypass built into the dip pipe or have an air valve fixed near the outlet of the trap (Figure 11.8).

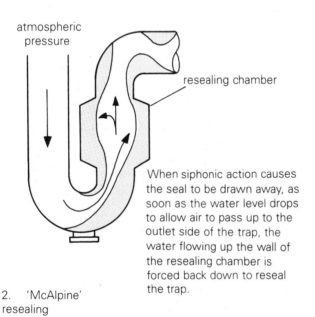

1.  'Grevak' resealing trap

When siphonic action causes the seal to be drawn away, as soon as the water level on the inlet side drops to reveal the anti-siphon tube, air enters the tube and balances the pressure on the outlet side to stop siphonage; the water in the reserve chamber then just flows back down the trap to reseal it.

When siphonic action causes the seal to be drawn away, as soon as the water level drops to allow air to pass up to the outlet side of the trap, the water flowing up the wall of the resealing chamber is forced back down to reseal the trap.

2.  'McAlpine' resealing

*Figure 11.7*  Resealing of trap details

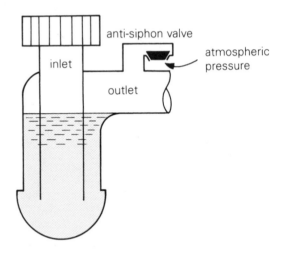

If the pressure drops on the outlet side of the trap, creating a partial vacuum and therefore setting up the conditions for siphonage of the seal, the greater pressure of the atmosphere will be able to lift the valve off its seating and pass through to balance the pressures once more.

*Figure 11.8*  Modern anti-siphon trap

## Sanitary pipework systems

### The one-pipe system

This is where all soil and waste appliances discharge into one main soil and waste pipe or stack through branch soil and waste pipes. Where two or more waste appliances are grouped together they can connect to one common branch pipe before connecting to the main stack. The main soil and waste pipe above the highest appliances connected to it acts as a ventilating or vent pipe and terminates at a 'safe outlet', away and above window openings, with the open pipe covered with a wire cage or balloon sometimes called a **birdcage**, which prevents birds, leaves etc. blocking up the vent (Figure 11.9).

All appliances must be separately vented with the vent stack either connecting to the soil and waste stack at a high level, above the highest connection, or terminating separately in a similar position to the soil and waste vent pipe (Figure 11.10).

So, although this system is called the one-pipe system, there are in fact two stacks, a soil and waste stack and a vent stack.

Appliances on ground floors can connect directly to the drains, and waste appliances can connect through a trapped back-inlet gully (Figure 11.11).

Soil pipes should be 75 mm minimum diameter if no appliance has a larger outlet, but 100 mm is more usual because of the 100 mm diameter outlet of washdown WCs. This size may need to be bigger depending on the size of building and the number of appliances. The soil and waste stack connects directly to the drainage system through a wide radius rest-bend, helping to prevent blockages and

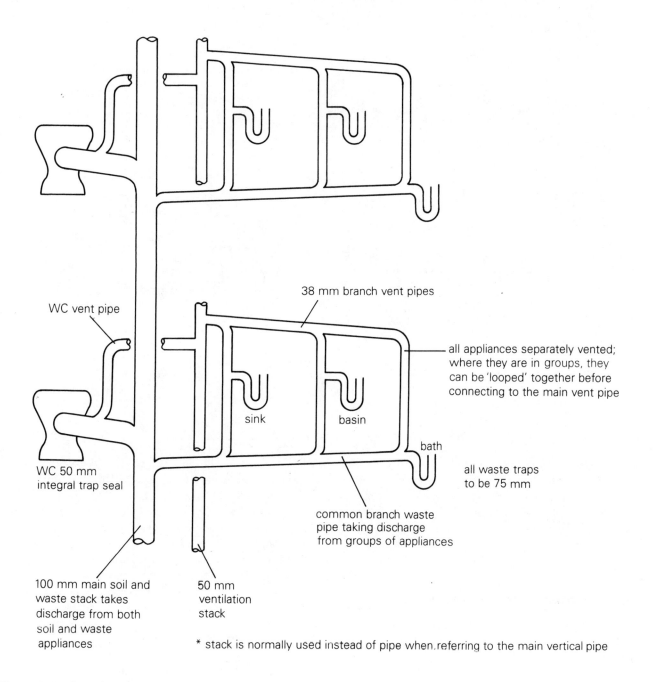

38 mm branch vent pipes

WC vent pipe

all appliances separately vented; where they are in groups, they can be 'looped' together before connecting to the main vent pipe

sink          basin

bath

WC 50 mm integral trap seal

all waste traps to be 75 mm

common branch waste pipe taking discharge from groups of appliances

100 mm main soil and waste stack takes discharge from both soil and waste appliances

50 mm ventilation stack

* stack is normally used instead of pipe when referring to the main vertical pipe

Figure 11.9   One-pipe above-ground drainage system

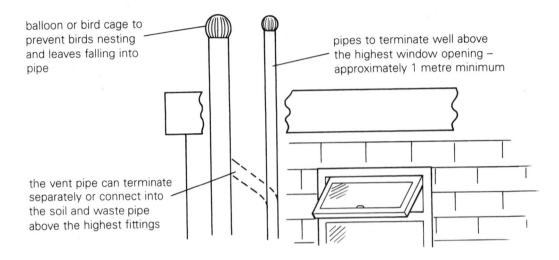

*Figure 11.10*  Soil, waste and ventilation pipe termination

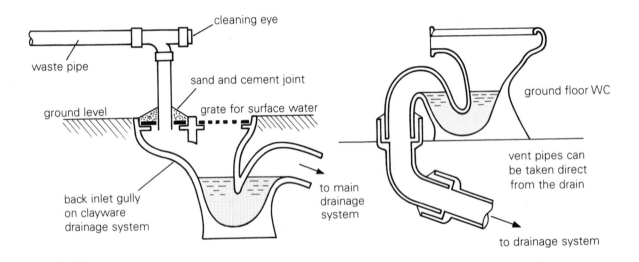

*Figure 11.11*  Ground-floor appliances connecting direct to the drains

reduces turbulent flow, which can cause increased air pressure at the base of the stack. Vent pipes are normally 38 mm diameter connecting into a 50 mm vent stack. Branch waste pipes are 38 mm minimum, rising to 50 mm, depending on the number of appliances. All waste traps should have a 75 mm deep seal, except appliances like WCs which have an integral 50 mm seal.

## The two-pipe system or dual system

In this system, all soil appliances discharge into a soil stack and all waste appliances discharge into a separate waste stack. It is often used where a separate system of drainage is in operation. Most of the other details are the same as for the one-pipe system except the waste stack must connect to the

drain through a back inlet trapped gully. The waste trap seals can be smaller in this system, usually 38 mm (Figure 11.12).

For housing with no more than one upper floor, vent pipes will be unnecessary if the waste appliances discharge into an open hopper. With only one WC connected to the soil stack, the upper vent part of the stack means that a separate appliance vent will be unnecessary (Figure 11.13).

Although an open hopper acts as a vent, the position of it may cause foul smells from the waste stack to escape from the hopper. In larger systems in flats etc., soil appliances must be vented through a soil vent and waste appliances through a waste vent pipe. So again, the name two-pipe system does not always accurately describe the system because there are usually four stacks – soil, waste and two vent stacks (Figure 11.12).

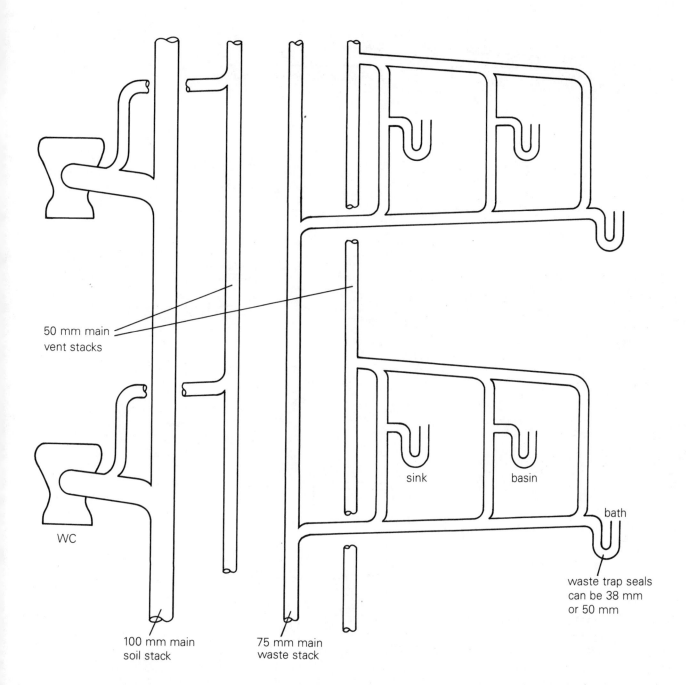

50 mm main
vent stacks

sink                    basin

bath

WC

waste trap seals
can be 38 mm
or 50 mm

100 mm main
soil stack

75 mm main
waste stack

*Figure 11.12*  Two-pipe or dual system of above-ground drainage

Both one and two-pipe systems have their relative advantages and disadvantages.

**One-pipe system**

**Advantages**    For larger systems there is less pipework so it is less unsightly if fixed externally and there is less maintenance and painting etc.

**Disadvantages**    For low-rise housing it is more costly and takes longer to install because of additional vent pipework. Unless large ducting is available it must be fixed externally.

Both soil and waste appliances need to be grouped near the main stacks. If there is a blockage, both soil and waste appliances are out of use.

**Two-pipe system**

**Advantages**    For low-rise housing there is less pipework therefore shorter installation time. Soil and waste appliances can be grouped separately if required. If one stack becomes blocked, the other may still be usable.

**Disadvantages**    In large installations, it is more costly due

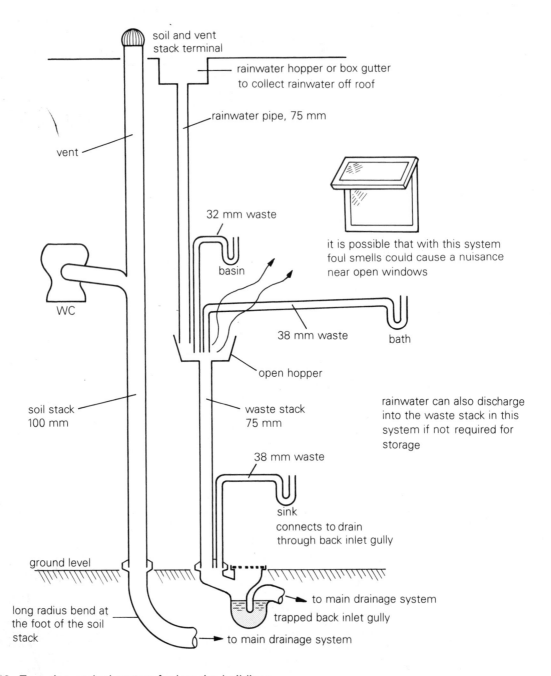

soil and vent
stack terminal

rainwater hopper or box gutter
to collect rainwater off roof

rainwater pipe, 75 mm

vent

32 mm waste

it is possible that with this system
foul smells could cause a nuisance
near open windows

basin

38 mm waste          bath

WC

open hopper

soil stack          waste stack
100 mm             75 mm

rainwater can also discharge
into the waste stack in this
system if not required for
storage

38 mm waste

sink
connects to drain
through back inlet gully

ground level

long radius bend at
the foot of the soil
stack

to main drainage system
trapped back inlet gully

to main drainage system

*Figure 11.13* Two-pipe or dual system for low-rise buildings

to additional pipework, longer installation time, more maintenance and painting etc. Large ducts are needed if fixed internally, and are unsightly if fixed externally.

For most low-rise buildings it has been generally accepted that appliance venting is often not needed if the main stacks act as vents at a high level. Very strict design guidelines using the one-pipe approach can also ensure that vent pipes are not needed on larger installations. This single-stack system is also ideal for low-rise and low-cost buildings because of the lower installation costs.

## The single-stack system

This system is accurately named; there is only one single stack that takes the discharge from both soil and waste appliances with no appliance vent pipes other than the main stack.

Using typical arrangements for a large house as an example (Figure 11.14), the main design requirements are:

1. The upper part of the stack acts as the main vent. This must terminate above and beyond the highest window opening and be capped with a suitable cage.

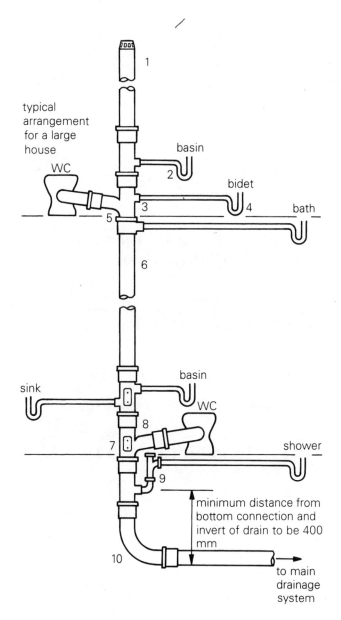

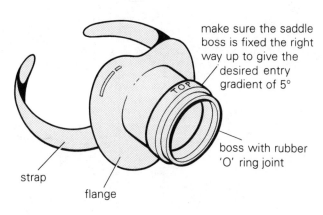

make sure the saddle boss is fixed the right way up to give the desired entry gradient of 5°

boss with rubber 'O' ring joint

strap

flange

after marking out and cutting the hole in the surface of the pipe, the straps and flange should be coated in solvent cement on the meeting surfaces then held in position

*Figure 11.15*  Solvent-welded saddle boss for PVC pipe

typical arrangement for a large house

WC

basin

bidet

bath

sink

basin

WC

shower

minimum distance from bottom connection and invert of drain to be 400 mm

to main drainage system

*Figure 11.14*  Single stack system of above-ground drainage

2. All appliances must connect to the stack separately, with maximum branches of:
- bath/sink/shower 2.3 m;
- basin/bidet 1.7 mm;
- WC 1.5 m.

3. All waste pipe connections/bosses to the stack should be set at 90° with a maximum fall in waste branch pipes of 5°. This greatly reduces the possibility of induced siphonage. Strap-on solvent-welded saddle bosses are convenient and easy to use for PVC stacks (Figure 11.15).

4. All traps to waste appliances should be 75 mm deep seal P-type. This greatly reduces the possibility of self-siphonage.

5. WC connections to the stack should be 'swept entry' to reduce turbulent flow down the stack and the possibility of induced siphonage on lower waste traps.

6. There should be no offsets in the main stack. This could create turbulence and cause air compression in the stack. They can be used in the non-wetted vent part of the stack above the highest connection.

7. No waste connections should be made to the stack between the centre line of a WC connection and 200 mm below it. This is to prevent back flow from the WC up the waste branch connection, usually a bath or shower. Special multi-branch fittings are available for most pipework materials with all main connecting bosses already made to the right dimensions and angles which just need fixing on the stack in the appropriate position. These are particularly useful for larger installations (Figure 11.16).

8. Access covers should be provided at or near all multi-branch connections.

9. There must be a minimum distance between the lowest connection to the stack and the invert level of the drain to reduce loss of seal due to compression. For two-storey buildings this is 460 mm and for buildings above this it is 760 mm. If this cannot be done, the appliance could connect directly to the drain through a back-inlet trapped gully.

10. The foot of the stack should connect to the drain through a long radius rest bend of 150° minimum to prevent turbulence and compression.

The recommended diameter of the main stack is 76 mm for up to two storeys, providing the WC outlets are not above that, 100 mm for up to five storeys with no more than two

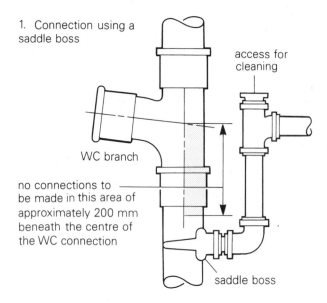

1. Connection using a
saddle boss

access for
cleaning

WC branch

no connections to
be made in this area of
approximately 200 mm
beneath the centre of
the WC connection

saddle boss

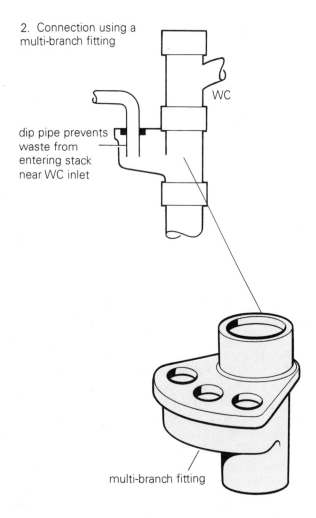

2. Connection using a
multi-branch fitting

WC

dip pipe prevents
waste from
entering stack
near WC inlet

multi-branch fitting

*Figure 11.16*  Waste connections near WC

groups of appliances (WC, bath, basin and sink), 125 mm for up to ten storeys with two groups of appliances and 150 mm for anything above this.

In certain circumstances where branch pipes exceed the recommended lengths significantly or in buildings with over twenty storeys where stack pressure fluctuations are likely, additional vent pipes usually from the WC may be necessary. Such systems are known as modified one-pipe systems (Figure 11.17). Modified one-pipe systems are usually cross-vented from the main discharge stack to a vent stack on each floor or on alternate floors.

# Washing machines and dishwashers

These labour saving waste appliances which are gaining popularity with domestic users around the world should connect into main stacks in the same way as other waste appliances. The only difference is that the trap should be positioned at a low level, with an upstand pipe into which the machine waste hose simply hooks. It is also possible to connect waste hoses directly into special sink traps where a combined waste pipe would be convenient (Figure 11.18).

# Testing sanitary pipework systems

As with all pipework systems it is always advisable to test the installation before use. Sanitary pipework systems should not only be watertight but they should also prevent foul gas escaping into the building.

The best way of testing for both water and airtightness is to carry out an air test.

### How to carry out an air test

1.  Seal the stack at both top and bottom by using drain plugs. Water poured on top of the upper plug and through an appliance to rest against the lower plug will enable you to check that the stack is securely sealed (Figure 11.19).
2.  Fill all the traps with water.
3.  Using a manometer/pressure gauge with a connecting hose and hand pump, pass the hose through a convenient trap, a WC trap is usually best, and using the hand pump, pump until 38 mm pressure head shows on the gauge.
4.  You will be able to see clearly the difference in the two legs of water in the U-tube. This difference of 38 mm head of pressure should remain for at least *3 minutes* by which time the system can be considered sound.
5.  Allow a few minutes after pressurising the stack for stabilisation of pressure and some absorption in the

joints, then adjust the pressure back up to 38 mm. If the stack cannot maintain the pressure, check all joints and connections for obvious faults, then try again. You may have to carry out a water test or smoke test to pinpoint the actual place the air is escaping (see the chapter on drainage for water and smoke test procedures).

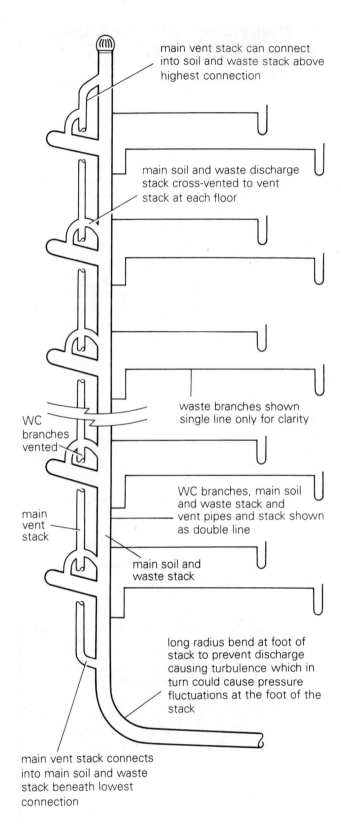

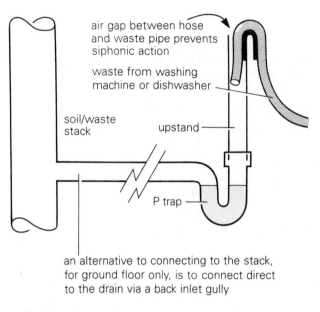

an alternative to connecting to the stack, for ground floor only, is to connect direct to the drain via a back inlet gully

1. Traditional way of connecting to the soil and waste pipe

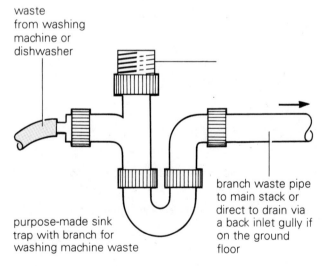

2. Alternative and easier way of connecting to soil and waste pipe

*Figure 11.17* Modified one-pipe system of above-ground drainage

*Figure 11.18* Washing machine and dishwasher connections to soil and waste systems

---

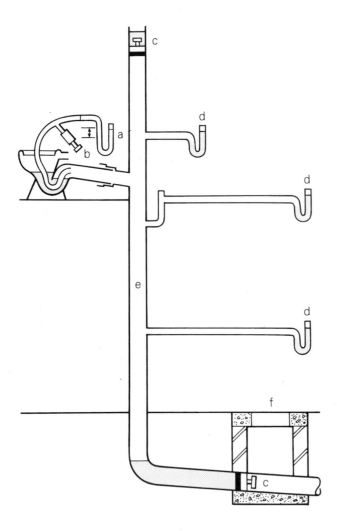

a U gauge/manometer

b pump

↕ 38 mm head of water to remain stationary for 3 minutes

c drain plugs or stoppers at top and bottom of stack to seal it

d all traps to be sealed with water

e compressed air in stack when pumped from WC

f manhole or other access to bottom of main stack

*Figure 11.19* Carrying out an air test on soil and waste pipes

# Rainwater collection and disposal

The method of rainwater collection and disposal chosen will depend mainly on the intensity, duration and frequency of rainfall experienced in the area. This will also influence any local bye-laws relating to the drainage system used.

In areas that experience heavy or tropical rainstorms the system used needs to collect all rainwater run-off from roofs and discharge it without overloading the drainage system. This is usually best achieved by discharging it through a separate system of drainage direct to a stream, river or the sea. An alternative would be to discharge it to a storage cistern where it could be used for crop irrigation or domestic purposes. If it is to be used for drinking water it must be treated.

The easiest way of dealing with rainwater is to have long overhanging eaves which discharge the run-off on to a concrete pavement, which in turn discharges it into a concrete channel running around the building. The channel then drains into a soakaway, which is simply a deep pit filled with stones where the water will slowly soak into the soil and away from the building (Figure 11.20).

Many builders and clients prefer to have a more effective method of rainwater collection and disposal, using gutters and downspouts or downpipes. On pitched roofs, gutters should be fixed around the eaves to collect the run-off and discharge it into a downpipe which would then connect into the drainage system.

Most gutters are either half-round or rectangular in section, in common sizes from 100–150 mm in diameter or cross-sectional length. Downpipes range from 63–75 mm diameter or cross-sectional length. The materials used include light gauge cast iron, cast aluminium alloy, zinc, galvanised steel, asbestos and UPVC.

Advice should be sought from the manufacturer before fixing plastic rainwater goods in situations where they will be subject to constant sunlight and high temperatures. Although most are resistant to light degradation, further protection may be necessary for constant sunlight. Constant high temperatures will also pose installation problems due to thermal movement.

Where plastic rainwater goods are fitted, expansion gaps of approximately 6 mm should be allowed between the end of the gutter and the stop in all gutter and downpipe connecting joints (Figure 11.21).

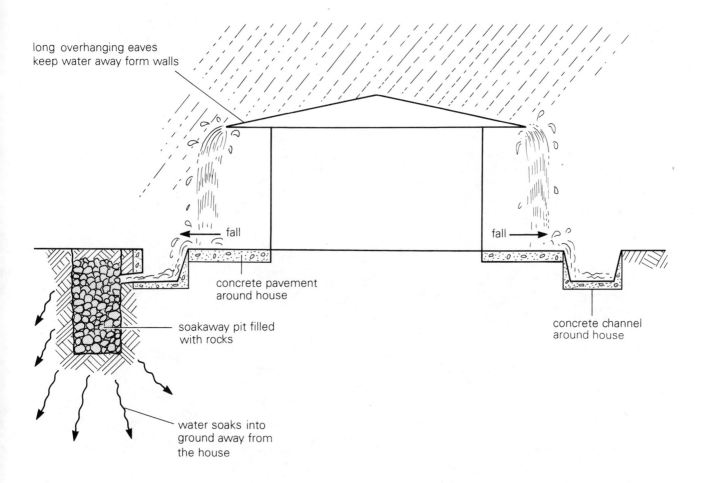

*Figure 11.20*  Simple rainwater disposal into a soakaway

long overhanging eaves keep water away form walls

fall

fall

concrete pavement around house

concrete channel around house

soakaway pit filled with rocks

water soaks into ground away from the house

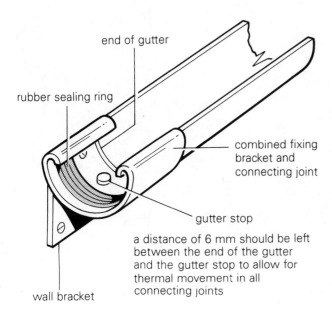

end of gutter

rubber sealing ring

combined fixing bracket and connecting joint

gutter stop

a distance of 6 mm should be left between the end of the gutter and the gutter stop to allow for thermal movement in all connecting joints

wall bracket

*Figure 11.21*  Expansion details on plastic gutters

The fixing methods will depend on the material the gutters and pipes are made from and also the structure of the building. Typical methods are shown in Figure 11.22.

Both gutters and downpipes should be capable of carrying the run-off from roofs during the periods of heaviest normal rainfall experienced in the area. In practice, for most domestic and light industrial building applications a 125 mm diameter half-round gutter discharging into a 75 mm diameter downpipe should be suitable. With the downpipe outlet fixed at one end of the gutter it should be capable of carrying approximately 85 litres per minute from a roof area of 67 m when the gutter is fixed with a minimum fall to the outlet. This will increase if the outlet is positioned in the middle of the gutter or if the gutter is laid to a fall of 1 in 600 or 10 mm in 6 m.

On flat roofs, a slight fall to one end of the roof is usual where a gutter can be fixed to receive the run-off. An alternative usually found on larger buildings is to have a box-gutter built into the structure as part of a concrete roof slab. This would then discharge into either an internal or an external downpipe (Figure 11.23).

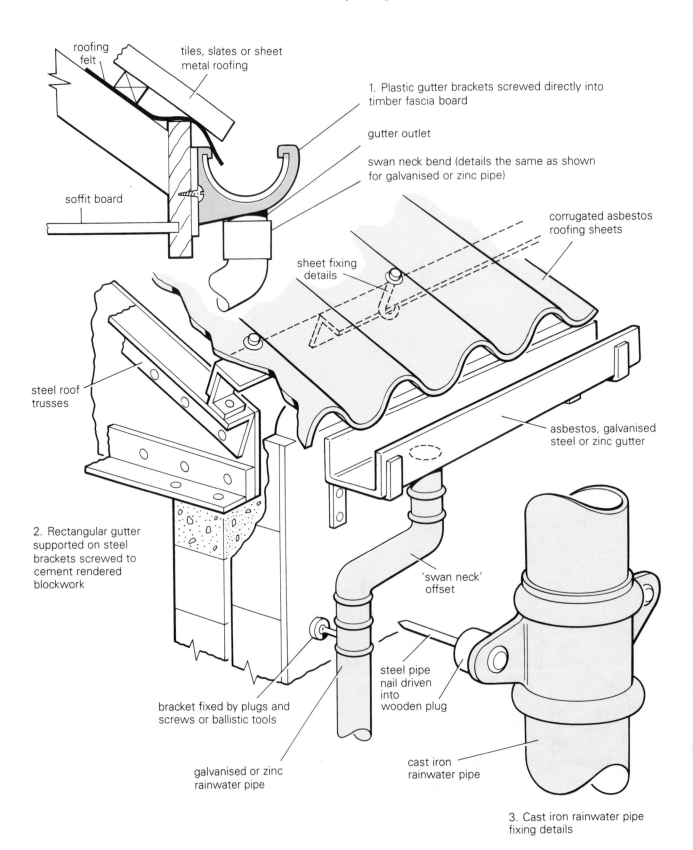

roofing felt

tiles, slates or sheet metal roofing

soffit board

1. Plastic gutter brackets screwed directly into timber fascia board

gutter outlet

swan neck bend (details the same as shown for galvanised or zinc pipe)

corrugated asbestos roofing sheets

sheet fixing details

steel roof trusses

asbestos, galvanised steel or zinc gutter

2. Rectangular gutter supported on steel brackets screwed to cement rendered blockwork

'swan neck' offset

bracket fixed by plugs and screws or ballistic tools

steel pipe nail driven into wooden plug

galvanised or zinc rainwater pipe

cast iron rainwater pipe

3. Cast iron rainwater pipe fixing details

*Figure 11.22* Examples of gutter and rainwater pipe fixings

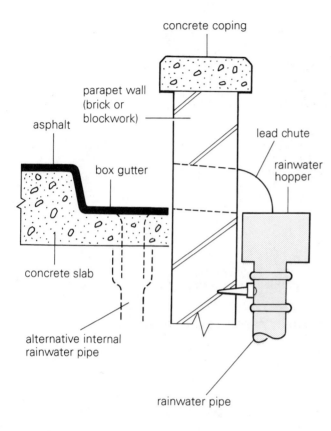

concrete coping

parapet wall
(brick or
blockwork)

asphalt

lead chute

box gutter

rainwater
hopper

concrete slab

alternative internal
rainwater pipe

rainwater pipe

*Figure 11.23*  **Box gutter details at parapet wall**

## ■ CHECK YOUR UNDERSTANDING

● Sanitary pipework or above ground drainage systems should be designed to convey soil and waste matter either together or separately to a drainage system without causing a hazard to health by allowing foul matter or gases to enter the building.

● The internal surface of all sanitary pipework should be smooth, non-corrodible and self-cleansing in operation.

● To help prevent foul gases from sanitary pipework systems entering rooms where sanitary appliances are fixed, appliances should be fitted with a trap containing a water seal.

● The water seal in all traps should remain both during and after use.

● Loss of trap seal due to air pressure fluctuations can be reduced by fixing vent pipes or fitting resealing anti-vac traps.

● All vent pipes should terminate above and away from window openings so that foul gases cannot enter the building.

● Most sanitary pipework systems are based on either the one-pipe system, the two-pipe system or the single-stack system.

● In single-stack systems, all waste appliances should be fitted with 75 mm deep-seal P-traps.

● Offsets in single-stack systems should be avoided and no branch connections made less than 200 mm below the centre line of the WC connection.

● The size of rainwater pipes and gutters will be dependent upon the size of the roof and the average intensity, duration and frequency of rainfall in the area.

Answer questions 1 to 5 by selecting one of the four options given.

1   In the drawing of the trap, which dimension lines show accurately the depth of the seal?
   i)    A
   ii)   B
   iii)  C
   iv)   D

2   Which of the following sanitary appliances would normally have an integral trap?
   i)    WC
   ii)   basin
   iii)  bidet
   iv)   sink

3   A trap that loses its seal as a result of air being drawn from the trap branch pipe is said to have seal loss due to:
   i)    momentum
   ii)   induced siphonage
   iii)  capillarity
   iv)   compression

4   In single-stack pipework, it is usual for all branch pipes to be:
   i)    at a steep angle
   ii)   connected to a vent pipe
   iii)  connected to the stack separately
   iv)   fixed at a lower level than the WC.

5   The simplest way of dealing with rainwater is to channel it into a:
   i)    soakaway
   ii)   box-gutter
   iii)  eaves-gutter
   iv)   combined system

6   Sketch a section through a simple bottle-trap and identify clearly where the dimensions of the trap seal are.

7   List the main advantages and disadvantages of the two-pipe system of sanitary pipework over the one-pipe system.

8   Describe in simple terms, using a sketch to illustrate, how a trap seal may be lost due to compression.

9   Describe the problems associated with using plastic rainwater goods in countries with very hot climates.

10  Sketch a section showing a typical half-round gutter and downpipe at the eaves of a pitched roof.

# Below ground drainage

## Introduction

The below ground drainage system is the set of pipes, drains and sewers that carries waste water from buildings to a collecting point ready for treatment and disposal. Effectively it returns the water that was taken from the water cycle for consumption and use, back into rivers and ultimately to the sea. In modern cities the drainage system is buried underground, but there are still some areas of the world where open drains carry domestic wastes and rainwater in gutters over the pavements.

## Drainage systems

Drainage systems can be classified into three types:

- separate;
- combined;
- partially separate.

### Separate drainage system

In the separate system (Figure 12.1) one pipe carries all the surface water while another pipe carries domestic effluent and industrial waste water. The advantage of this system is that, in theory, no foul sewage should be discharged without treatment. However, with two pipe networks required, the separate system is more expensive to construct.

### Combined drainage system

The combined system uses only a single pipe; this collects surface water as well as domestic and industrial waste water (Figure 12.2). Combined systems are fitted with overflow weirs at strategic points. These allow excessive amounts of storm water to escape into streams or rivers during periods of heavy rainfall. The effect of this is that, from time to time,

pollution will occur when waste water is flushed over the weirs with the storm water.

### Partially separate drainage system

This system is a compromise; it usually has a pipe network to collect surface water in the newer parts of residential suburbs and a combined system for older developed areas. For individual dwellings which are built on suitable ground a partially separate system will use soakaways or natural water courses to dispose of rainwater (Figure 12.3).

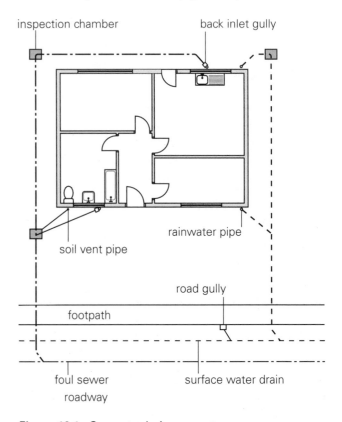

*Figure 12.1* Separate drainage system

226

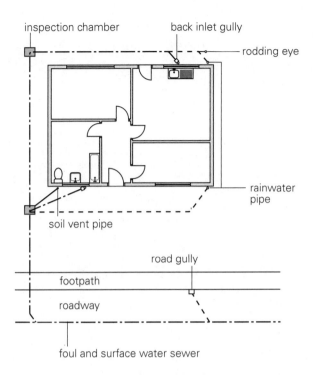

*Figure 12.2* Combined drainage system

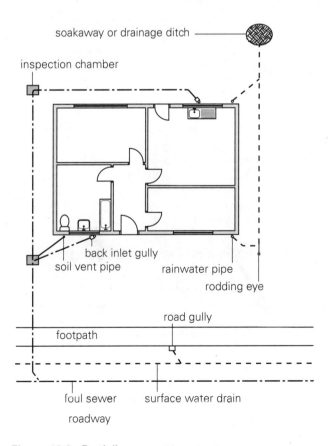

*Figure 12.3* Partially separate system

## Choice of system

For new developments, a number of factors have to be balanced in determining the most appropriate system for a given area. The local geography, the natural and artificial features of the area, its climate and the mixture of building types (domestic or industrial) will determine the best choice. Where a drainage system already exists, the actual type of system can be found by questioning the local authority responsible for drainage. Alternatively, **fluorescent dye** can be added to the water discharging into the drains to trace the pipework outflows.

## Flow through the system

Gravity flow through the drainage system is best, but where this would require the pipes to be buried to great depths **pumping stations** can be used. To prevent deposits of solids from eventually blocking the system, pipes should be laid to give the water flow a **self-cleaning velocity** of about 0.75 m/s. Where a 100 mm diameter pipe serves a few dwellings at the head of the drain, a slope of between 1:40 and at least 1:70 is required. If the slope is too shallow, the flow will be deep and slow enabling solid matter to settle out. If the fall is too steep, the flow will be shallow and solid matter is likely to be left behind (Figure 12.4).

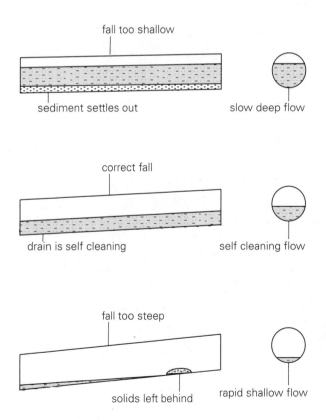

*Figure 12.4* Illustration of self-cleaning velocity effect

# Sewage treatment

The purpose of sewage treatment is to stabilise the sewage and make it suitable for discharge into natural waterways without it affecting the natural balance of the water. For many years sewage was disposed of by dilution or irrigation. Crude methods such as these are becoming impractical as populations increase and so other methods have been introduced. They are usually based on the natural processes of oxidation of the waste by microorganisms, with various methods employed to speed up the work of the microorganisms. This is done to create a good source of air (the oxygen being the essential requirement) so that the biological process of oxidation can occur as quickly as possible. This can be done in shallow artificial ponds or in deep ponds into which air is pumped.

Where the climate is suitable, sunshine and algae will combine to effect the oxidation, giving as a by-product algae that can be used as a fertiliser due to their nitrogen content. Probably the oldest method of treatment, still in use today is the **trickling filter**. In this, the waste water is allowed to flow in a thin stream over a bed of limestone chippings; the microorganisms form a biofilm on the stones feeding off the sewage content before the treated water is allowed to percolate through a grass plot or reed bed that acts as a self-cleaning filter.

## Septic tank

This consists of a buried concrete, masonry or fibreglass tank with two (or more) compartments through which the sewage flows (Figure 12.5). Septic tanks treat sewage from dwellings that are not connected to the public drainage system; they must be sited at least 15 m away from the building and the outlet must be piped away to a suitable location.

When the sewage enters the tank it flows slowly through it and is kept out of contact with the air for at least 24 hours. This allows anaerobic biological action to liquefy the organic matter and fine particles settle to the bottom of the tank. Bacteria can then convert most of this to methane and carbon dioxide. Eventually the accumulation of sediment has to be removed by pumping into a tanker to transport it away for disposal.

## Packaged sewage treatment plant

The packaged sewage treatment plant (rotating biological contactor unit) is an improved version of the septic tank. When waste water and sewage flow into the unit it enters a primary settlement zone that allows large solids to settle out. The liquid then flows into a pre-treatment zone from where it is passed to the main treatment zone at a controlled rate. This enables the microorganisms (growing in the rotating

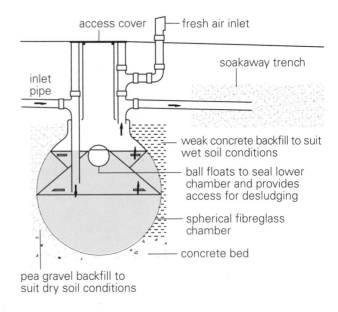

*Figure 12.5*   Section through a septic tank

biological contactor unit) to produce an effluent that is very clean and which can be discharged into a suitable ditch or water course. As with the septic tank, settled solids have to be removed by tanker from time to time.

## Cesspool tanks

The cesspool tank is used where there is no suitable disposal point for effluent. It is simply a buried concrete or fibreglass holding chamber into which the waste water from a dwelling can be piped (Figure 12.6). Cesspools should have a minimum capacity of 18 000 l; they have no outlet and so need to be regularly emptied by a vacuum tanker when full, the frequency depending on the number of occupants in the building and their use of water.

# Materials and joints for drains

The traditional pipe material used for underground drains has been salt-glazed earthenware. It was jointed by means of a socket and spigot. The spigot was centralised in the socket by means of a length of course hemp rope, or **gaskin**, and the seal was achieved by a sand and cement fillet (Figure 12.7).

In ground that is liable to movement due to changes in moisture content, such as clay, rigid sand and cement joints can give rise to problems as any movement can crack the joint and cause it to leak. To counteract this, flexible jointing systems for use with clayware pipes have been developed. Figure 12.8 shows a section through the joint; this consists

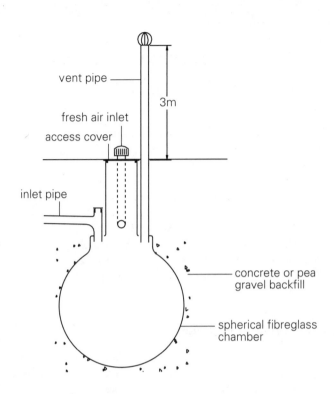

Figure 12.6   Section through a fibreglass cesspool tank

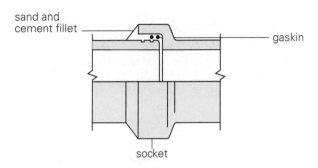

Figure 12.7   Section through a socket and spigot joint

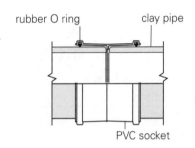

Figure 12.8   Section through a push-fit socket joint

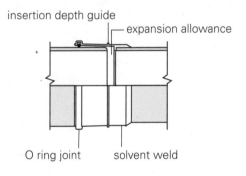

Figure 12.9   Section through a UPVC joint

of a plastic double socket with nitrile rubber rings to form a seal. In use, the pipe end is lubricated with soft soap and then pushed into the socket. Because the joints are flexible, any small movements do not cause problems. Furthermore, the joints are designed to allow for small changes in alignment of up to 5°.

Unplasticised polyvinyl chloride can also be used for underground drains. It is lighter and quicker to install because it is available in long lengths and so requires fewer joints compared to short clayware pipes. Again, a push-fit rubber ring joint is used. Remember to allow room for expansion when measuring and jointing UPVC. The sockets have a witness line moulded on to give 10 mm of expansion allowance per 3 m length (Figure 12.9).

Cast iron is also used for underground drains, particularly for large public buildings and for suspended pipework in cellars. The cast iron is protected against corrosion by a bitumen coating. Cast iron was originally jointed by means of socket and spigots, using gaskin and poured and caulked lead to form a seal. In modern systems, a mechanical joint is formed by bolting a collar around a rubber sleeve that clamps the pipes together making the joints much easier and quicker to complete. Also, the cast iron is often coated with epoxy resin, rather than bitumen for improved corrosion resistance.

# Safety when working with drains

There are three basic risks when working on drains:

- Trench collapse resulting in people being buried.
- Danger from poisonous and inflammable gases.
- Risk of disease, such as hepatitis or Weil's disease.

## Trench collapse

The danger of a trench collapsing depends on its depth and the nature and water content of the ground. If the trench is deeper than 1.2 m in poor or waterlogged soil, it might be necessary to board the sides. The deeper the trench the greater the need for support. Furthermore, placing the spoil close to the edge of the trench increases the risk. Figure 12.10 shows typical methods of supporting the sides of the trench. Alternatively, where the trench is to be dug by machine and is not too deep, it may be more economical to dig the trench with sloping sides (so that the angle of the slope is about 50°) to prevent the risk of collapse.

## Risk from sewer gases

Take great care when working on existing drains! Always station a helper at ground level and have a safety rope tied round you if you have to descend into a deep inspection chamber, it could be full of hydrogen sulphide gas which can suffocate in a few minutes. Similarly, risks from methane and carbon dioxide gases occur in existing drains. Allow time for any gas to disperse after removing the cover.

## Risk of disease

Always take care to prevent splashes of contaminated water from entering any cuts or body orifices; wear goggles and a mask if necessary and always wash thoroughly after work is completed and before eating or drinking to prevent ingestion of contamination. Exposure to sewage or its products can result in a number of illnesses. These include:

**Gastroenteritis** This is characterised by cramping stomach pains, diarrhoea and vomiting.

**Weil's disease** A flu-like illness with severe and persistent

headaches. Weil's disease is transmitted by rat urine; it can damage the liver, kidneys and blood and can be fatal.

**Hepatitis** This causes inflammation of the liver and jaundice.

## Planning drainage systems

When deciding on the design and route of drains, always bear the following points in mind:

- Keep the runs of drain straight between access points.
- Lay the drains with a fall that creates a self-cleaning velocity.
- Provide access for inspection and rodding at changes of direction, at the head of the drain and at a maximum of 90 m intervals on long straight runs of drain.
- Ensure that the drain is watertight and properly supported by bedding on granular material. If necessary, where the drain runs close to the building below the foundations, the trench must be filled with concrete up to the level of the foundation (as in Figure 12.11) to prevent possible building collapse.

## Drains below buildings

If a drain has to be run under a building it should be surrounded with at least 100 mm of granular fill. If the top of the drain is less than 300 mm below the underside of the over-site concrete slab, the drain needs to be encased in concrete formed with the slab (Figure 12.12).

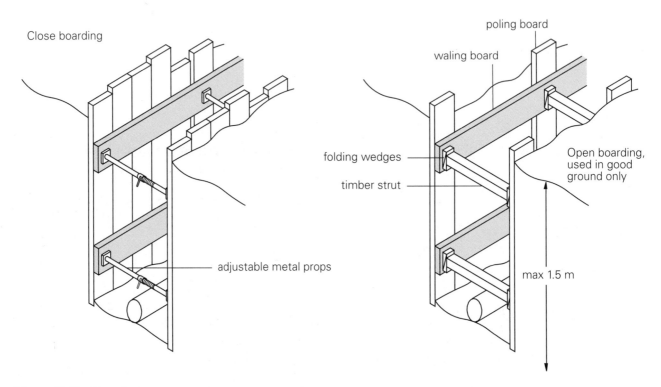

*Figure 12.10* Trench support

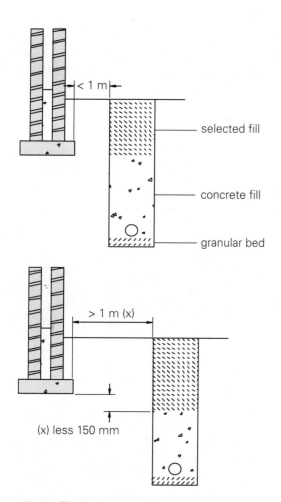

selected fill

concrete fill

granular bed

(x) less 150 mm

*Figure 12.11*   Drains running close to buildings

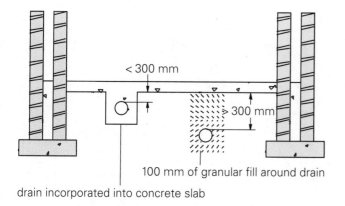

100 mm of granular fill around drain

drain incorporated into concrete slab

*Figure 12.12*   Protection of drains under buildings

## Drains passing through walls

Where the drain passes through a wall, the pipe should be provided with an opening that is at least 50 mm larger all around. The space can be sealed off by rigid sheet material or packed with rockwool. Alternatively, short **rocker pipes** can

be used either side of the wall. These must be fitted with flexible joints to enable differential movement between the wall and the drain (Figure 12.13).

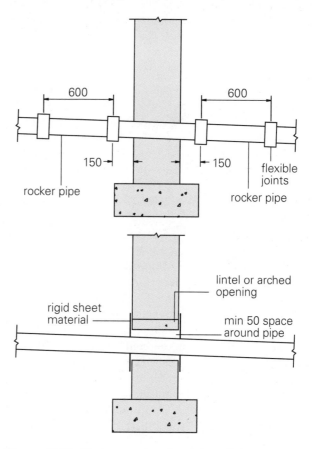

rocker pipe          flexible joints          rocker pipe

rigid sheet material

lintel or arched opening

min 50 space around pipe

*Figure 12.13*   Drains passing through walls

## Bedding and back-filling

Drains need to be protected against ground movement. This is achieved by laying the pipe on a bed of **pea gravel** or other granular material. The pipe should be covered with soil that does not contain large stones, lumps of clay or vegetable matter (Figure 12.14).

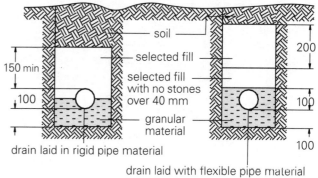

soil

selected fill

selected fill with no stones over 40 mm

granular material

150 min

100

200

100

100

drain laid in rigid pipe material

drain laid with flexible pipe material

*Figure 12.14*   Bedding and back-filling

## Provision for access and rodding

It is important to provide access to the drainage system at strategic points to enable blockages to be cleared. Inspection chambers and fittings with rodding eyes can be installed at suitable locations. Rodding eyes are much cheaper to provide and can be used where the drains are close to the surface. Access should be provided:

- At changes of direction of less than 135° and at junctions where a branch joins the main at between 90° and 135°.
- At or within 12 m of the connection of the drain to the sewer.
- At the highest point of the drain.
- Where a ramp or backdrop is required to change the level of the drain.
- In long straight runs of drain at a maximum of 90 m intervals.

### Inspection chambers

Inspection chambers have traditionally been made from brick or concrete and need to be large enough to enable work to be carried out. The drain running through the inspection chamber is carried by a half round channel with concrete **benching** to cause any water-flow to fall back into the channel. Step irons should be built into the side of deep inspection chambers to enable access. If the inspection chamber incorporates a backdrop, this can be within the chamber provided the pipe is made from cast iron or UPVC. If made of clay, the pipe should be outside the chamber and encased in concrete. Typical brick inspection chamber construction details are shown in Figure 12.15.

Ready-made plastic inspection chambers are available (Figure 12.16). Made from polypropylene, they are quick to install simply by cutting the chamber up-stand to give the correct height. The moulded base usually has five inlets and an outlet. Any unused inlets are simply plugged off to seal them.

### Rodding eyes

By installing a capped junction or bend at the head of the drain, and piping the branch to ground level, access for rodding can be achieved (Figure 12.17).

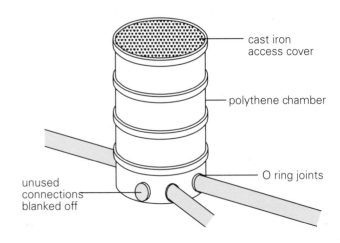

Figure 12.16  Plastic inspection chamber

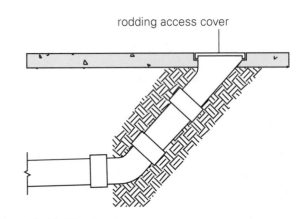

*Figure 12.17*  **Rodding eye**

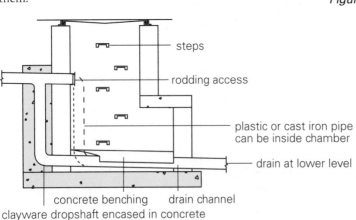

Section through deep chamber with drop-shaft

*Figure 12.15*  **Typical brick inspection chamber**

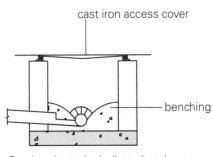

Section through shallow chamber

## Bends and access fittings

A variety of angles and radii are used for bends in drainage systems. Long radius bends should be used in preference to elbows because they channel the flow better without reducing its velocity. Various angles are available: 90° ($\frac{1}{4}$ bend), 135° (1/8 bend) and 157$\frac{1}{2}$° (1/12 bend) being the preferred options.

Use a **rest bend** at the base of soil stacks. The moulded-on foot will support the weight of the stack giving it a stable base. **Access bends** and junctions are also available. On cast iron fittings, the access door is held in place by brass nuts and bolts, whereas on PVC fittings the access door is screwed into place. A variety of bend fittings are shown in Figure 12.18.

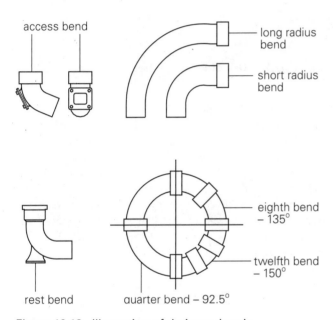

Figure 12.18   Illustration of drainage bends

# Gullies and traps

A drainage gully is a fitting that enables waste water to enter the drainage system without allowing smells or sewer gases to escape. A variety of designs have been developed to suit different situations; some common types are illustrated in Figure 12.19.

**Back inlet gully**   This is used to connect rainwater pipes and waste pipes from ground floor sinks.
**Garage or yard gully**   This contains a galvanised steel sediment bucket that can be lifted out to enable easy cleaning and prevent silt blocking the drain.
**Grease traps**   These are used to prevent grease entering and clogging the drain. A grease trap holds a relatively large volume of water that, theoretically, enables the grease to cool, float and solidify on the surface of the water in the trap from where it can be removed for disposal. The advent of

detergents has reduced the need for grease traps because they break down the grease more effectively and enable it to be washed away (Figure 12.20).
**Petrol interceptor**   This is used to prevent petroleum vapours entering the drains. Petrol interceptors consist of two or three chambers that hold water. Waste water entering the interceptor flows slowly through, trapping any oil or petrol vapours and enabling them to evaporate and escape via vent pipes (Figure 12.21).

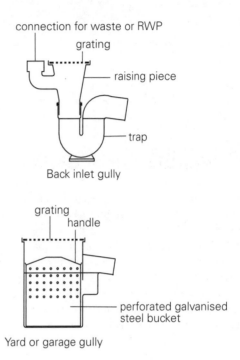

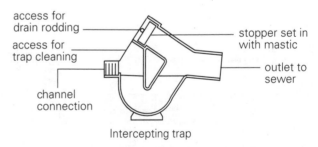

Figure 12.19   Typical gully traps

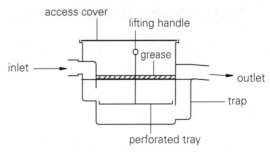

Figure 12.20   Grease trap

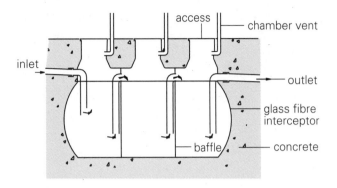

*Figure 12.21*  Petrol interceptor

**Intercepting trap**  This is fitted to the last inspection chamber before the public sewer; intercepting traps prevent sewer gases from entering private drains.

## Ventilation of drains

It is important to allow the passage of air through the drainage system to enable any foul gases to escape. This is achieved by providing air inlets at the low point and vent pipes which terminate at a high level at the head of the drain. Convection currents cause a slow flow of air through the system (as in Figure 12.22) Also, if the air pressure in the drain were to be reduced, for example by the pipes flowing full, the trap seals of gullies and WCs could be lost and sewer gases would be able to enter the building.

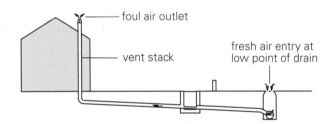

*Figure 12.22*  Ventilation of drainage system

## Setting out drain levels

Where the drain serves only one or two dwellings it is likely that the flow will be intermittent. In this case, a fall of 1:40 should be used for a 100 mm diameter drain. If the drain serves enough dwellings to provide a more continuous flow, the fall can be reduced to 1:80 provided that at least one WC is connected.

For short runs of drains, an **incidence board** can be used to check the fall. This is simply a wooden board that is tapered to match the fall. When placed on to the top of the drain, a spirit level will show level when the drain is falling at the correct slope (Figure 12.23).

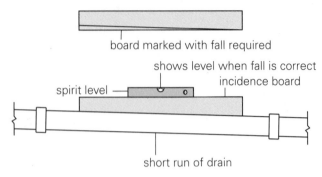

*Figure 12.23*  Use of incidence board

On longer runs of drain, a water level or surveyor's site level can be used to transfer a level on to **sight rails** at each end of the trench. A traveller (or boning rod) can then be used to check the slope by sighting through the sight rails. If the drain is too high, the traveller will show above the rails. If too low, the traveller will be hidden. The height of the traveller should be equal to the difference between the trench base at the head of the drain plus the height of the sight rail above this point; see Figure 12.24 for details of sight rails and traveller.

## Drain testing

It is normal practice to carry out two soundness tests on drainage systems. The first before backfilling the trench, followed by a second test after backfilling, which may have to be witnessed by a building control officer.

### Methods of testing

Two methods of soundness testing are possible: these are the **water test** or the **air test**. A water test is illustrated in Figure 12.25. The length of drain to be tested is blanked off at its lower end by means of a **drain stopper** (Figure 12.26). Another stopper is fitted at the top of the run of drain with an upstand pipe of 1.5 m height attached. The drain is then filled with water. If testing before backfilling, the joints can be inspected for leaks. If the trench has been backfilled, then the filled drain should be left to stand for up to two hours, topping up the water level if necessary to allow for absorption by clayware pipe materials. Provided the rate of water loss is less than 0.05 l/m for 100 mm diameter over a 30 minute period, the drain can be deemed sound. Table 12.1 suggests maximum rates of loss for drains of larger

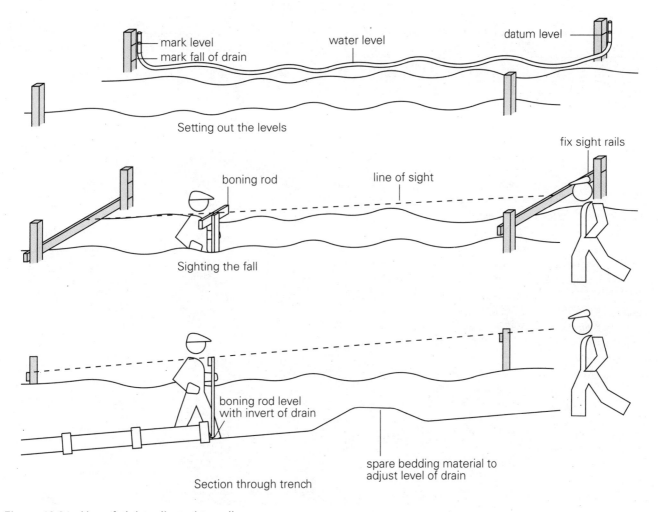

mark level
mark fall of drain
water level
datum level

Setting out the levels

fix sight rails
boning rod
line of sight

Sighting the fall

boning rod level
with invert of drain

spare bedding material to
adjust level of drain

Section through trench

Figure 12.24 Use of sight rails and traveller

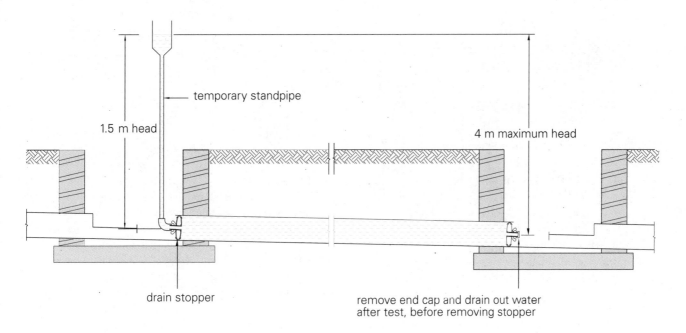

temporary standpipe

1.5 m head
4 m maximum head

drain stopper

remove end cap and drain out water
after test, before removing stopper

Figure 12.25 Water test

*Table 12.1* Acceptable water loss for 30 minute drain test

| Diameter of drain (mm) | Water loss (l/m run of drain) |
|---|---|
| 100 | 0.05 |
| 150 | 0.08 |
| 225 | 0.12 |
| 300 | 0.15 |

diameter. To prevent possible bursting of clayware pipes, the total head of water should not exceed 4 m, so it may be necessary to test the drain in sections.

The air test (Figure 12.27) is quicker to carry out and more searching than the water test, and should be used in preference. To carry out the test, drain stoppers are fitted to any open ends and gullies have their traps filled with water. A length of hose is then passed through a trap and air is gently blown into the drain until a pressure of up to 5 mb is indicated on the manometer. Provided a pressure of at least 3 mb remains after the 2 minutes of the test, the drain can be considered sound.

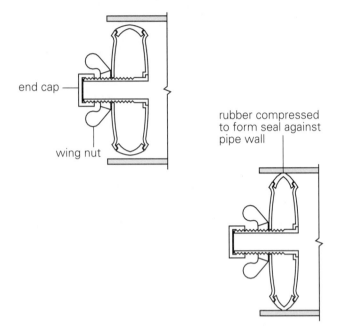

*Figure 12.26*   Section through drain stopper

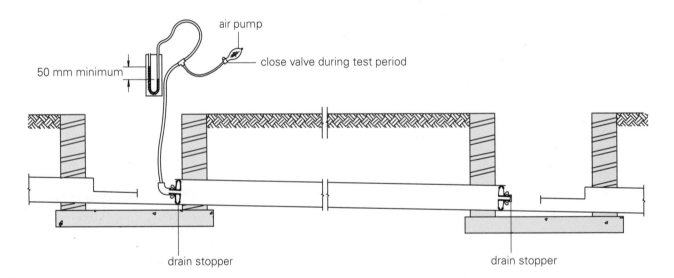

*Figure 12.27*   Air test

## CHECK YOUR UNDERSTANDING

● In the separate drainage system, one pipe carries all the surface water while another pipe carries domestic effluent and industrial waste water.

● The combined drainage system uses only a single pipe; this collects surface water as well as domestic and industrial waste water.

● To prevent deposits of solids from eventually blocking the drainage system, pipes should be laid to give the water flow a self-cleaning velocity.

● Flexible jointing systems are best because they allow ground movement without cracking the joints.

● Cast iron pipes and fittings should be used for drains under large public buildings and suspended drains in cellars.

● Take care to prevent danger from trench collapse by sheeting the sides of deep excavations.

● Do not enter deep inspection chambers without a safety line and an assistant at ground level; allow time for sewer gas to dissipate before starting work.

● Take care not to allow splashes of contaminated water to

enter cuts or body orifices to prevent the danger of disease when working on existing drains.

● Carry out an air test before backfilling the trench; it is much easier to find and repair faulty joints at this stage than after backfilling.

● Backfill trenches carefully after installing the drain pipes so as to minimise the risk of damage causing leaking joints and a failed final drain test.

● Provide access for rodding at strategic points to enable maintenance and cleaning.

## REVISION EXERCISES AND QUESTIONS

1  List the basic principles that should be followed when planning a drainage system for a dwelling.

2  Explain one method of protecting a drain passing through a wall.

3  What safety precautions should be taken when working
   i)   in a trench 2.5 m deep?
   ii)  to unblock an existing drain requiring rodding in a deep inspection chamber?

4  Why it is important to ensure that drains are adequately ventilated?

5  How can the correct fall of a short run of drain be established?

6  A drain is to be laid with a fall of 1:40. By how many mm will the pipe fall per metre run?

7  How can the outlet from a gully be traced if it runs to an inspection chamber that has multiple inlets?

8  Explain the term self-cleaning velocity.

# Sheet weatherings

## Introduction

Sheet weatherings, made with non-ferrous metal and used around chimneys to abutments and for the covering of roofs, are an interesting part of a plumber's work. Properly installed, sheet weatherings will help to keep the building fabric dry and weather-tight for many years. This chapter illustrates typical roofing details that can be fabricated using a variety of joints and techniques. It also covers the various technical factors that have to be considered when planning and installing the work.

## Materials for sheet weatherings

Lead, copper, aluminium and zinc are all non-ferrous metals that can, with practice, be easily worked and will give a long service life even when exposed to the weather. This is because they have the ability to form a self-protecting oxide skin when in contact with the air.

Lead is a soft, dense, malleable metal that can be **bossed** to form complex shapes from a flat sheet without cutting or folding. Alternatively, lead can be cut, folded and **welded** to create larger numbers of similar pieces if required.

Soft-condition annealed copper and pure aluminium sheet are both ductile metals that can be formed and installed using similar techniques of folding and **welting**. Note: copper and aluminium must never be used together on the roof because of galvanic action. If they were to be used together this would lead to the aluminium being rapidly corroded.

Zinc, a slightly harder but still ductile metal, can be formed and jointed by welting and soldering.

Both lead and copper can be used in virtually any atmosphere due to their excellent corrosion resistance. Aluminium and zinc, on the other hand, will give good service in pollution-free, rural areas but are more likely to be affected by corrosive city and industrial atmospheres or the salt-laden air from the oceans.

## Preparation of roof understructure

It is important to make sure that the timber understructure that supports the sheet metal roofing is properly constructed and suitable. Seasoned planed softwood and most other timbers are satisfactory, either as tongue and groove boards or exterior grade plywood. Timbers to avoid are those containing large amounts of organic acid, such as western red cedar or sweet chestnut.

The surface of the timber should be reasonably smooth. Any fixing nails should be punched below the surface. If screws are used they should be countersunk below the surface. Where tongue and groove boards are used they should be run with, not across, the fall. If this is not practical, the boards can be laid diagonally.

Once the timber understructure and any wood-cored rolls have been fixed, sharp edges should be planed or rasped to give a smooth edge of about 3 mm radius that will not cut into the metal. Next the roof must be swept to remove all shavings and dirt that might scratch and damage the metal, before proceeding to install the flashings. If the entire roof is to be covered, a thin felt **underlay** is required. This can be made from polyester or geotextile material or, if the timber is smooth, **waterproof building-paper** can be used. Take care not to use felt that is impregnated with bitumen as this can cause the metal to bond to the roof understructure. This will prevent thermal expansion and can lead to stress failure through fatigue.

## Types of joints and fixings

Where joints are to run across the fall of the roof it is important that they do not create an upstand that will hold back the water run-off. Depending on the situation, **lap joints, drips** and **single or double welts** can be used, as illustrated in Figures 13.1 to 13.3.

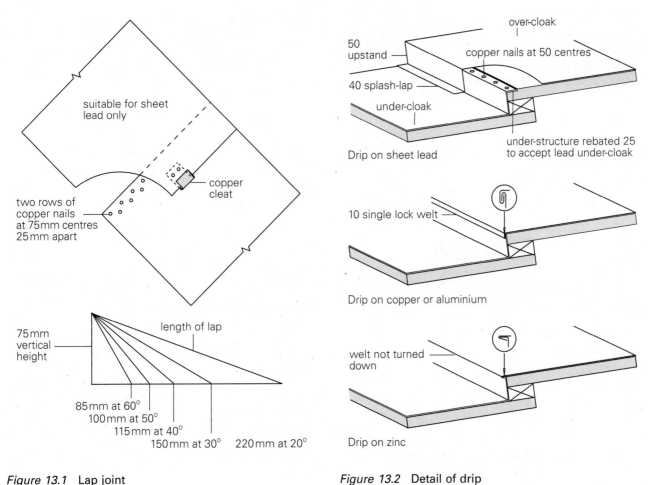

**Figure 13.1**  Lap joint

**Figure 13.2**  Detail of drip

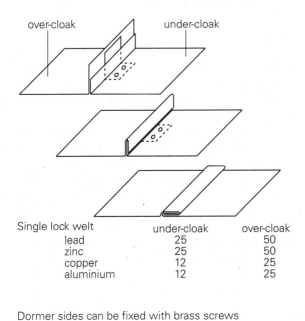

Single lock welt
| | under-cloak | over-cloak |
|---|---|---|
| lead | 25 | 50 |
| zinc | 25 | 50 |
| copper | 12 | 25 |
| aluminium | 12 | 25 |

Dormer sides can be fixed with brass screws then soldered over. These are called dots.

**Figure 13.3**  Single and double lock welt

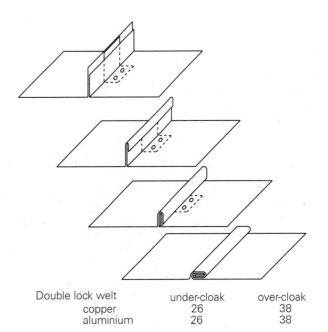

Double lock welt
| | under-cloak | over-cloak |
|---|---|---|
| copper | 26 | 38 |
| aluminium | 26 | 38 |

Joints that follow the line of fall can be raised without stopping the water run-off and so **standing seams** and **batten rolls** or **wood-cored rolls** are used. These are shown in Figures 13.4 to Figure 13.6.

As well as forming a water seal, the joints have another important function to perform. By incorporating sheet metal clips or **cleats**, they also fix the sheet weatherings   to the roof structure. Furthermore, by allowing the metal to expand and contract, the joints prevent damage due to thermal cycling.

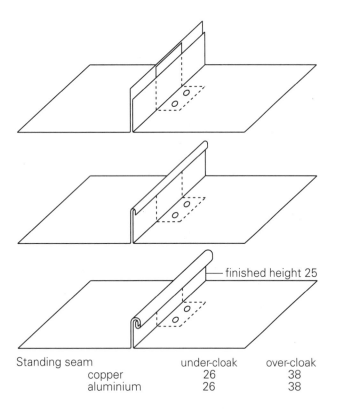

| Standing seam | under-cloak | over-cloak |
|---|---|---|
| copper | 26 | 38 |
| aluminium | 26 | 38 |

*Figure 13.4*  **Standing seam**

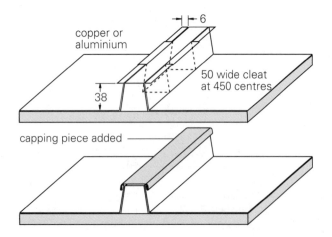

*Figure 13.5*  **Batten roll**

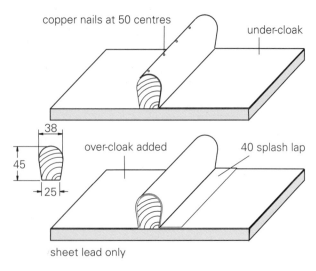

*Figure 13.6*  **Wood-cord roll**

## Nail and screw fixings

It is important to use the correct type of nails and screws when fixing sheet metal roofing. If the wrong choice of material is made, galvanic action will corrode one or other of the metals. Copper nails, preferably with a serrated shank and clout head, and brass screws can be used for both lead and copper. Stainless steel screws can be used with lead. Never use copper nails with aluminium or zinc. Galvanised, sherardised, aluminium alloy or stainless steel fixings are suitable in this case.

## Working techniques for lead

**Lead bossing** is a term that describes the forming of sheet lead (or other malleable metals) into shape by beating with wooden tools. This is possible because lead is the softest of all the common metals and is also ductile and does not harden when worked. This means that it can be readily shaped, using skilled techniques, without cracking or becoming hard and brittle. Once the skills have been learned from a teacher, practice will lead to their improvement and eventual proficiency.

Because lead is very soft, only chalk or a felt-tip pen should be used for marking out; this is to prevent the metal becoming scratched. Any scratches will tend to increase the danger of splitting where folds or bossing is to take place.

The basic point to remember when bossing is that the lead must not be thinned by stretching or thickened by working the lead into the corner being formed. Where there is too much lead in the corner (as in Figure 13.7) the lead is bossed out and away. When forming a corner that requires more lead, such as a break-corner, chimney apron or back-gutter, the extra lead has to be moved into the corner. In either case, by keeping the lead smooth and forming 'waves' that can be

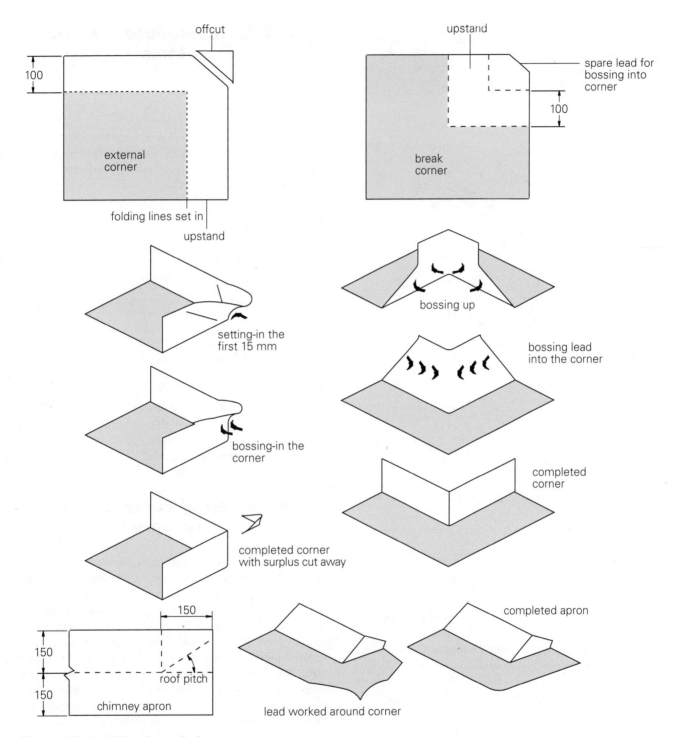

offcut

100

external corner

folding lines set in

upstand

setting-in the first 15 mm

bossing-in the corner

completed corner with surplus cut away

150

150

150

roof pitch

chimney apron

lead worked around corner

upstand

spare lead for bossing into corner

100

break corner

bossing up

bossing lead into the corner

completed corner

completed apron

*Figure 13.7* **Lead bossing techniques**

moved by the tools, the lead sheet is formed into the shape required.

**Lead welding** can also be used to form the shapes required for roofing. As with bossing, the skill must be learned by demonstration and tutored practice. Ideally oxy-acetylene welding equipment with a small welding shank and nozzles will be used. Simple, good quality welds can also be achieved by using a small, specially designed nozzle fitted to an LPG torch. The basic points to note are that:

● a neutral flame must be used (Figure 13.8);
● clean surfaces are required; the surface film of grey oxide must be removed by shaving, including the underside of any lapped joints;

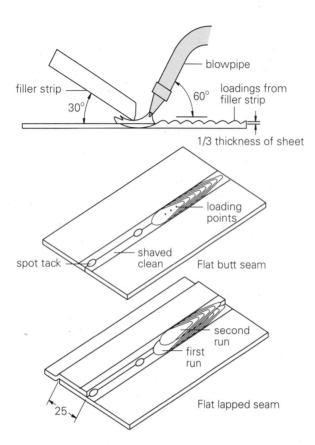

*Figure 13.8*  Lead-welding seams

## Working techniques for other metals

These relatively harder roofing metals, although not used together on the roof, all require similar working techniques. Accuracy in measuring and marking out is the vital first stage in achieving a quality job. Use a pencil or a fine felt tip marker and try to work to a tolerance of ±1 mm if possible.

Copper roofing sheet is supplied in **dead-soft temper**. When forming seams and welts, try to use as few firm blows with the tools as possible. This is to prevent the metal work-hardening too much. The pure aluminium sheet used for roof work is very soft and easy to work. Zinc sheet is relatively stiff and needs a firm approach with the tools when joints are being formed.

### Soldering zinc

Zinc sheet can also be shaped and jointed by soldering in triangular gusset pieces. Use a 50:50 or 60:40 low antimony lead/tin solder and killed spirits as the flux, with a large-headed soldering iron to provide the heat. Do not use a blowtorch directly as it will cause the sheet metal to distort. The seams should be close fitting (to encourage capillary attraction), 10 mm wide and should be tacked at 75 mm centres before completing the joint. Once soldered, any flux used must be thoroughly washed off.

- correct full penetration is achieved, so that a strong weld is formed;
- the weld is properly reinforced, by building up a bead that is $\frac{1}{3}$ thicker than the lead sheet;
- undercutting is avoided, because it reduces the thickness of the lead at the very edge of the weld; these points are shown in Figure 13.8.

Filler strips, 10 mm wide, can be cut from the lead sheet; these also need to be shaved clean before use. Flat butt seams are used to insert **gussets** (triangular-shaped pieces) into chimney aprons or back-gutters or other welds done on the bench. For welds that have to be made *in-situ* on the roof, lapped seams are better. This is because any slight variations in fit can be accommodated by the joint without leaving a gap. Furthermore, because the lead undersheet extends beyond the welded edge, the chances of accidentally igniting the roof timber are reduced.

⚠ Always have a fire extinguisher available while welding, and wait, once the welding is complete, before leaving the site in case smouldering wood ignites, causing a fire.

## Weathering upstands to masonry

Where the sheet weatherings meet the masonry or brickwork, **upstands** are formed to weather the joint. These are covered with cap flashings that are turned into the brick joint by 25 mm, with the lower edge hanging over the upstand by 75 mm to form the seal (Figure 13.9). The maximum length of each piece is 1.5 m, and a lap of 100 mm is required between pieces. The cap flashing is held in place by wedges made from scrap roofing metal. These are driven into the brick joint at about 450 mm centres. The lower edge is held by metal clips to prevent wind lift. Where the masonary joints are very wide, or where only a few brick courses cover the flashing, it is better to build in the cap flashings. Alternatively, they can be fixed by brass or stainless steel screws and plugs (Figure 13.10).

## Typical roofing details

Figure 13.11 illustrates how sheet weatherings can be fabricated and fitted to a variety of roofing structures.

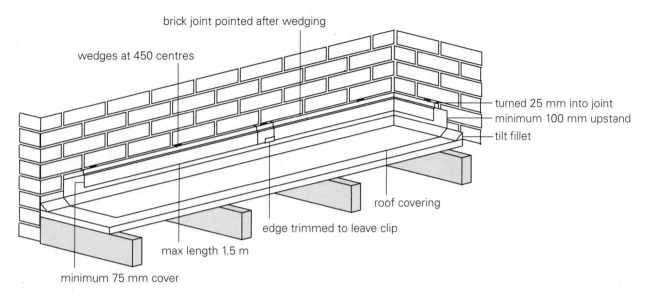

*Figure 13.9*  Cap flashing

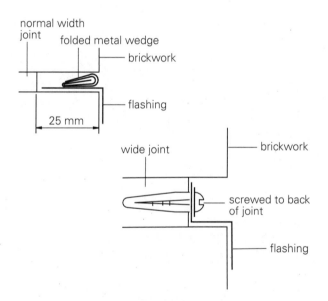

*Figure 13.10*  Fixing cap flashing to wide masonry joints

## Chimney weatherings

These comprise an **apron** that covers the lower front edge of the chimney. Where the roof is covered with plain tiles or slates, **soakers** are interposed between the tiles and upstand against the brickwork of the chimney sides. The soakers are covered with a **cap flashing** that is turned and wedged into the brick joints. The rear of the chimney is covered by a **back gutter** that extends under the tiles; the joint between this and the brickwork is made by another wedged cap flashing. Where the chimney coincides with the roof ridge, two aprons are fitted, one to each side. A saddle (Figure 13.12) is used to weather the ridge where it meets the chimney.

## Canopy weatherings

Where entrance doors need protection against the weather a **canopy** can be used. If small in size, a single piece of metal can be used to cover this. Where the canopy is too long, a standing seam or wood-cored roll can be used to form joints in line with the fall (Figure 13.13).

## Dormers

Dormers are used to provide light into attic rooms. The front can be weathered with an apron similar to that used on a chimney; soakers are also used up the sides of the dormer. These are covered by triangular-shaped dormer **cheeks** that are nailed along the top and turn round the front of the dormer. This edge can be covered by a timber capping or a continuous cleat can be used with the metal turned behind. The dormer top can be weathered in a similar way to the canopy, with the metal running up under the tiles in the same way as the chimney back gutter (Figure 13.14).

## Abutment flashings

Where the roof abuts against a vertical brick wall, the flashing detail is similar to that at the side of the chimney. Figure 13.15 shows how to set out the cover flashing using a straight edge. The triangular off-cuts are used to form the wedges required to fix the cover flashing.

## Roof penetrations

Where pipes have to pass through the roof, a weathering slate can be fabricated. Figure 13.16 shows how to set out the shape of the upstand and elliptical hole required.

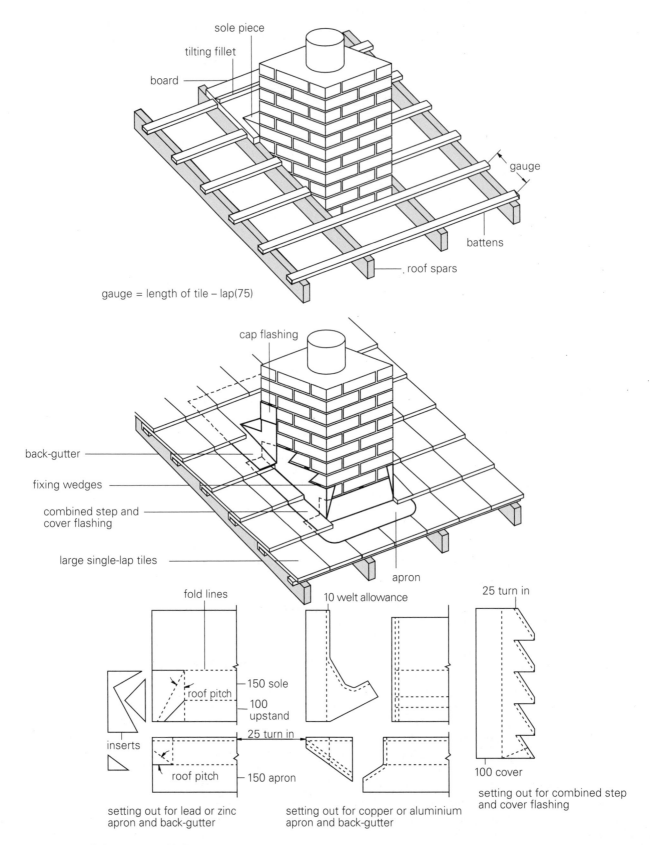

gauge = length of tile – lap(75)

*Figure 13.11*  Chimney weathering

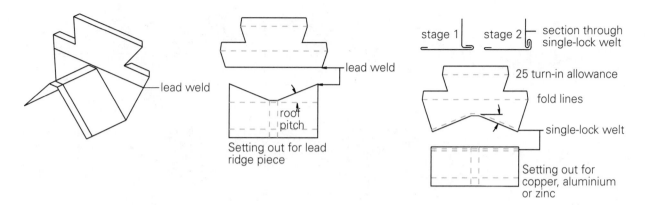

*Figure 13.12*  Ridge saddle

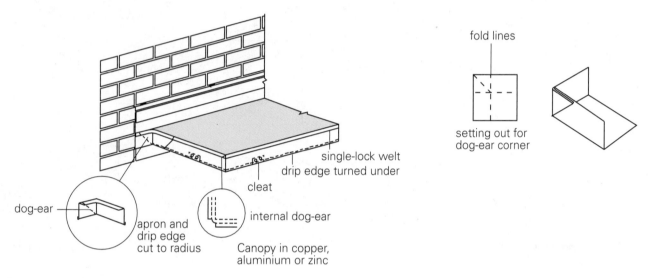

*Figure 13.13*  Canopy weathering

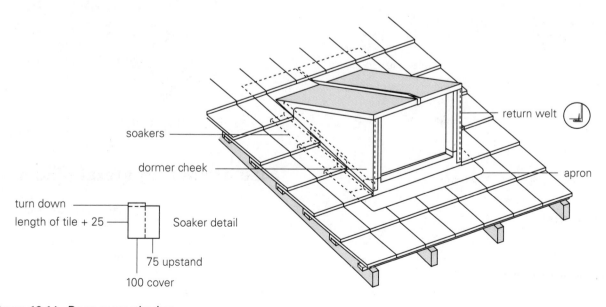

*Figure 13.14*  Dormer weathering

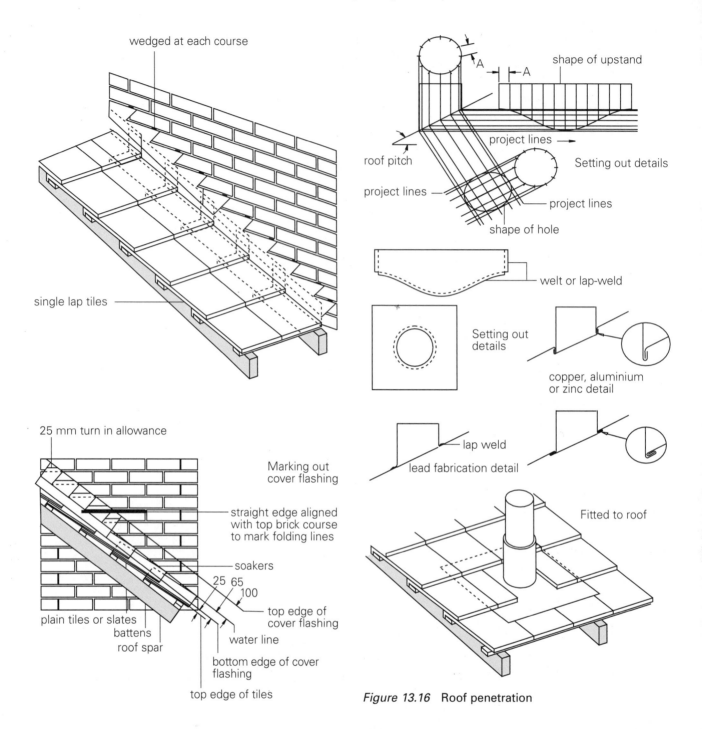

Figure 13.15  Flashing to abutment

*Figure 13.16*  Roof penetration

## Valley gutters

Where two pitched roofs meet, a valley gutter is required. Make sure that the pieces of metal used are not too long and are fixed with a double row of nails at the top, and that the lap is long enough to provide 75 mm of vertical height. (Figure 13.17).

## Size of roofing metal pieces

Table 13.1 sets out some of the physical properties of sheet roofing metals and can be used to compare them in terms of weight and rates of expansion. Table 13.2 and Table 13.3 set out the suggested thickness and size of pieces for a variety of different roofing details; it is important to limit the size of each piece for a long lasting, trouble-free and reliable job to result.

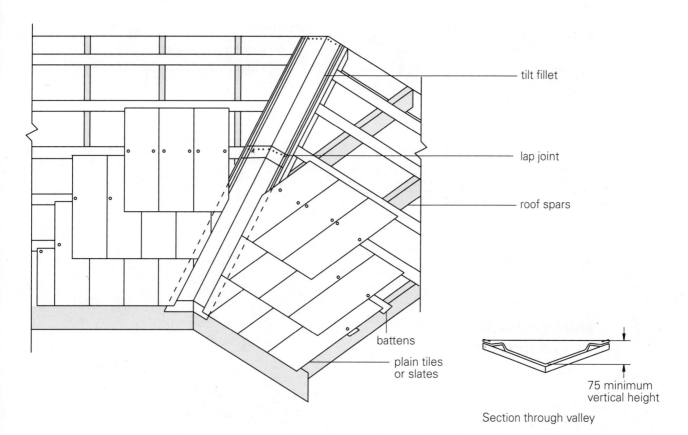

Section through valley

*Figure 13.17*   Valley gutter

*Table 13.1* Properties of roofing metals

| Metal | Density (kg/m$^2$) | Melting point (°C) | Tensile strength (MN/m$^2$) | Coefficient of linear expansion (°C) |
|---|---|---|---|---|
| Lead | 11 300 | 327 | 16 | 0.000029 |
| Copper | 8900 | 1083 | 308 | 0.000016 |
| Aluminium | 2705 | 660 | 81 | 0.000026 |
| Zinc | 7130 | 419 | 170 | 0.000029 |

*Table 13.2* Suggested sizes and thickness for sheet lead roofing details

| Thickness (mm) | Code number | Typical use | Spacing of joints (m) with fall | across fall |
|---|---|---|---|---|
| 1.25 | 3 | Soakers | – | – |
| 1.80 | 4 | Chimney aprons and cap flashings | 1.5 | 0.5 |
| 2.24 | 5 | Back gutters and roof work up to 60° pitch | 2.0 | 0.6 |
| 2.50 | 6 | Roof work up to 60° pitch | 2.25 | 0.675 |
| 3.15 | 7 | Roof work up to 60° pitch | 2.4 | 0.675 |

*Table 13.3* Suggested sizes and thickness for sheet copper, aluminium and zinc roofing details

| Metal | Thickness (mm) | Typical use | Spacing of joints (m) with fall | across fall |
|---|---|---|---|---|
| Copper | 0.5 | Soakers | – | – |
| | 0.6 | All other normal roof work | 3.0 | 0.6 |
| Aluminium | 0.7 | Soakers and flashings | – | – |
| | 0.9 | All other normal roof work | 3.0 | 0.6 |
| Zinc | 0.6 | Soakers and flashings | – | – |
| | 0.8 | All other normal roof work | 2.5 | 0.6 |

## Problems with sheet weatherings

### Capillarity

It is important to remember that capillarity can occur in roofing joints. If the metal surfaces are closely fitted, water can be drawn up into the joints. To prevent this problem, **anti-capillary grooves** are incorporated into drips and boiled linseed oil can be used to form a water resistant seal on single and double lock welts by coating the metal before the welt is formed.

### Effect of solar heat gain and weather conditions

Flashings usually fail because of inadequate fixing, the most common causes being:

* restriction of thermal movement;
* using pieces that are too long;
* poor fixing into mortar joints.

Thermal cycling of the roofing metal occurs as the weather changes as well as with the time of day. This can result in changes of temperature of over 80°C. If the pieces of metal are too long or large in area, the stresses set up as the temperature changes can result in stress cracks (Figure 13.18) or, in the case of lead, failure due to **fatigue**. Failure can also occur where the lead is damaged due to its own weight being too much for the number of fixings used. **Creep** can affect lead that is fitted to a steep roof slope; this is the tendency of the metal to stretch slowly with the passage of time under sustained loading. Intermediate fixings, such as **soldered dots** or **secret tacks** can be used to prevent creep (as shown in Figure 13.19).

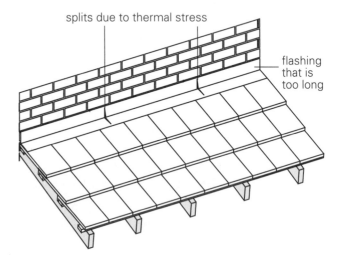

*Figure 13.18* Thermal stress cracking

Stress cracks can develop due to work-hardening of the metal caused by wind lift if the pieces are too large. Wind lift can also be a problem where the edge of, for example, cover flashings are not correctly secured (as in Figure 13.20). Where the roof is very exposed and the wind conditions are severe, clipping frequency should be increased.

## Sequence of installation

When planning the installation of sheet weatherings it is important to remember that the rainwater run-off is by gravity flow. In effect, the water will run down the slope from the surface of a higher piece on to the lower ones. So,

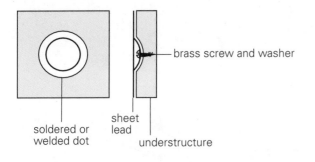

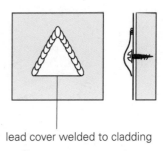

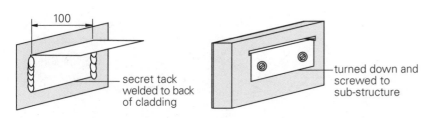

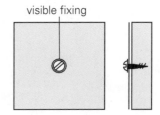

*Figure 13.19*  Intermediate fixings for sheet lead

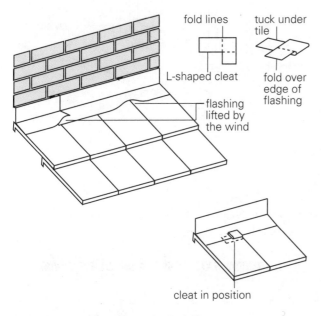

*Figure 13.20*  The effect of wind lift

by installing the pieces starting at the lowest point of the roof (or flashing) and working up the slope to the top (or ridge), the water will be kept out of the building. This basic principle is shown in Figure 13.21.

Once the sequence of installation has been decided, the locations of the various seams and welts can be decided before calculating the quantity of metal required. Remember to allow for the height of upstands, drips and welts when choosing the width of bays or pieces of metal for estimating purposes.

## Patination

In time, lead and copper will develop a natural, attractive patina. In the case of lead, this is a silver grey colour. The patina is insoluble and once formed, the water run-off from the lead roof cannot stain adjoining masonry or other materials. Where the lead is visible and the run-off from the initial light grey carbonate (that is formed before the final patina) could cause staining problems, a smear coating of **patination oil** (or raw linseed oil if this is not available) applied to the newly fixed lead-work will prevent the problem. In the case of copper, tarnishing initially takes place; this results in a dark or blackened surface due to the formation of copper salts. In time, further changes to the layer gradually take place forming an attractive pale green patina.

## Maintenance of sheet weatherings

Properly fabricated and correctly fixed, sheet weatherings will give very long service without maintenance or trouble. Where problems arise, the principle causes are inadequate fixings or installing pieces that are too large. Gales or thermal cycling may cause a problem and then heavy rain will expose it. If cover flashings are lifted by the wind, extra fixings should be added to secure the free edge before dressing the cover flashings back into place.

Where trees overhang the roof, leaf fall can block gutters and roof outlets. Once these are blocked, the roof can flood and water will leak through what are otherwise sound joints. Clearing falling leaves before they cause blockages will prevent this problem.

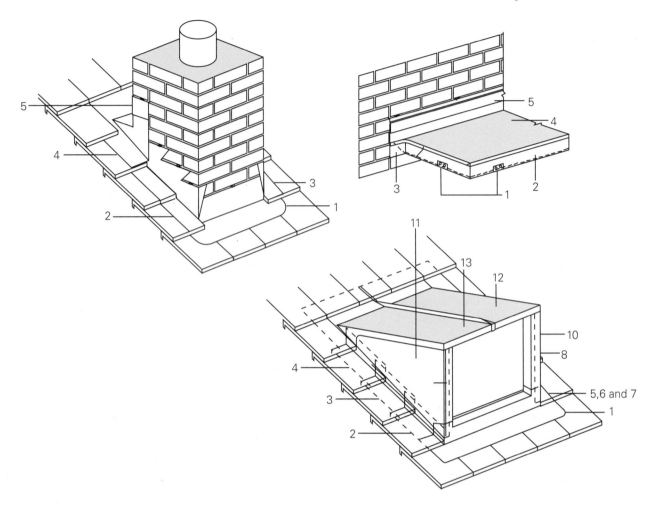

*Figure 13.21*  Installation sequence for typical roofing details

### ■ CHECK YOUR UNDERSTANDING

● Lead or copper can be used in both city and rural areas but aluminium and zinc are best used in unpolluted atmospheres.
● Make sure that the timber understructure that supports the sheet metal roofing is properly constructed and suitable.
● Use seasoned planed softwood tongue and groove boards or exterior grade plywood for any understructure.
● The surface of the timber should be smooth; punch any nails below the surface and rasp sharp edges to a small radius before sweeping the roof clean.
● Do not use pieces that are too long or large in area; they will eventually crack and fail.
● Make sure that each joint has the appropriate number of fixing cleats incorporated and that these are correctly fixed.
● Wedge any cover flashings before pointing the masonry joints. Where the roof is exposed to gales, use extra wedges and secure any free edges with extra clips.

● Never mix copper with aluminium or zinc; the resulting corrosion will soon destroy your work.

### *REVISION EXERCISES AND QUESTIONS*

1   Why are the non-ferrous metals – copper, lead, aluminium and zinc – suitable for use as sheet weatherings?
2   What preparations should be made before laying sheet lead on a flat roof?
3   What type of nails should be used to fix the under-cloak of a sheet lead lap joint?
4   As well as forming a water seal, joints on sheet metal weatherings perform two other vital tasks. What are they?
5   State three reasons why flashings might fail?
6   How can creep be prevented on lead sheet fixed to a steep sloping roof?

# Interpreting drawings and data

## Introduction

The purpose of building drawings and their associated specifications is to show the designer's intentions about the shape and details of the building components or systems in relation to the other parts of the building. This is so that the installer can understand how to construct or fit the component or system. Furthermore, the materials required and the sequence of operations, tools and equipment needed can be estimated from the information contained in the drawings and specifications.

## Types of drawings and data

At the **design stage**, sketch drawings and preliminary drawings or diagrams will be used to show the designer's intentions. Sketch drawings are also often used by site supervisors and craftsmen to show other operatives how a particular problem might be resolved or how a component can be fabricated on site.

Once the design is accepted and agreed, **production drawings** can be done. These consist of two forms: **location drawings** and **component drawings**.

Location drawings include:

- **block plans** to identify the site and locate the outline of the building in relation to the town plan (Figure 14.1);
- **site plans** to show the location of the building in relation to setting out points, means of access, the general layout of the site and the principle runs of drains (Figure 14.2);
- **general location drawings** to show the position of components, the layout of rooms and component assembly details (Figure 14.3).

Component drawings include:

- **ranges** to show the basic sizes, reference numbers and performance data of sets of standard components (Figure 14.4);

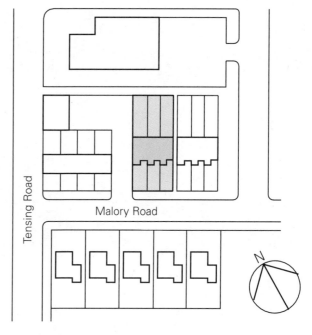

Map Ref NE463231  Scale  1:1250

*Figure 14.1*  Block plan

- **details** to show the information necessary to enable manufacture and installation of components (Figure 14.5);
- **assembly drawings** to show in detail the particular construction methods of buildings, elements and components (Figure 14.6).

## Other information not shown on drawings

Drawings are not used to show information that is better given in schedules, such as schedules of types of sanitaryware, and tables of data, for example radiator dimensions and heat outputs, or specifications.

**Conditions of contract**  This is a legal document that defines the responsibilities of the employer (the client), the

251

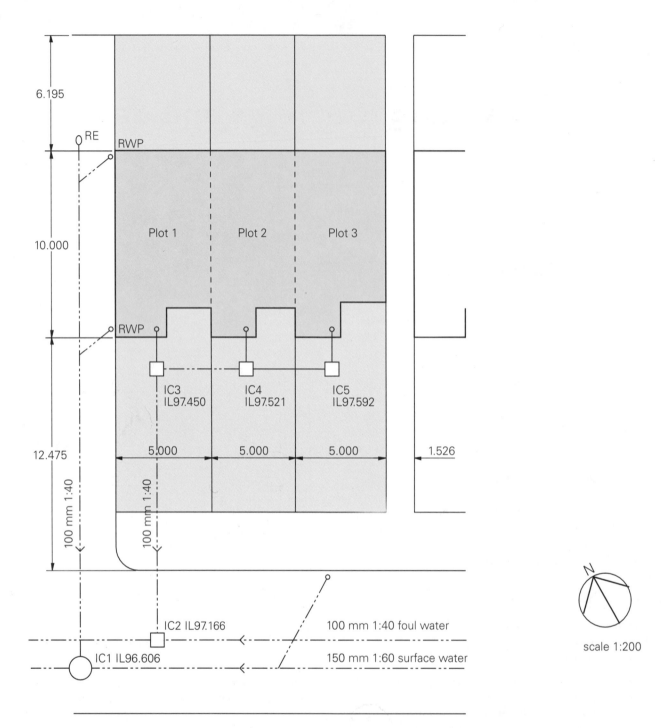

*Figure 14.2*  Site plan

architect and the contractors who will carry out the building work.

**Specification**  The specification is a precise description of the materials and methods of workmanship to be employed while carrying out the contract work.

**Schedules**  Schedules give tables of information on ranges of similar items (such as radiators or sanitaryware).

**Bill of quantities**  The bill of quantities is a measure (price) of the amount of materials and labour and other items required for the building work.

Drawings, specifications and schedules should always be read together so a full idea of the work to be carried out is obtained and the likelihood of potentially expensive mistakes is minimised.

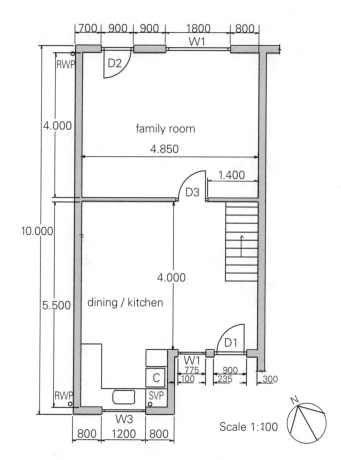

*Figure 14.3*   General location drawing

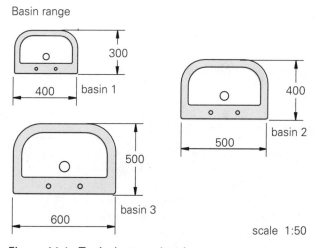

*Figure 14.4*   Typical range drawing

## Use of symbols

Drawings are made up of symbols; these are simplified images of the components or things they represent. A selection of typical building and engineering drawing symbols is shown in Figure 14.7. Using symbols greatly speeds the production of

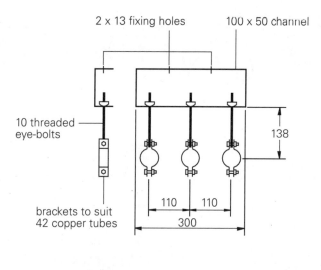

Hanger bracket type 7                    scale 1:10

*Figure 14.5*   Typical detail drawing

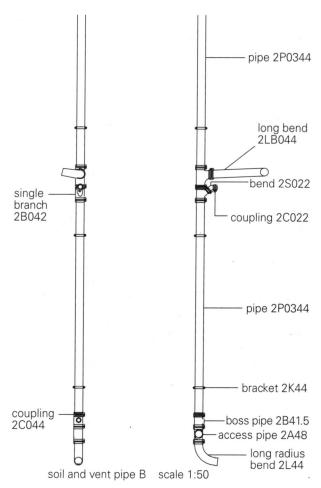

*Figure 14.6*   Typical assembly drawing

the drawing, but there is the possibility of misinterpretation, so a key is often included to try to ensure accurate understanding by the reader of the drawing.

To enable the identification of different pipe services on the drawing, different types of line are used, including lines of similar type with differing width. **Continuous lines** are used for walls and fixtures, such as sanitaryware. **Dashed lines** are used for hidden details, while **chain lines** with one or more dots or dashes between the long sections are used for the various services (Figure 14.8). Fine chain lines are also used to show the centre lines of various components.

## Typical building drawing symbols

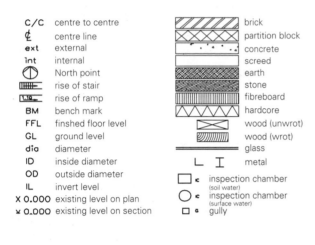

## Typical pipework drawing symbols

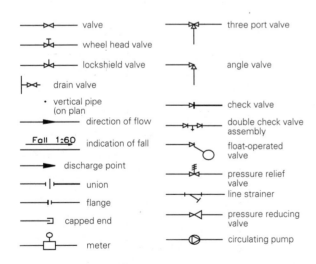

*Figure 14.7* Typical building and engineering drawing symbols

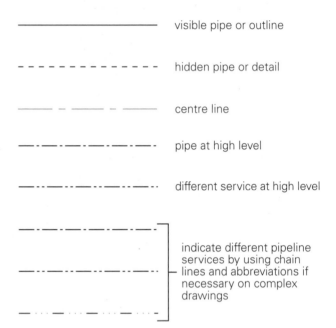

*Figure 14.8* Types and uses of lines

## Identification of pipelines

Once installed in large buildings with many services, the problem of identification of pipes can occur. This can be overcome by coding using bands of various colours. A typical colour coding scheme is shown in Figure 14.9.

The coloured bands should be applied where the pipes enter rooms and then at intervals as required to enable identification.

# Methods of drawing and projections

Drawings, being only two-dimensional, sometimes do not illustrate the three-dimensional world well. Because of this, various methods of drawing have been developed, such as the

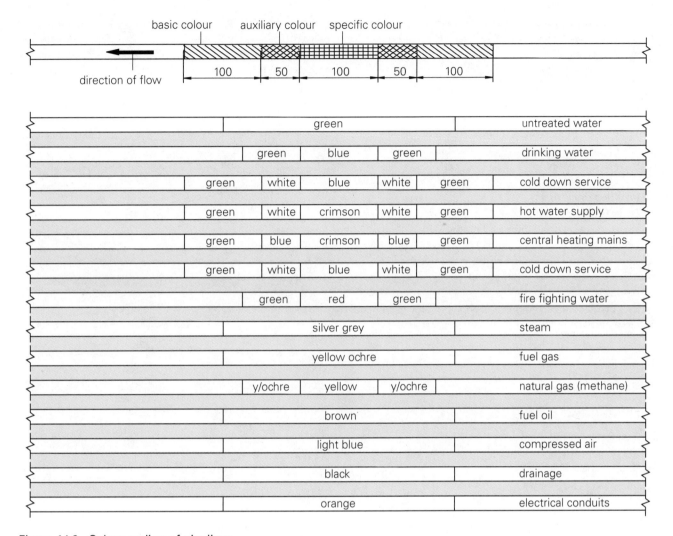

Figure 14.9   Colour coding of pipelines

orthogonal projection, as well as isometric and oblique drawings and exploded views.

**First angle orthogonal projection**

This type of drawing is recommended for building drawings. Draughtsmen use it to show various views of the building. The views are projected or thrown on to planes similar to the way a cinema film is projected on to a screen. Usually a plan view is drawn together with, if necessary, a front and or side elevation at right angles to it. The basic form of first angle projection is shown in Figure 14.10.

**Isometric drawings**

Isometric projection is a pictorial view of objects. The illusion of three dimensions is achieved by inclining horizontal edges at 30° (Figure 14.11).

**Oblique drawings**

In oblique drawing only one horizontal edge is inclined, in this case to 45°. It is usual to shorten the inclined edge by

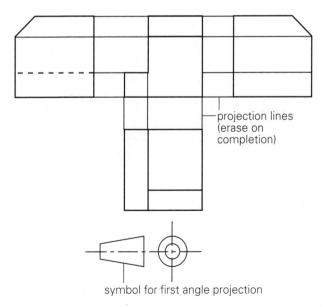

Figure 14.10   Example of first angle projection

50% to improve the proportions of the drawing (Figure 14.12). Oblique drawings are useful where measurements need to be shown, for example on the side of a water storage cistern to facilitate drilling for connections.

### Exploded views
Exploded views are often used by manufacturers to show how equipment is to be assembled (Figure 14.13). They are also used to illustrate parts and part numbers to enable correct selection when ordering spares.

### As installed drawings
While in the course of construction, modifications are often made to the design of a building. Once the work is completed, particularly on large buildings, a set of 'as installed' drawings should be produced to facilitate future maintenance.

### Valve charts
Where plant rooms and ducts contain many valves and different services, it is useful if a valve chart is drawn up.

This will show the valve positions, valve numbers and whether the valves should be normally open or closed. The valves themselves can have a small numbered tag attached (Figure 14.14) to enable correct identification.

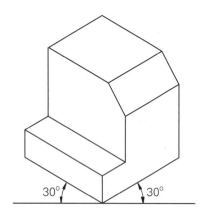

Figure 14.11   Isometric drawings

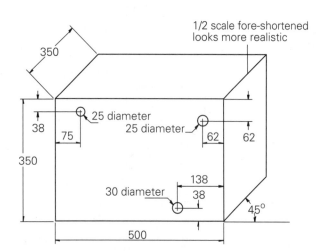

Figure 14.12   Oblique drawing of cistern showing position of connections

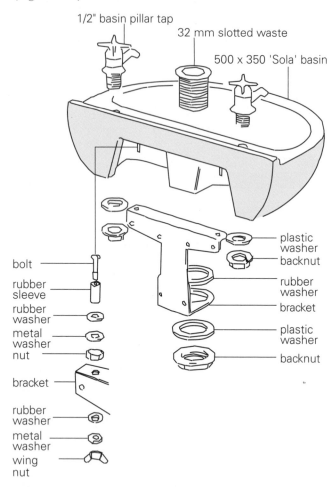

Figure 14.13   Typical exploded view

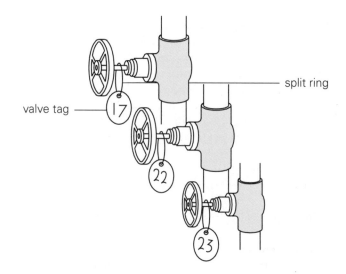

Figure 14.14   Examples of valve identification tags

# Drawing scales

To enable large objects and buildings to be shown on manageable-sized pieces of paper, reducing scales have to be used. Scales are simply ratios where one unit of the drawing represents a greater (or lesser) number of units than the real object. Various scales can be used; a full-sized drawing will have a scale of 1:1. Other preferred scales range from: 1:5 and 1:10 for detail drawings; 1:50, 1:100 and 1:200 for general site drawings; and 1:1250 or 1:2500 for block plans.

To determine the length of the drawn line, the real length of the object to be drawn is *divided* by the scale factor. For example, a real length of 1 m becomes a line of 10 mm when drawn to a scale of 1:100 (1000/100 = 10). Conversely, when reading the drawing, the measured length of the drawn line is *multiplied* by the scale factor to obtain the real length of the object. For example, a measured length of line of 20 mm at a scale of 1:100 represents 20 × 100 = 2000 mm or 2 m.

## Dimensions and grids

Drawings can be produced either with sufficient dimensions marked on them to enable understanding or on a grid (usually either at 500 or 100 mm intervals), as shown in Figure 14.15.

Where dimensions are critical, for example in the manufacture of engineering components or brackets, **chain dimensioning** (as normally used on building drawings) is not recommended. In this case, dimensions should be shown from a common datum. This ensures that errors cannot build up (Figure 14.16).

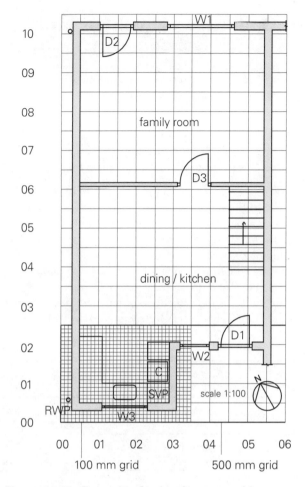

*Figure 14.15* Example of a drawing on a grid

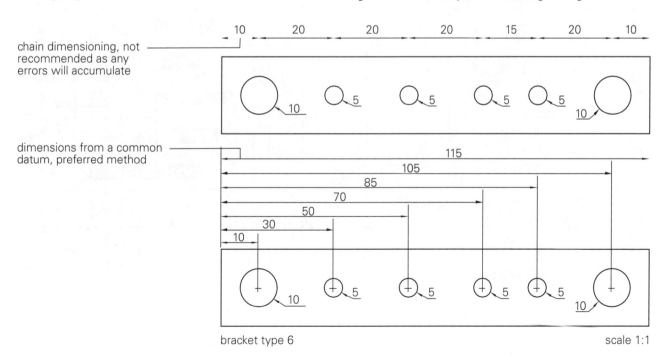

*Figure 14.16* Dimensions from a common datum

## Operation sequences and schedules

To facilitate planning and timing of building work, a system of bar charts or **operation sequences** can be used. These can show:

- when the work is to be carried out;
- the order in which it is to be done;
- the dates when materials have to arrive on site;
- the number of operatives and their skills.

As the work progresses, the bar charts can be coloured or shaded to show the work completed up-to-date. The basic principles of these planning charts are shown in Figures 14.17 and 14.18.

Another type of operation sequence used by plumbers is often to be found in manufacturer's instructions. When installing or servicing complicated equipment, the operative refers to the manufacturer's instruction booklet to find the

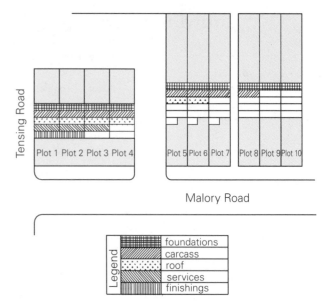

*Figure 14.17* A simple progress record

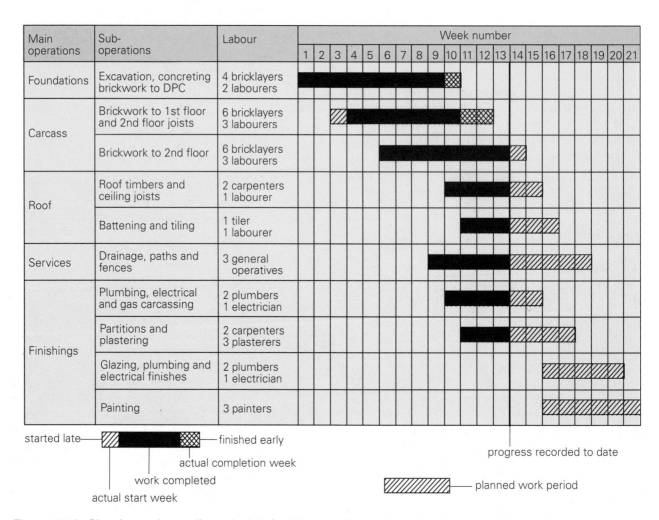

*Figure 14.18* Planning and recording schedule for labour and operations

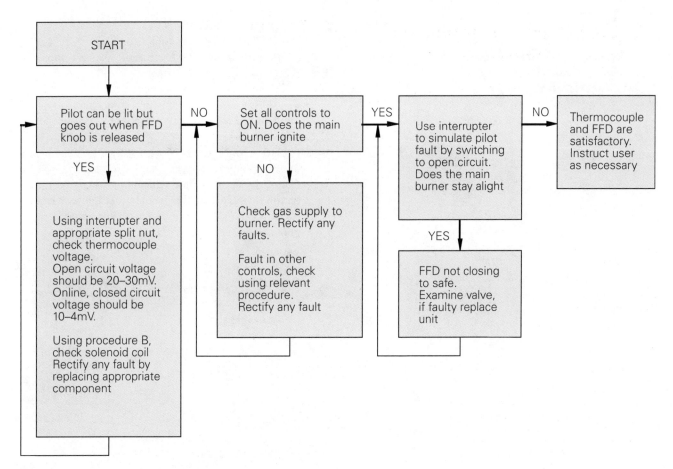

*Figure 14.19*  Typical fault-finding algorithm

correct sequence and parts required to do the work. Usually diagrams are used to aid identification and assembly. Fault-finding algorithms or operation flow-charts are included in the instructions to suggest ways of determining and rectifying faults efficiently (Figure 14.19 shows an example).

## CHECK YOUR UNDERSTANDING

● Always read the drawings, specifications and schedules together to enable a better understanding of the designer's intentions.

● Check with the drawing key to ensure correct interpretation of unfamiliar symbols.

● Make sure you have the most up-to-date copy of the drawing! If it has been amended, costly mistakes are more likely.

● Check the scale before taking measurements from the drawing to avoid over- or under-ordering materials.

● Where measurements are critical, do not scale, only use marked dimensions or check on site.

● Draw up dimensions from a common datum when producing drawings of items with critical sizes.

● Produce 'as installed' drawings and a valve chart to aid future maintenance for large or complex contracts.

● Use the information shown in operation sequences to plan for the ordering and arrival of materials and to calculate the number of operatives required to carry out the work.

### REVISION EXERCISES AND QUESTIONS

1   Which type of drawing should be used to show the location of principle runs of drainage?

2   In which document would a complete list of the materials required to construct a building be found?

3   Where can the information be found to identify a particular valve in a large, complex plant-room?

4   With reference to Figure 14.2, approximately how much 100 mm diameter tube would be required (to the nearest 5 m above) to lay the foul-water drains shown?

5   What type of fluid would be found in pipes that were colour-coded as follows:
   i)    green, red, green?
   ii)   yellow ochre, yellow, yellow ochre?
   iii)  green, blue, crimson, blue, green?

6   The isometric drawing (scale 1:50) in Figure 14.20 shows the 15 mm diameter pipe runs necessary to feed a kitchen sink. Make a list of the galvanised steel tube and fittings required to install the pipe runs as shown.

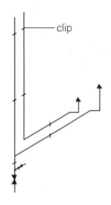

*Figure 14.20*

7   With reference to Figure 14.17:
    i)     How many plots are completed?
    ii)    Approximately how much of the work is completed?

8   With reference to Figure 14.18:
    i)     Which sub-operation commenced 1 week late?
    ii)    Which sub-operation is 50% complete?
    iii)   How many carpenters are required on-site during week 14?

9   According to Figure 14.19, what should be done next if the following facts were found when testing a flame failure device: the pilot remains lit when the igniter button is released and the main burner ignites when the controls call for heat, but does not extinguish when the pilot is switched to open circuit?

# Appendix: Mathematics for plumbers

## Introduction

One of the most important and frequent things you will have to do as a plumber is to calculate how much material you will need to do any particular job. In fact you will do this so frequently that eventually it will become second nature to you. It is because estimating and calculating are seen as second nature that they are often overlooked when it comes to learning how to do them correctly. If you overestimate the amount of materials required it will cost you or your customer more money; if you underestimate, it will also cost you more money in time, having to go out and get more materials.

This appendix will cover some of the basic mathematical processes that you are likely to need as a plumber and also some related geometry that will enable you to interpret and produce workshop drawings and templates.

## Basic arithmetic

### Fractions

A fraction is a part of a whole number. In Figure A1 the shaded area of the square is *one fourth* or *one quarter* of the whole. This is written as $\frac{1}{4}$.

The 4 represents how many parts make up the whole and the 1 represents how many parts we are looking at in this example. The number above the line, the 1 in this case, is called the **numerator**, and the number below the line, the 4 in this case, is called the **denominator**. You can also see in Figure A1 that A + B + C is equal to *three-fourths* or *three-quarters* or 3 parts of the whole and is written as $\frac{3}{4}$.

If you split one of the quarters, D, in half you can see that each half will be equal to *one-eighth* i.e. d is $\frac{1}{8}$ and e is $\frac{1}{8}$.

the shaded area = 1/4
A + B + C      = 3/4
D = 1/4 or 2/8 = d + e

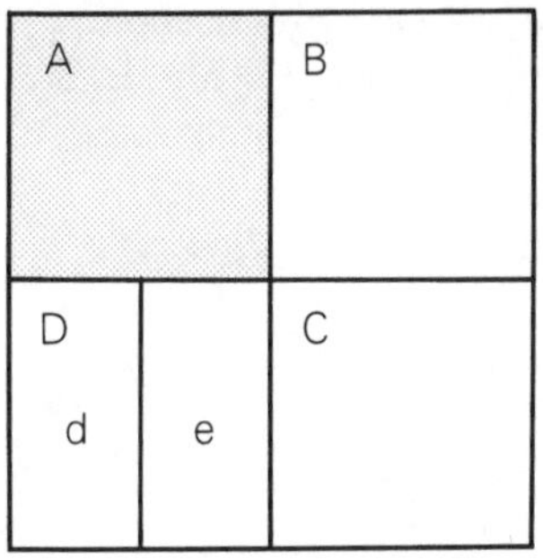

*Figure A1*

### Addition and subtraction of fractions

When adding and subtracting fractions that have the same denominator, e.g. $\frac{3}{8} + \frac{1}{8}$ you can simplify it by writing it out as follows:

$$\frac{3+1}{8} = \frac{4}{8}$$

Because both these fractions have what is called a **common denominator**, it only needs writing out once. The result of this calculation can be further simplified. If you look at Figure A2 you will see that $\frac{4}{8}$ is the same as $\frac{1}{2}$.

the shaded area = 1/2
1/2 = 4/8

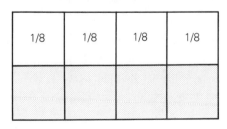

*Figure A2*

What we have done is to divide both numerator and denominator by the same number that does not leave a remainder, in this case 4. This is called cancelling out. It means simply that whatever you do to the numerator you must also do to the denominator. When cancelling in this way the actual value of the fraction does not change.

When adding or subtracting fractions that do not have common denominators, they must first of all be altered until they do have a common denominator. This must be done without altering the value of the numbers. You must find the smallest number that both denominators will divide into without leaving a remainder. This number is called the **lowest common denominator**.

### Example
Add $\frac{5}{16}$ to $\frac{7}{8}$ The lowest common denominator here is 16, as the denominators 16 and 8 both divide into 16. The fraction $\frac{5}{16}$ does not need to be altered as it already has a denominator of 16. However, the fraction $\frac{7}{8}$ needs to be changed by multiplying both the top and bottom of the fraction by 2.

So $\frac{7}{8} = \frac{14}{16}$

The addition is now:

$$\frac{5}{16} + \frac{7}{8} = \frac{5}{16} + \frac{14}{16}$$
$$= \frac{19}{16}$$

Examples such as $\frac{19}{16}$, where the numerator is bigger than the denominator, are called **improper fractions**; those where the denominator is the biggest number are called **proper fractions**. Improper fractions are often converted to **mixed numbers** by dividing the numerator by the denominator, writing the figure down and writing the remainder down as a fraction next to this:

$$\frac{19}{16} = 1\frac{3}{16}$$

When dealing with calculations involving mixed numbers it is easier to convert them all to improper fractions.

### Example
$$5\frac{2}{8} + 4\frac{3}{8} - 2\frac{1}{4}$$

when converted to improper fractions becomes:

$$\frac{42}{8} + \frac{35}{8} - \frac{9}{4}$$

The lowest common denominator is 8 because 8 is the smallest number that is divisible by both 8 and 4 (the denominators of the fractions). The fractions $\frac{42}{8}$ and $\frac{35}{8}$ do not need to be changed as their denominators are already 8. Both the numerator and the denominator of $\frac{9}{4}$ are multiplied by 2.

So $\frac{9}{4} = \frac{18}{8}$

The sum is now:

$$\frac{42}{8} + \frac{35}{8} - \frac{9}{4} = \frac{42}{8} + \frac{35}{8} - \frac{18}{8}$$
$$= \frac{59}{8}$$
$$= 7\frac{3}{8}$$

### Multiplication and division of fractions
When multiplying fractions, multiply both numerators and both denominators, e.g.

$$\frac{3}{4} \times \frac{1}{2} = \frac{3}{8}$$

This is easy but if you are working out longer calculations involving more than one process do each part separately. The following example involves both addition and multiplication:

$$\frac{5}{16} \times \frac{1}{2} + \frac{3}{4}$$

First do the multiplication:

$$\frac{5}{16} \times \frac{1}{2} = \frac{5}{32}$$

Now the addition. First find the lowest common denominator:

$$\frac{5}{32} + \frac{3}{4} = \frac{5}{32} + \frac{24}{32}$$
$$= \frac{5 + 24}{32} = \frac{29}{32}$$

When dividing, you are simply finding out how many times one number will fit into another. So 6 divided by 3 is 2 because the 3 will go into 6 twice. This can be written out as $\frac{6}{3} = 2$. When dividing fractions, **invert** the fraction you are dividing by and multiply instead. The values will not change but the calculation becomes easier. We can see this by using the same example of dividing 3 into 6.

If you want to convert a whole number into a fraction, simply write the number as the numerator and give it a denominator of 1, e.g. 6 becomes $\frac{6}{1}$.

So to see how this 'inversion' rule works when dividing 3 into 6 we need to make both numbers into fractions i.e.

$$\frac{6}{1} \div \frac{3}{1}$$

Now by inverting it becomes:

$$\frac{6}{1} \times \frac{1}{3} = \frac{6}{3}$$

which when simplified further by dividing the 3 into the 6 gives the correct answer of 2.

# Decimal fractions

Although it is important to understand and be able to work with basic fractions, most actual calculations you will do will involve decimal fractions or decimals as they are more commonly called.

   Decimal fractions are easy to work with because they are based on a scale of units relating to a base figure of 10. Instead of writing the denominator under a division line it is written after a **decimal point**, which is written after the whole number. The size or value of the fraction depends on how many **decimal places** or numbers appear after the decimal point. Because each decimal place is based on fractions of 10, the first number after the decimal point denotes the number of tenths, the second the number of hundredths, the third the number of thousandths etc.

## Example

If written as a common fraction, the figure 25.592 would be written as:

$$25 + \frac{5}{10} + \frac{9}{100} + \frac{2}{1000} \text{ or } 25\frac{592}{1000}$$

   If there is no whole number, just a decimal fraction, a zero must be written in front of the decimal point to show clearly that the number is less than 1.

## Example

0.75 written as a common fraction would be $\frac{75}{100}$,

which can be simplified by cancelling down: $\frac{75}{100} = \frac{3}{4}$

   It is normal practice when working with decimals to calculate to a given number of decimal places, depending on the accuracy required. For most day-to-day plumbing, calculating to *two* decimal places is sufficient. This means that you should work out the calculation to *three* places and if the third number is 5 or greater the second number is increased by 1; if the third number is lower than 5 it is ignored and the second number remains the same.

## Example

59.566 = 59.57 (to 2 decimal places).
   On the other hand 59.564 = 59.56 (to 2 decimal places).

### Addition and subtraction of decimals

The only rule to remember here is to write the numbers down with the decimal points directly underneath each other.

## Example

52.355 + 2.66 is written:
$$\begin{array}{r} 52.355 \\ +2.66 \\ \hline 55.015 \end{array}$$

## Example

755.456 − 12.79 is written:
$$\begin{array}{r} 755.456 \\ -12.79 \\ \hline 742.666 \end{array}$$

To 2 decimal places the answer to the first calculation will be 55.02 and the answer to the second calculation will be 742.67

### Multiplication and division of decimals

The multiplication of decimals is straightforward and is carried out the same way as for whole numbers by ignoring the decimal point during the actual calculation and inserting it in the answer, the position being determined by the sum of the decimal places in the original figures.

## Example

6.5 × 5.5

$$\begin{array}{r} 65 \quad \text{(1 decimal place)} \\ \times 55 \quad \text{(1 decimal place)} \\ \hline 325 \\ 3250 \\ \hline 3575 \quad \text{(2 decimal places in answer)} \end{array}$$
= 35.75

## Example

5.55 × 20.275

$$\begin{array}{r} 555 \quad \text{(2 decimal places)} \\ \times 20275 \quad \text{(3 decimal places)} \\ \hline 2775 \\ 38850 \\ 111000 \\ 11100000 \\ \hline 11252625 \quad \text{(5 decimal places in answer)} \end{array}$$
= 112.52625

   Division of decimals is straightforward when the denominator is a whole number. If the denominator is not a whole number it can be made into one by moving the decimal point to the right until it is at the end of the number. The main rule here is to do the same to the numerator as you do to the denominator so that the relative value of the number remains the same. For every place that you move the decimal point to the right, you are multiplying it by multiples of 10, i.e. move 1 place = 10, move 2 places = 100, move 3 places = 1000, and so on.

## Example

4.55 ÷ 2.5 can also be written as $\frac{4.55}{2.5}$

   This shows clearly that 4.55 is the numerator and 2.5 is the denominator. This is awkward to calculate so make the denominator 2.5 into a whole number by moving the decimal point to the right one place, which is in effect multiplying the number by 10 so it becomes 25. We must also now multiply the numerator by 10 making it 45.5.

The process can be seen clearly here:

$$\frac{4.55}{2.5} \times \frac{10}{10} = \frac{45.5}{25}$$

The division can now be carried out in the normal way but making sure that the decimal point is put in the correct position in the answer:

$$25 \div 45.5 = 25\overline{)45.5} \quad \begin{array}{r} 1.82 \\ \end{array}$$

$$\begin{array}{r} 25 \\ \hline 205 \\ 200 \\ \hline 50 \end{array}$$

$$= 1.82$$

When multiplying or dividing decimals by 10, 100, 1000 etc., all you have to do is move the decimal point 1 place for every unit, i.e. once for 10, twice for 100, three times for 1000 etc. When multiplying, the decimal point moves to the right, when dividing it moves to the left.
For example :    63.5 × 10 = 635.0 or 635
                 2.6 × 100 = 260.0 or 260
                 6.5 ÷ 10 = 0.65
                 42.5 ÷ 100 = 0.425

Once you have mastered the basics of working with decimals you should have little difficulty in working with metric or S.I. (Systeme International d'Unites) units as a whole. The primary units in the S.I. system are shown in Table A1. To enable easier use of the system, a bigger range of derived units have been developed. These derived units are based on multiples or sub-multiples of the primary units.

For example, many plumbing calculations involve the use of units derived from the primary unit for length: the metre (m). These include the derived unit for area: the square metre ($m^2$), and the unit for volume: the cubic metre ($m^3$).

Examples of derived units are shown in Table A2. For countries that use imperial measurements, a conversion to metric units is shown in Table A3.

**Table A1 Primary base units of the S.I. system**

| Quantity | Unit | Symbol |
|---|---|---|
| length | metre | m |
| mass | kilogram | kg |
| time | second | s |
| electric current | ampere | A |
| temperature | kelvin | K |
| luminous intensity | candela | cd |

**Table A2 Examples of derived units of the S.I. system**

| Quantity | Unit | Symbol |
|---|---|---|
| area | square metre | $m^2$ |
|  | square millimetre | $mm^2$ |
| volume | cubic metre | $m^3$ |
|  | cubic millimetre | $mm^3$ |
| capacity | litre | l |
| density | kilograms per cubic metre | $kg/m^3$ |
| mass flow rate | kilograms per second | kg/s |
| volume flow rate | cubic metres per second | $m^3/s$ |
| power | watts | W |
| energy | joules | J |
| force | newton | N |
| pressure | newtons per square metre | $N/m^2$ |
| calorific value | kilojoules per cubic metre | $kJ/m^3$ |
| normal temperature | degree Celcius | °C |
| U value | watts per square metre per degree Kelvin | $W/(m^2 K)$ |

**Table A3 Conversion chart: imperial units to metric units**

| Imperial unit | Metric unit | Multiply by |
|---|---|---|
| kilograms force | newtons | 9.81 |
| pounds force | newtons | 4.45 |
| pounds per square inch | newtons per square metre | 6894.76 |
| feet of water pressure | newtons per square metre | 2989 |
| feet per second | metres per second | 0.3048 |
| calorific value in Btus/lb | kilojoules per kilogram | 2.33 |
| inches | millimetres | 25.4 |
| miles | kilometres | 1.609 |
| gallons | litres | 4.546 |
| feet | metres | 0.305 |
| cubic feet | cubic metres | 0.028 |
| square feet | square metres | 0.093 |
| square yards | square metres | 0.836 |
| yards | metres | 0.914 |
| ounces | grams | 28.349 |

Because most metric calculations involve units based on multiples or sub-multiples of 10, they can conveniently be converted into derived units. For example, the relationship between the following linear units is easy to see:

1 metre     = 1000 mm or 100 cm or 0.001 km
1 centimetre = 10 mm or 0.01 m
1 millimetre = 0.001 m
1 kilometre  = 1000 m or 10 000 cm

A space of 1 m³ will hold 1000 litres of water and 1 litre of water has a mass of 1 kg, so 1000 litres of water will have a mass of 1000 kg. This is useful when doing a range of calculations involving such things as volume, capacity and mass of water in tanks and cisterns, and heat quantity.

## Rearranging formulae

Formulae are simply methods of writing down calculations using various symbols and/or letters to represent unknown quantities or mathematical operations. We have already seen that by inverting fractions we can alter the process without altering the overall value or outcome, but more involved calculations need further understanding of the process.

All formulae contain an equals (=) sign. When rearranging formulae, this sign plays an important part. When a number or symbol is moved from one side of the = sign to the other, the role of that number or symbol is reversed, i.e. a plus (+) sign moved to the other side of the = sign becomes a minus sign (−) and vice versa. A multiplication sign (×) moved to the other side of the = sign becomes a division (÷) sign and vice versa.

**Example**

Make $a$ the subject of the following formulae by rearranging:

$a + 2 = b$ becomes $a = b - 2$
$a - 2 = y$ becomes $a = y + 2$
$a \times 2 = y$ becomes $a = y \div 2$
$a \div 2 = b$ becomes $a = b \times 2$

Where multiplication (×) and division (÷) signs are not written, a process of cross-multiplication is used to rearrange the formula, i.e. a figure on the top line at one side of the = sign, when moved to the other side goes to the bottom line and vice versa. Figure A3 shows the principle.

the principle of cross multiplication

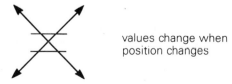

values change when position changes

*Figure A3*   **The principle of cross-multiplication**

**Example**

Make $a$ the subject of the following formulae by rearrangement using cross-multiplication:

$2a = f$ becomes $a = \dfrac{f}{2}$

$\dfrac{a}{2} = f$ becomes $a = 2f$

$\dfrac{xa}{z} = y$ becomes $xa = yz$ which then becomes $a = \dfrac{yz}{x}$

## Indices and square roots

The **index** of a number (the plural is indices), or **power** of a number is a small number written to the top right of a number which shows how many times that number has to be multiplied by *itself* (not by the index number) to give its true value.

**Example**

$2^2 = 2 \times 2 = 4$, the true value. In this case, if the number was multiplied by the index number it would give the same result but if the index was 3 it would give a very different result, i.e. $2^3 = 2 \times 2 \times 2 = 8$, the true value, but if the number was multiplied by the index it would be $2 \times 3 = 6$ which is *incorrect*.

The **square root** of a number is, in effect, the opposite of an index. The square root of a number is a number that when multiplied by itself will give the original number.

For example, $\sqrt{9} = 3$, because 3 multiplied by itself = 9 or $3 \times 3 = 9$ or $3^2 = 9$

The use of indices and square roots is necessary when doing calculations involving right-angled triangles.

## Perimeter

**Perimeter** is a linear measurement around the edge of a given closed space.

For example, the perimeter of the square shown in Figure A4 is $4 \times 1$ m because the square has 4 sides each 1 m in length.

a square with sides 1 m long will have a perimeter of 4 m

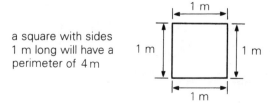

*Figure A4*

- A square is a four-sided enclosed shape, with opposite sides parallel and equal in length with all corners forming right angles or 90° angles.
- A rectangle is similar to a square, with 4 sides and 4 × 90° angles, but one pair of the opposite parallel sides is longer than the other. The longer sides are the length and the shorter sides are the breadth.
- Squares and rectangles are both called quadrilaterals, i.e. they are plane figures bounded by 4 straight lines. Other quadrilaterals include trapeziums and parallelograms.

A rectangle with 2 sides (length) of 3 m and 2 sides (breadth) of 2 m would have a perimeter of $3 + 3 + 2 + 2 = 10$ m. This can be written out more easily as $(3 \times 2) + (2 \times 2) = 10$ m

Note: Where parts of a calculation are shown in brackets, these must be done first.

To find the perimeter of shapes made up of squares or rectangles, i.e. where all internal angles are right angles, you do not always need the dimension of every side.

**Example**

Find the perimeter of Figure A5.

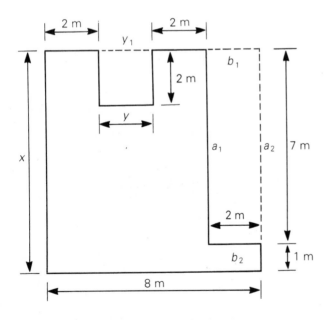

when finding the perimeter of regular shapes made up of right angles, convert them to rectangles with dotted lines, as shown. Note that: $b_1 = b_2$   $a_1 = a_2$   $y = y_1$
Add the inset line dimensions to the full rectangle perimeter dimensions i.e.

(8 x 4 sides) + (2 x 2 sides) = 36 m

*Figure A5*  Straight-sided figures with all angles 90°

Dimension $x$ is not given but the two dimensions on the opposite side, 7 m and 1 m, are clearly the same total length as $x$, therefore $x = 7\,m + 1\,m = 8\,m$. Dimension $y$ can be found in a similar way. The total length of the base can be seen as 8 m. If you add together all the horizontal dimensions given, apart from the base, they add up to 6 m. It is clear to see now that if you subtract 6 m from 8 m, the base side, you are left with 2 m, which must be the length of $y$.

The perimeter can now be worked out. It is easier if you first of all make the shape a full square by adding dotted lines as shown then working the total perimeter out as you would a square:

length of 1 side (8 m) × 4 sides = 32 m

The inset dimensions, to the right of the figure, of 7 m and 2 m, are equal to the dimensions of the dotted lines added at that position to make the square and have been accounted for so can be ignored. In the inset at the top, $y$ (2) is equal to the dotted line making the square at that point, so can also be ignored. The two inset dimensions that cut into the figure, however, have not been accounted for and are additional perimeter measurements that must be added to the square perimeter dimensions already worked out. The full calculation can now be seen:

8 m × 4 sides + 2 m × 2 sides

$(8 \times 4) + (2 \times 2) = 36$ m

# Area

Area is the measurement of an amount of surface or a two-dimensional measurement, and is measured in square units, for example a surface which has sides 1 m long and is square has an area of 1 square metre (Figure A4). The unit is written as $1\,m^2$ because we are multiplying metres by metres: $m \times m = m^2$

The small letter 2 or index shows that dimensions along 2 planes or in 2 directions have been multiplied together.

To find the area of any rectangle or square, multiply the long side (length) by the short side (breadth). If large rectangles or squares were split up into 1 m squares you could find the area by simply adding up all the squares. It is clearly more practical, however, to measure the length and breadth and multiply them together.

**Example**

In Figure A6 the length is 3 m and the breadth is 2 m. Split up into squares you can easily see that it contains 6 squares each $1\,m^2$. With larger shapes it would be impractical to do this and since you can see clearly that the area calculation of length × breadth gives us the correct answer, there is no need to split shapes into 1 m squares:

$3\,m \times 2\,m = 6\,m^2$

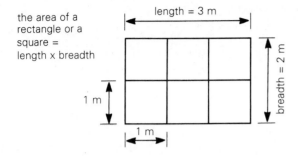

the area of a rectangle or a square = length × breadth

length = 3 m

breadth = 2 m

1 m

1 m

*Figure A6*  Area of rectangles and squares

For more complicated right-angled figures, or figures that are made up of rectangles and squares, it is easier to split these into true rectangles or squares, calculate the area of them separately then add them all together.

**Example**

Work out the area of Figure A7.

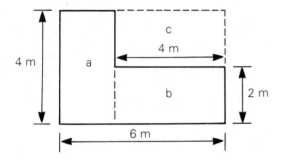

4 m

a

c

4 m

b

2 m

6 m

*Figure A7*

area of $a = 4 \,\text{m} \times 2 \,\text{m} = 8 \,\text{m}^2$
area of $b = 4 \,\text{m} \times 2 \,\text{m} = 8 \,\text{m}^2$
area of $a + b = 16 \,\text{m}^2$

Another way would be to make the shape into one large rectangle by extending the edges with dotted lines, working out the area of this rectangle, then working out the area of the 'added' space and subtracting it from the whole, i.e.

area of whole rectangle $= 4 \times 6 = 24 \,\text{m}^2$
area of $c = 4 \times 2 = 8 \,\text{m}^2$
area of whole − area of $c = 16 \,\text{m}^2$

You may not always be asked to find, for example, the area of a figure having been given dimensions for the length and breadth. You may be given the length of one side and the area but be asked to work out the breadth. In such cases, you will have to rearrange the given formula as shown.

**Example**

If only the length of 6 m and the area of 24 m² are given and the breadth dimension is an unknown quantity, call the unknown $x$ and write the formula out as:

$6 \times x = 24$

If we divide $6x$ by 6 it will cancel out the 6 and leave $x$ on its own, but we must also divide 24 by 6 to keep the same value:

$$\frac{6x}{6} = \frac{24}{6}$$

This now becomes $x = \dfrac{24}{6} = 4 \,\text{m}$, which is the breadth.

## Triangles

A triangle is a three-sided figure; the internal angles of a triangle add up to 180° (Figure A8). For all triangles, the area is equal to half the area of the smallest rectangle that the triangle will fit into. Figure A9 shows a rectangle with lines forming one large triangle $a$ and two smaller ones $b$ and $c$. If you reproduce this on a piece of paper (the top of the triangle can be any position along the top) and cut out triangles $b$ and $c$, you will find that it is possible to join them together so that they will fit exactly over triangle $a$. One triangle is equal to half the area of the smallest rectangle the triangle will fit into.

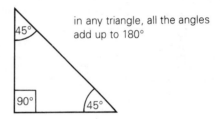

45°

in any triangle, all the angles add up to 180°

90°

45°

*Figure A8*  In any triangle all the internal angles add up to 180°

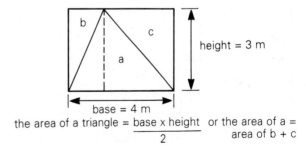

b

c

a

height = 3 m

base = 4 m

the area of a triangle = $\dfrac{\text{base} \times \text{height}}{2}$   or the area of a = area of b + c

*Figure A9*  Area of a triangle

The area of a triangle
$$= \frac{\text{base} \times \text{height}}{2}$$

**Example**

The area of triangle *a* in Figure A9 $= \dfrac{4 \times 3}{2}$

$= \dfrac{12}{2}$

$= 6\,\text{m}^2$

## Right-angled triangles and Pythagoras' theorem

A right-angled triangle is one that contains one internal angle of 90° or a right-angle (Figure A10). The sides making the right angle are the base and the perpendicular side, with the side opposite the right angle being the hypotenuse.

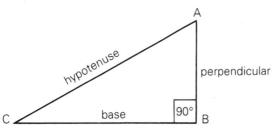

Pythagoras' theorem states that in a right-angled triangle, the square on the hypotenuse is equal to the sum of the squares on the other two sides i.e. $AC^2 = AB^2 + BC^2$

*Figure A10*  Pythagoras' theorem

> Theorem of Pythagoras: the square on the hypotenuse of a right-angled triangle is equal to the sum of the squares on the other two sides.

In relation to Figure A10 this can be written as $AC^2 = AB^2 + BC^2$

Using this information, if you know the length of two sides you can easily find out the length of unknown sides.

**Example**

Find the length of base BC if AC is 5 m and AB is 3 m

Using the formula $AC^2 = AB^2 + BC^2$

$\qquad\qquad 5^2 = 3^2 + BC^2$

By rearranging the formula, the $+3^2$ moves to the other side of the = sign but now becomes $-3^2$ to balance the overall calculation.

$5^2 - 3^2 = BC^2$

$25 - 9 = BC^2$

$16 = BC^2$

$\sqrt{16} = BC$

$4 = BC$

## Trapeziums

A trapezium is a four-sided figure which has a pair of parallel sides unequal in length (Figure A11). The area can be found by splitting the figure up into two triangles and a rectangle, working out their areas and adding them together, or you can use the following simple formula:

> The area of a trapezium = half the sum of the parallel sides × the distance between them.

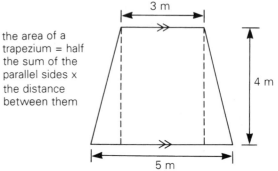

the area of a trapezium = half the sum of the parallel sides × the distance between them

⋙ indicates parallel sides

*Figure A11*  Area of a trapezium

**Example**

The area of Figure A11 $= \dfrac{3 + 5}{2} \times 4$

$= \dfrac{8}{2} \times 4$

$= 4 \times 4 = 16\,\text{m}^2$

## Parallelograms

A parallelogram is a four-sided figure with both sets of opposite sides parallel, but unlike a square or rectangle it contains no right angles (Figure A12). The area can be found by splitting the figure up into triangles and rectangles,

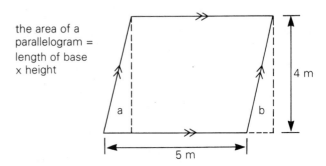

the area of a parallelogram = length of base × height

*Figure A12*  Area of a parallelogram

working out their areas and adding them together, or you can use the following simple formula:

> The area of a parallelogram = length of the base × the perpendicular height

You can see that if perpendicular lines are drawn down from the top two corners, the triangle created at *a* is equal to the triangle created at *b*. If triangle *a* was moved and placed directly over *b* it would leave a rectangle. To find the area of parallelograms therefore you treat them in the same way as rectangles by multiplying the length (base) by the breadth (perpendicular height).

**Example**
The area of Figure A12 $= 5\,m \times 4\,m = 20\,m^2$

## Circles

Circles play an important part in the work of a plumber. From hot water storage cylinders and water pipes to drainage pipes and channels, all involve an understanding of circles, especially when calculating such things as capacities of vessels and the force exerted by water.

A circle is a perfectly round figure with one line enclosing it (Figure A13). The main parts of a circle are: the **circumference** – this is the line enclosing the circle or perimeter; the **diameter** – this is a straight line passing through the centre of the circle from one point on the circumference to an opposite point, cutting the circle in two; the **radius** – this is a straight line from the centre point of the circle to a point on the circumference, or half of the diameter.

All calculations relating to circles involve the use of a constant figure called 'pi' represented by the symbol $\pi$, which is roughly equal to 3.142 and is equal to the number of times the diameter of a circle divides into the circumference.

> The area of a circle $= \pi \times r \times r$
>
> When figures or symbols are written next to each other or next to numbers in formulae it means they are to be multiplied together so the above formula can be written simply as: $\pi r^2$

**Example**
Find the area of a circle with a radius of 0.5 m

$Area = \pi\,r^2$
$Area = 3.142 \times 0.5\,m \times 0.5\,m = 0.7855\,m^2$
$= 0.79\,m^2$ (to 2 decimal places).

> The circumference of a circle $= \pi d$

**Example**
Find the circumference of a circle having a radius of 0.5 m. If the radius is 0.5 m the diameter will be $0.5\,m \times 2 = 1\,m$ the circumference $= 3.142 \times 1\,m = 3.142\,m$

**Example**
Find the amount of sheet steel needed to make the cylindrical vessel shown in Figure A14. It has a flat base with an open top.

If the base was removed and the cylinder cut down its length, you would see that opened out the cylinder would become a rectangle. Therefore to find out how much steel is required, all you have to do is find the area of this rectangle and add it to the area of the circular base.

area of cylinder wall = circumference $(\pi d) \times$ height
$area = 3.142 \times 0.8\,m \times 1.4\,m = 3.51904\,m^2$
$= 3.52\,m^2$ (to 2 decimal places).

area of a circle
$= \pi r^2$ or $\pi d^2/4$

circumference $= \pi d$

diameter = d

radius = r

circumference

*Figure A13* Area of a circle

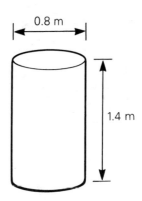

*Figure A14*

It is easier to convert dimensions given in mm to m before working out: divide by 1000 or move the decimal point 3 places to the left. In the above example the radius was given as 400 mm, which becomes 0.4 m, and since it is the diameter that is needed here it is 0.4 m × 2 which is 0.8 m.

The area of the cylinder wall now needs adding to the area of the base which is a circle.

Area of base $= \pi r^2$
Area $= 3.142 \times 0.4 \times 0.4 = 0.5027 \,\text{m}^2$
or $0.50 \,\text{m}^2$ (to 2 decimal places).

Added together, the total area of metal required will be the area of the sides plus the area of the base:

$$
\begin{aligned}
\text{total area} &= 3.52 \\
&\phantom{=}\ +0.50 \\
&\phantom{=}\ \overline{4.02} \\
&= 4.02 \,\text{m}^2
\end{aligned}
$$

# Volume

Volume can be defined as the amount of space a body takes up. It is measured in cubic units, i.e. a cube which has sides 1 m long will occupy a space of $1 \,\text{m}^3$ (Figure A15). The unit is written as $1\text{m}^3$ because it shows that we are multiplying metres by metres by metres: m × m × m. The small number 3 or index shows that dimensions along 3 planes or in 3 directions have been multiplied together.

Objects that are made up of cubes are called **cuboids**. To find the volume of a cuboid, multiply the length by the breadth then multiply this by the height.

> The volume of a regular cuboid = length × breadth × height

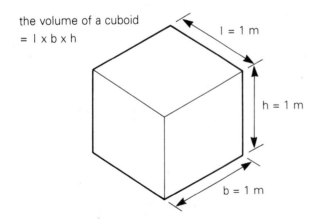

the volume of a cuboid
= l x b x h

*Figure A15*   Volume of a cube

Figure A16 for example has been split up into 1 m cubes, each cube is $1 \,\text{m}^3$. You can easily count the number of cubes and find that there are 16. In other words, it has a volume of $16 \,\text{m}^3$. It is easier, however, to use the given formula of $1 \times b \times h = \text{volume}$

Therefore the volume of Figure A16 $= 4 \,\text{m} \times 2 \,\text{m} \times 2 \,\text{m}$
$= 16 \,\text{m}^3$

This formula is useful for finding out the volume and capacity of rectangular tanks and cisterns. Regular shapes that have the same cross-sectional shape throughout their length and with both ends parallel, like Figure A16, are also known as **prisms**. The best way of finding the volume of a prism is to use the following formula:

> The volume of a prism = cross-sectional area × height

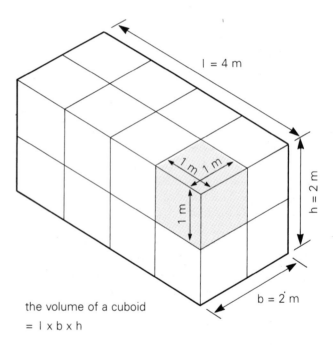

the volume of a cuboid
= l x b x h

*Figure A16*

The height is usually taken as the longest dimension or length. You can see that Figure A16 is a prism so using the formula:

Volume of Figure A16 $= 2 \,\text{m} \times 2 \,\text{m} \times 4 \,\text{m} = 16 \,\text{m}^3$

This which gives the same result of course. There are other kinds of prisms which require a slightly different formula but for most plumbing applications the above formula is used.

This formula is useful for finding out the volume and capacity of cylinders.

**Example**

Find the volume of the cylinder shown in Figure A14.

Volume of cylinder = cross-sectional area × height

= area of base × height
= $\pi\, r^2 \times$ height
= 3.142 × 0.4 m × 0.4 m × 1.4 m
= 0.70 m$^3$ to 2 decimal places

1 cubic metre contains 1000 litres of water, so to convert volume into capacity of water simply multiply the volume in cubic metres by 1000 to give the capacity in litres.

Therefore the cylindrical vessel in the example with a volume of 0.70 m$^3$ will contain 0.70 × 1000 litres = 700 litres of water.

**Example**

How many litres of water will a cistern measuring 0.5 m × 2.5 m × 0.75 m hold?

Volume = 0.5 m × 2.5 m × 0.75 m = 0.94 m$^3$
Capacity in litres = 0.94 × 1000 = 940 litres.

1 cubic metre also weighs 1000 kg, therefore if 1 cubic metre holds 1000 litres, 1 litre of water weighs 1 kg.

## Intensity of pressure

We have seen that 1 litre of water weighs 1 kg and that 1 cubic metre of water weighs 1000 kg. In fact the kilogram is a unit of mass, so strictly speaking 1000 litres of water has a mass of 1000 kg. To express this in terms of weight we must account for gravity and to do this we must use the unit of the newton. One newton will accelerate 1 kg at 1 m per second, or per second$^2$. The gravitational force on 1 kg is 9.81 N.

---

Intensity of pressure is measured in newtons per square metre (N/m$^2$).

Because 1 kgf = 9.81 N, one cubic metre of water must exert a pressure 1000 kgf or 1000 × 9.81 N which is 9.81 kN. Therefore for every 1 m head or height of water, a pressure of 9.81 kN/m$^2$ will be exerted, i.e. a pressure of 9.81 kN/m$^2$ will be exerted at the base of 1 m$^3$ of water.

In simple terms, intensity of pressure (IOP) = 9.81 kN/m$^2$ × head in metres.

---

It is easier to use the kilonewton which equals 1000 newtons in these calculations to avoid long figures.

**Example**

What is the intensity of pressure acting on the base of the boiler shown in Figure A17?

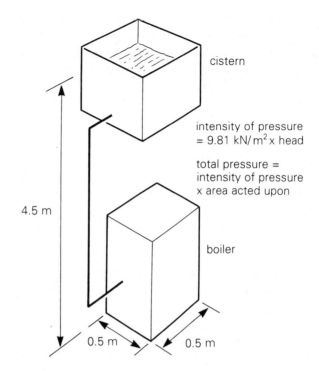

cistern

intensity of pressure = 9.81 kN/m$^2$ x head

total pressure = intensity of pressure x area acted upon

boiler

4.5 m

0.5 m        0.5 m

*Figure A17*  Intensity of pressure

IOP = 9.81 kN/m$^2$ × 4.5 m (head)
    = 44.15 kN/m$^2$

It is clear that intensity of pressure is the pressure acting on every m$^2$ at any given depth. Total pressure is the pressure acting on a *specific* area at a given depth.

Total pressure is measured in newtons and because it relates to a specific area it must therefore take account of that area.

Total pressure (TP) = 9.81 kN × head in metres × area acted upon.

Therefore, the total pressure acting on the base of 1 m$^3$ of water is 9.81 × 1 × 1 = 9.81 kN

**Example**

What is the total pressure acting on the base of the boiler shown in Figure A17?

TP = 9.81 kN × 4.5m × 0.5 × 0.5 = 11.03 kN

The formula can also be written as the IOP × area acted upon

## Temperature and specific heat

Once you have mastered working with decimals, have an understanding of the relationship between different metric units and are able to rearrange formulae, you will be able to carry out calculations across a range of related areas. You can see from Table A2 that normal temperature is measured in degrees Celsius (°C) and that heat and work, both of which are forms of energy, are measured in joules (J).

It requires 4.186 joules to raise the temperature of 1 gram of water by 1°C. Because it is more usual to talk about quantities of water in litres, to carry out any heat calculations we must convert this formula. There are 1000 grams of water in 1 kilogram, and 1 kilogram of water is equal to 1 litre. Therefore 4.186 × 1000 joules will raise 1 litre by 1°C and 4186 J is equal to 4.186 kJ. For most heat calculations therefore we use 4.186 kJ. This is known as **specific heat capacity** i.e. the amount of heat necessary to raise 1 kg of material by 1°C.

Therefore water has a specific heat capacity of 4.186 kJ/kg °C.

### Example

How many kilojoules are needed to raise 50 litres of water from 10°C to 70°C?

The temperature rise from 10°C to 70°C is 60°C, therefore the heat required is:

$$4.186 \times 50 \times 60 = 12\,558\,kJ$$

When calculating heater or boiler power, the heat energy must be converted to watts (W) and watts = joules/seconds. With this information you can now work out how long it will take to heat a certain amount of water up or what power will be required to heat water up over a certain period.

In the previous example, we saw that it took 12 558 kJ to raise 50 litres by 60°C. The power required to do this in 1 hour (3600 seconds) will be:

$$\frac{12\,558}{3600} = 3.488\,kW$$

Note: because we put kJ instead of J in the formula the answer will be in kW instead of W.

## Percentages

Percentages are used when comparing given quantities to a hundred parts, i.e. percentage means 'per hundred' and a percentage shows how many 1/100 parts are present. The 100 symbol used to represent percentages is % (per cent).

### Example

$$1\% = 1 \text{ in every } 100 \text{ or } \frac{1}{100} \text{ or } 0.01$$

$$25\% = 25 \text{ in every } 100 \text{ or } \frac{25}{100} \text{ or } 0.25$$

$$75\% = 75 \text{ in every } 100 \text{ or } \frac{75}{100} \text{ or } 0.75$$

$$100\% = 100 \text{ in every } 100 \text{ or } \frac{100}{100} \text{ or } 1$$

To convert a percentage into a fraction, write the percentage as the numerator and 100 as the denominator. To convert a percentage to a decimal, move the decimal point 2 places to the left, i.e. divide by 100. To convert a fraction to a percentage, multiply by 100. To convert a decimal to a percentage, move the decimal point 2 places to the right, i.e. multiply by 100.

### Example

$$\frac{6}{30} = \frac{6}{30} \times 100 = \frac{600}{30} = 20\%$$

$$0.65 = 65\%$$

$$50\% = \frac{50}{100} = 0.50$$

To increase a given quantity by a certain percentage, simply multiply the quantity by the percentage increase expressed as a fraction and then add the result to the original quantity to give you the new figure.

### Example

To allow for cutting and wastage, 15% needs to be added to the measured quantity of 75 m² of sheet steel required to roof a small warehouse.

$$\% \text{ increase } = \frac{75}{100} \times 15$$

$$= \frac{45}{4} = 11.25$$

The total amount of sheet steel required $= 75 + 11.25 = 86.25\,m^2$

### Example

If 60 people are employed on a building site and 20% of them are trainees, exactly how many trainees are there?

Number of trainees

$$= \frac{60}{100} \times 20$$

$$= \frac{60}{5}$$

$$= 12 \text{ trainees}$$

## Geometry and working drawings

Working drawings, workshop drawings or templates are often needed as a guide to bend pipes to given angles and measurements. They can be chalked roughly on the floor or on the bench or they can be drawn on paper or wooden sheets to be used over again. Before you are able to draw these accurately, a basic understanding of geometry in relation to the construction of angles and how to create them is essential. An angle is formed when two lines meet at a point, called the **vertex**, and they are measured in degrees (°). All angles are based on the circle and the number of degrees around the point at the centre of a circle is 360°. When a circle is divided into four equal parts, each angle formed will be 90° (Figure A18). A 90° angle is called a right angle, other angles are:

- **acute angle**: less than 90°
- **obtuse angle**: more than 90° but less than 180°
- **reflex angle**: more than 180° but less then 360°
- **complementary angles**: 2 angles adding up to 90°
- **supplementary angles**: 2 angles adding up to 180°

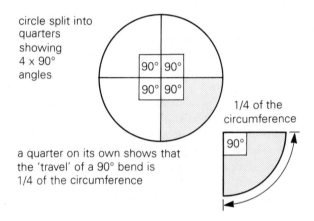

*Figure A18*

It is possible to construct any angle using a protractor but if you do not have a protractor you can still construct a range of angles using standard workshop set-squares and compasses.

## Set-squares

There are two available, the 45° set-square and the 30°/60° set-square. By putting the squares together in various combinations you can create several different angles (Figure A19).

## Compasses

These can be used to create a number of angles without the aid of either a protractor or set-squares. There are just three basic constructions involved:

**Bisecting a line to create a perpendicular or 90° angle**
Put the compass point at one end of a given line and extend the other end until it is beyond half-way down the line and scribe arcs above and below the centre of the line. Using the same compass setting or radius, repeat the process from the other end of the line so that the arcs created intersect the previous ones. Using a straight edge, draw a straight line between the intersections to create a 90° angle on the original line (Figure A20).

To bisect a line to create a perpendicular at a given point on a line, first put the compass point at the given point and extend it to create a convenient radius and draw a semi-circle above the line cutting it at both sides. Using both intersections as points, and a compass radius bigger than the one used to create the semi-circle, scribe intersecting

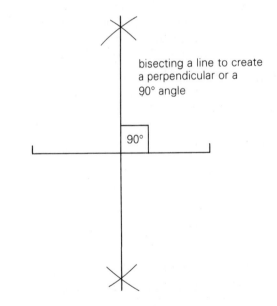

*Figure A20*   Bisecting a line to create a 90° angle

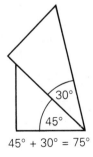
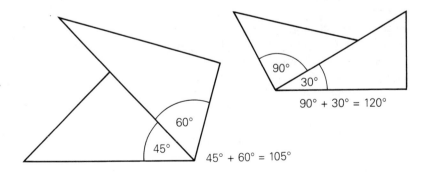

*Figure A19*

arcs above the line then draw a line from the intersection to the given point to create a perpendicular at this point (Figure A21).

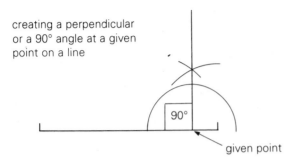

creating a perpendicular or a 90° angle at a given point on a line

90°

given point

*Figure A21*   Creating a 90° angle at a given point

**Bisecting an angle**   Put the compass point on the centre of the given angle and extend it to scribe an arc on both lines forming the angle. Using the same compass radius, put the compass point on the intersections created on each line to scribe arcs which intersect each other midway between the angles. Draw a line from the centre of the given angle to the **intersection** to bisect the angle. For example, to bisect a 90° angle to create a 45° angle see Figure A22.

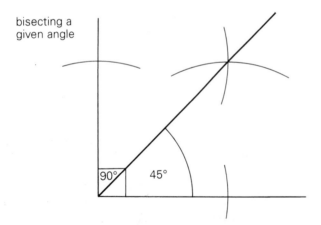

bisecting a given angle

90°   45°

*Figure A22*   Bisecting a given angle

**Constructing a 60° angle**   Put the compass point on a given line at the centre of the proposed angle and extend the other end to a convenient radius and scribe an arc that intersects the line and extends above the centre point. Using the same compass radius, put the compass point at the line intersection and scribe an arc which cuts the previous arc above the line. Draw a line from the intersection of the arcs to the centre line of the proposed angle to create the 60° angle (Figure A23).

By bisecting the 60° angle you are now able to create a range of angles including: 15°, 30°, 45°, 120°, 165° etc. (Figure A24).

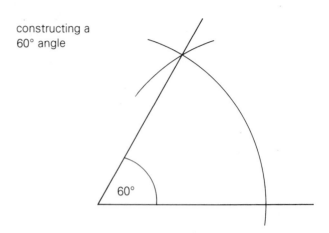

constructing a 60° angle

60°

*Figure A23*   Constructing a 60° angle

If you include the procedures already covered for creating 90° and 45° angles you will be able to create most of the angles that will ever be required for general plumbing and pipework purposes.

Although you should now be able to draw a straight single-line template to given angles, it is much more useful and accurate to add both the radius and pipe thickness on to create effective working drawings. To draw the radius of a bend on a pipework template, you will first of all have to find the centre line of the circle that forms the bend.

The radius of a bend depends on whether it is going to be a machine bend, a heat bend or a spring bend.

---

- For a machine bend, the radius = the radius of the machine former for the size of pipe being bent.
- For heat and spring bends, the radius = a minimum of 4 × outside diameter of the pipe.

---

The most common bends required in pipework are either right angle (90°) bends, 45° and 135° bends. To create an angle of 135° you only actually bend the pipe 45° (Figure A25).

**Drawing a 90° bend to a given radius (machine bend)**
Assuming you have already drawn the 90° angle, open the compasses up to the radius of the former for the pipe being bent; if the former groove covers the whole pipe, the radius measurement is taken from the centre of the former to the centre line of the former pipe groove; the edge of most other formers align with the centre of the pipe (Figure A26).

With the compass set, bisect the 90° angle. The intersection of the arcs to form the bisection forms the centre line of the circle to create the bend. Using the same compass setting, put the compass point on the centre line of the circle and scribe the bend. It should start and finish perfectly on the line intersections (Figure A27).

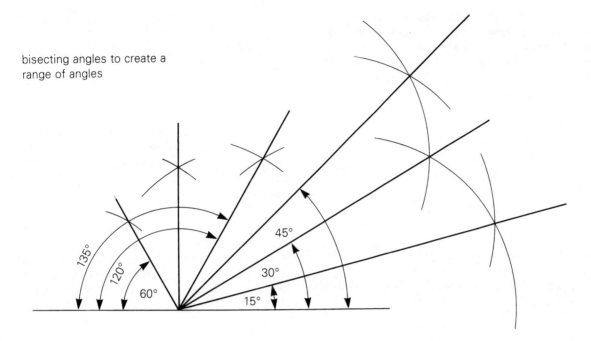

bisecting angles to create a range of angles

*Figure A24* **Bisecting angles**

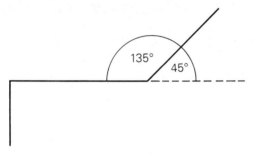

to create a 135° bend the pipe is only bent through 45°

*Figure A25* **Creating a 135° bend**

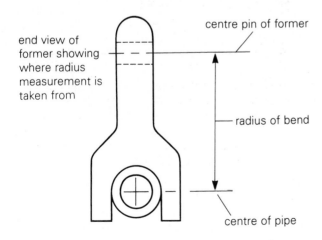

end view of former showing where radius measurement is taken from

centre pin of former

radius of bend

centre of pipe

*Figure A26* **End view of a former**

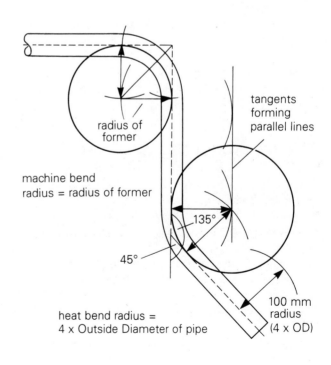

radius of former

tangents forming parallel lines

machine bend radius = radius of former

heat bend radius = 4 x Outside Diameter of pipe

100 mm radius (4 x OD)

*Figure A27* **Drawing 90° and 135° bends to a given radius**

**Drawing a 135° bend to a given radius (heat bend)**

Assuming you have already drawn the 135° (45°) angle, open up the compasses to the desired radius for a heat bend (4× outside diameter of pipe); for 15 mm nominal bore steel pipe with an outside diameter of approximately 25 mm this will be 4 × 25 = 100 mm.

To find the centre point of the circle, you will need to draw parallel lines to both lines forming the angle at a distance of 100 mm, i.e. the circle radius. To do this, scribe two arcs from any two positions on one of the lines forming the angle at 100 mm above the inside of the line and drawn a line that just touches the outside edge of both arcs without cutting them (this is known as a **tangent**). This line will be parallel to the line forming part of the angle. Repeat this process above the other line making up the angle. The point at which both parallel lines intersect will be the centre line of the circle forming the bend (Figure A27).

With the compass still set at 100 mm, the radius of the bend, put the point on the intersection and scribe the bend.

**Adding the pipe thickness**

To form the complete template or workshop drawing, one that you can place the pipe on and see clearly the outside dimensions and angles, you must now add on the pipe thickness.

All you need to do here is set your compasses to the radius based on the outside diameter of the pipe and draw parallel lines as shown throughout the pipe length or measure the pipe thickness along perpendiculars from the centre line at each end of the pipe and join up.

For long straight sections you may need to scribe more than two arcs to form accurate tangents. At the bends, use the same centre points but extend the compass for the outside diameter and retract it for the inside diameter, being careful to do so along a perpendicular line from the centre of the circle to the centre of the pipe.

## CHECK YOUR UNDERSTANDING

- When adding or subtracting fractions they need to have a common denominator.
- Instead of dividing fractions, it is easier to 'invert' the fraction you are dividing by, and multiply without altering the results.
- To multiply decimal figures by 10, 100, 1000 simply move the decimal point 1 place to the right for every 0 after the 1. To divide, move the decimal point to the left.
- A container with a capacity of 1 cubic metre will hold 1000 litres of water. 1000 litres of water will have a mass of 1000 kg and a force of 9.81 kN.
- The area of a rectangle = $l \times b$ and is measured in m³.
- The area of a triangle = base × height ÷ 2 or half the base × height.

- The volume of a cuboid = $l \times b \times d$ and is measured in m³.
- The volume of a prism = cross-sectional area × height and is measured in m³.
- The area of a circle = $\pi r^2$. The circumference of a circle = $\pi d$.
- With right-angled triangles, the square of the hypotenuse is equal to the sum of the squares of the other two sides.
- When rearranging formulae, the value of a figure is reversed if you move it to the other side of the = sign.
- The specific heat capacity of water is 4.186 kJ/kg per °C, which means it takes 4.186 kJ of heat to raise 1 kg of water (1 litre) 1°C.
- The radius for machine bends is always the radius of the former used.
- The radius for spring and heat bends should always be at least 4 × the outside diameter of the pipe being bent.
- Angles can be created in the workshop or on site without the aid of a protractor by using set-squares or compasses.

## REVISION EXERCISES AND QUESTIONS

Answer questions 1 to 5 by selecting one of the four options given.

1  $\frac{4}{5} \div \frac{4}{10} =$
   i)   $\frac{8}{25}$
   ii)  $\frac{1}{2}$
   iii) 2
   iv)  $3\frac{1}{5}$

2  56.50 ÷ 2.25 to 2 decimal places =
   i)   0.40
   ii)  25.11
   iii) 58.75
   iv)  127.13

3  95.75 × 1000 to 2 decimal places =
   i)   0.096
   ii)  0.10
   iii) 9575
   iv)  95 750

4  What is the area of a circle having a radius of 700 mm to 2 decimal places?
   i)   1539.58 mm
   ii)  1.54 m
   iii) 4.40 m
   iv)  153.96 m²

5   A rectangular cistern enclosing a space of $0.4\,m^3$ and with sides 500 mm and 600 mm will have a depth of:
   i)   0.12 m
   ii)  0.38 m
   iii) 0.75 m
   iv)  1.33 m

6   Work out to the nearest litre how many litres a hot storage cylinder will hold if it has a radius of 450 mm and a height of 1.25 m.

7   What will the intensity of pressure be on a valve situated 6.5 m below the feed cistern?

8   What power will be required to heat 100 litres of water from 15°C to 75°C in 1 hour?

9   If you add 12% on to the total measured length of 600 m of pipe needed for a job to account for wastage, how much pipe will you need?

10  What will the heat length or travel of a 90° bend be for a steel pipe having an outside diameter of 35 mm?

# Answers to revision exercises and questions

## Introduction

This section provides you with the answers to the end of chapter questions. Always try to answer the question yourself before you look for the answer here.

If you are not sure of the answer, re-read the relevant section to revise before trying the question again. To revise a topic quickly you can also look through the 'Check your understanding' section given at the end of each chapter as well as the list of key words and definitions at the end of the book.

### Hints on answering examination and course work questions

- Read all the questions carefully before you write anything. Make sure you know exactly what each question is asking you to do.
- Plan the time you will spend on each question. Use any marks given as a guide; the more marks any question is worth the more time it is worth spending answering it.
- If you have a choice of questions, make your choice and stick to it. Don't change your mind halfway through the examination.
- Make sure you get all the 'easy' marks. Do not spend too much time on a 'difficult' question. Leave it; if you have time you can go back to it later when you have completed all the others.
- Keep an eye on time. Make sure that you try to answer all the questions you are required to. Try and keep some time at the end for checking and improving your answers.
- Try to present your work as clearly as you can, whether writing or drawing. Make your work easy for the examiner to follow.
- When carrying out practical work, make sure that you understand what you are being asked to do. Re-read the question and check any drawings carefully before you start, then follow all instructions carefully.

- In multiple choice questions, select only one of the options given.

**Chapter 1**

1  i)

2  ii)

3  i)

4  iii)

5  iv)

6  Long hair and loose clothing should be covered or tied back when working so that it does not get caught or entwined in machinery, tools or equipment.

7  The single most important thing a plumber can do to help prevent accidents is to have a responsible attitude to safety and work responsibly at all times, taking note of all safety notices and wearing all recommended safety clothing if necessary.

8  It is necessary to keep the back straight when lifting materials or equipment off the floor to help prevent undue strain being put on the backbone which may cause damage to the intervertebral discs.

9  - Plank/platform too high, it is unstable. It needs to be repositioned so that it is no more than two-thirds up the height of the trestle.
   - Plank/platform is too narrow to work on. A wider plank or additional plank needed.
   - Plank/platform overhanging trestle forming a 'trap' that makes it unstable and liable to overbalance.
   - Dripping paint causing slipping hazard. Clean up paint and put tin of paint and brush over a drip tray.
   - Trestle not on level ground and wedged with small wedges making it unstable. Reposition trestle on to level ground or put larger wedges underneath and secure the trestle to the wall.
   - Trailing wire on the floor, bad electrical connection, presence of water near electrical equipment, drill too

near end of bench. Get a proper extension lead with the correct connections, plugs and sockets. If available use low-voltage equipment or battery-operated drill. Position drill away from the edge of the bench. Move water bucket and mop up spillage.
- Pipe extending out from vice causing hazard to people walking past. Reposition pipe in vice.
- Nails protruding from bench. Knock them down or remove them.
- No handle on file. Put handle on.
- Chisel has a 'mushroomed' head. Grind the head down or use another chisel.

- Oil can dripping on the floor causing a slip hazard. Mop up the spillage and position over a drip-tray.
- Wood lying on floor with nails sticking up. Take nails out and remove the wood.
- Rubbish on floor, banana skins causing a slip hazard. Remove all rubbish.
- Old packing cases with nails and strapping causing a hazard from cuts and a fire risk. Remove all nails and straps and put wood in stores.
- Packing cases stacked too high making them unstable. Remove the cases to stores and stack lower.

**10**

| Operation | Possible hazard | Recommended precaution |
|---|---|---|
| Chiselling | Particles getting into eyes, hitting hand with the hammer | Wear goggles and fit rubber sleeve to chisel |
| Grinding | Sparks getting into eyes, and clothes getting caught in machinery | Wear goggles and cover all loose clothing |
| Handling hot, greasy or rough materials | Skin allergies, cuts and burns | Wear protective gloves, use tools to pick materials up and use barrier cream |
| Working on or near scaffolds | Falling tools and materials | Wear a safety helmet |
| General site-work | Standing on nails, walking into objects, falling | Wear safety boots and helmet and keep your eyes open |
| Working in areas with high dust concentrations | Breathing in dust and fumes | Wear a respirator or face mask |
| Working with molten metals and welding | Burns to hands, body and eyes | Wear goggles and protective overalls and boots (dark goggles for welding) |
| Working in damp conditions | Various illnesses like colds and flu, lowering resistance to viruses. Water-borne diseases from worms, insects and rodents | Pump out water, wear protective rubber boots |

**Chapter 2**

1 ii)
2 i)
3 ii)
4 iii)
5 iv)
6 When you discover a safety hazard, if it is something that you can quickly and easily correct, for example a nail sticking out of a piece of wood, then remove it. If it is something more serious you must inform your immediate supervisor, employer or safety officer. If there is a hazard report book you must also fill in a hazard report form.
7 To treat a minor burn to the hand, carefully fold back clothing (if clothing is stuck to the burn do not attempt to remove it – wait for doctor to arrive) immerse it in cold water or put it under running cold water to cool it down and reduce the pain then apply a sterilised dressing. Call for the ambulance or doctor.
8 If someone gets bitten by an insect or snake try to identify the type of insect etc. involved by asking the casualty. If possible and safe to do so try to trap the insect etc. by throwing something over it like a box or bowl. Put the casualty at ease in the recovery position, contact the doctor or ambulance immediately. Keep talking to the casualty to reassure him/her until the doctor arrives. Do not give the casualty any food or drink. If the casualty loses consciousness, check that the airways are kept clear of obstructions, check breathing and pulse. If breathing stops carry out emergency mouth to mouth resuscitation; if no pulse, carry out emergency external chest massage.

9   Steps to be taken when treating a wound to stop it from bleeding, taking measures to cut down the possibility of contact with the casualty's blood:
    ● Wash your own hands and cover any cuts or scratches with a waterproof dressing.
    ● If available put on a pair of disposable plastic gloves.
    ● If the wound appears not to be too serious and the casualty is conscious and capable, encourage the casualty to close the sides of the wound together and apply pressure for a few minutes, then to apply a sterilised dressing him/herself with your help and guidance.
    ● If the casualty is not capable, close the wound and apply direct pressure for a few minutes until the flow of blood has stopped or reduced, then apply the dressing yourself.
    ● If the wound is on an unbroken limb, raise and support it to reduce the flow.
    ● If no-one has called for a doctor by this time call one immediately.
10  ● Lie the casualty on his/her back.
    ● Clear mouth for obstructions.
    ● Tilt the head right back to open the airway.
    ● Hold the jaw and open the mouth with one hand and hold the nostrils together with your other one.
    ● Take a deep breath, seal your mouth to the mouth of the casualty and breath into the casualty's mouth, filling his/her lungs.
    ● When you see the chest rise, remove your mouth, watch the chest fall and then check to see if it rises on its own.
    ● Continue to inflate lungs every 4 seconds until casualty starts to breath unaided.
    ● Put casualty into recovery position.

## Chapter 3
1   iv)

2   i)

3   i)

4   ii)

5   iii)

6   Key points to be observed when using a hacksaw:
    ● make sure the teeth are pointing away from you, in the direction of the cut; make sure there are no teeth missing;
    ● make sure there are no bends or kinks in the blade;
    ● keep a slow and steady cutting stroke, applying pressure on the forward cutting stroke only.

7   It is necessary to remove the burrs after cutting steel pipe to provide an accurate and straight external surface for jointing and to provide the true internal bore of the pipe to give full-bore flow. Burrs are removed externally by using a rough-cut file and internally by using a reamer or a half-round or circular rough-cut file.

8   The heat length for a 90° bend is equal to one quarter of the circumference of a circle drawn to a radius equal to $4 \times$ the outside diameter of the size of pipe being bent, therefore:
    ● mark off on the pipe the centre line of the projected bent leg of the pipe; this is easier to do using a working drawing or bending template which will show the fixed position of both legs of the bend (see Figures 3.20 and 3.21);
    ● from the marked position, which will be the end of the actual bend, measure back the distance equal to one quarter the circumference of a circle having a diameter of 200 mm (the radius of the bend is $4 \times 25$ mm, the outside diameter of the pipe, so the diameter of the circle will be $2 \times$ the radius of 100 mm $= 200$ mm). The distance will be D which is $3.142/200 = 157$ mm;
    ● this mark is the start of the heat bend.

9   A chain-wrench or 'chain dogs' should be used to screw a piece of pipe into a fitting at high level because there is less chance of it slipping off, therefore it is safer.

10  Three tools used in the forming of a hole in lead pipe to receive a branch are:
    i)   auger
    ii)  bent-pin or bending bolt
    iii) hammer

11  To mark a vertical line on a wall without the aid of a spirit level:
    ● mark the position on the wall where you want the line;
    ● attach a weight or plumb bob to the end of a long piece of string;
    ● rub chalk along the full length of the string;
    ● with the weight hanging close to the floor, fix the other end of the string at high level with a nail, so that the string hangs in front of the marked position;
    ● when the string has stopped swinging and is perfectly plumb, hold the string against the wall near the bottom and pull back on the string above this so that it flicks back against the wall and leaves a vertical chalk mark on the wall.

12  It is necessary to wear goggles when drilling holes into masonry to prevent dust and masonry particles getting into your eyes.

13  See Figure 3.63.

14  The tools used to form a thread in a hole drilled into a piece of steel are a tap wrench and taps and they form a female thread.

15  A setting-in stick is used to drive in the internal corners of sheet metal, mainly lead, so that the metal is fully against the decking timbers. Alternative tools that could do the same job are a chase wedge and mallet.

## Chapter 4

1 i)

2 i)

3 iii)

4 ii)

5 i)

6 Galvanised steel pipe is the most suitable steel for carrying cold water supplies because it is resistant to corrosion and is relatively cheap and easy to joint.

7 The 'washout' thread is the incomplete part of a thread formed by the dies to enable them to start cutting into the pipe and should be clearly seen on the pipe *after* a fitting has been screwed on to the pipe. If this incomplete thread formed part of the joint inside the fitting it may not form a watertight joint.

8 When installing thermoplastic pipes for domestic hot and cold water supplies you should consider the following: allowances for expansion because of their high expansion rate; secure siting and fixing because of their low impact strength; siting and protection to guard against degradation caused by excessive sun-light/ultra-violet light.

9 Vitreous china is a good material for the manufacture of sanitary appliances because it is impervious to water and is easily moulded before firing.

10 **Ceramic materials**:
Advantages: strong, durable, relatively inexpensive, good availability of raw materials making widespread manufacture possible, resistant to most acids and alkalis, easy to mould, easy to clean, easy to fix.
Disadvantages: can crack if subject to rough use, if the glaze does not match the clay crazing may occur, can stain under certain water conditions.
**Stainless steel**:
Advantages: light and easy to install, will not crack or break easily, will not stain.
Disadvantages: relatively costly, manufacturing methods and plant needed make its availability less widespread, can be 'noisy' in use.

11 Stop taps prevent back-siphonage of water by having a loose valve which acts as a non-return valve, forcing it on to the seating in the event of back-flow, which stops water flowing back into the main.

12 A gate valve should be fitted on a low pressure cold water pipeline because it offers little resistance to the flow. Most other taps would reduce the flow even further.

13 The valves on hot water draw-off taps are fixed and the valves on cold water draw-off taps are loose.

14 A plug cock fitted on a cold water mains pipeline inside a building would create water hammer because of the rapid shutting-off action.

15 As the water flows through the orifice it falls into the cistern which slowly fills with water. As the water rises so too does the ball float which is connected to a lever arm, the other end of which is connected to a valve. As the water rises, the lever arm causes the valve to close against the orifice, shutting the water off. If the water level drops, the reverse will happen, letting water flow once more into the cistern.

## Chapter 5

1 The most important factors to be considered include the weight to be supported, the number of fixings, and the nature of the structure to be fixed to. Also to be considered are cost and ease of use.

2 Because the grip of the shield anchor increases as the load increases.

3 By careful alignment of the fixing with the holes in the sanitary ware and use of a rubber washer between the fixing and the ceramic material.

4 By applying masking tape around the edges before sealing with silicone.

5 A cavity rivet should be used because the fixing remains secure in the plasterboard when the screw securing the bracket is removed.

## Chapter 6

1 The factors to be considered include: the material to be used for the pipe; the type of jointing system; the nature of the soil through which the pipe will run; the depth that the pipe should be buried; and the route from the water main to the point where the service enters the building, which should be as straight and direct as possible.

2 Underground water service pipes should not be buried in foul or aggressive soil or in drains, cess pits or inspection chambers.

3 A labelled diagram similar to Figure 6.18 will suffice.

4 i) The cistern must be made from suitable materials; it should be supported on a firm level base and fitted with a vented lid; the overflow should be filtered; the outlet connection should be at the opposite end to the inlet and have a valve fitted; the cistern should also be insulated against heat gain and frost if necessary.

   ii) There needs to be a minimum of 350 mm above the removable lid for access. Also, a servicing valve should be installed in the supply pipe feeding the cistern

5 A servicing valve must be fitted in the supply pipe at the boundary of the property. Another, the main stop-valve, must be fitted immediately on the pipe as it enters the property. Servicing valves should also be fitted on pipes feeding float-valves and, in larger installations, at

strategic points on the pipelines to allow for turning off sections of the installation for maintenance and repair.

6   A drain-valve must be fitted immediately downstream of the main stop-valve where the service entry enters the building. Further drain-valves should be fitted at all trapped low points in the system to enable draining for repair and maintenance.

7   The cistern should be protected by fitting a 25 mm bore warning pipe that runs with a slight fall to discharge in a conspicuous position. A separate overflow pipe should also be fitted; this should be at least one diameter larger than the supply pipe to the float-valve and should be run to terminate 150 mm above a suitable drain point.

8   i)   No more than 3 flushes of 2.5 l per hour.
    ii)  No more than 3 flushes of 5.0 l per hour.

9   Noise can be minimised by installing tube of adequate diameter to keep the flow velocity below 3 m/s; by removing burrs after cutting tube to length; and by ensuring that tube is correctly supported and clipped.

10  By installing a double-check-valve assembly into the pipe supplying the hose tap, or by using a tap that incorporates a check-valve and vacuum breaker.

## Chapter 7

1   Because the primary water remains in the system, scale formation is reduced.

2   A labelled drawing similar to Figure 7.12 will be satisfactory.

3   **Conduction** through the metal of the heat exchanger.
    **Convection currents** carrying heat from the boiler to the storage vessel by moving water.
    **Radiation** from the burning fuel into the boiler heat exchanger.

4   Airlocks are created by installing the pipework in unventilated arches.

5   Secondary circulation is installed to save water and fuel by preventing cold water run-off through dead legs.

6   $4.18 \times 250 \times (60-18) / 3600 \times 2 = 6.09$ kW boiler power.

7   Corrosion can be minimised by using corrosion resistant, compatible materials and preventing the entry of oxygen into the system.

8   Good insulation materials trap many tiny air pockets and have the following properties: fire resistant, not attractive to vermin, not too fragile, and impervious to moisture in damp conditions.

9   $0.000011 \times 20 \times (85-20) \times 1000 = 14.3$ mm of thermal expansion.

10  It is better because stratification will be encouraged and the hot water temperature will be maintained until the contents of the vessel are used up.

## Chapter 8

1   Air temperature and the temperature of the surfaces in the room.

2   Any three of: panel radiator, convector radiator, column radiator, skirting convector, fan convector, natural draught convector.

3   A labelled diagram similar to Figure 8.9 with correct feed, vent and pump position will suffice.

4   ● Faster hot water storage vessel heat up and recovery time.
    ● Smaller storage vessel and primary circulation pipes.
    ● Greater flexibility in siting the storage vessel.
    ● Independent control of both circuits.
    ● Improved fuel efficiency.

5   In the small-bore system, pipes of 15 and 20 mm diameter form a series of interconnected branched loops serving the heat emitters. Micro-bore systems have a pair of manifolds from where 8 or 10 mm pipes feed to individual heat emitters.

6   A programmer, room thermostat, cylinder thermostat and either a three-port valve or two zone valves.

7   The cold water supply should be checked for adequate pressure and flow rate.

8   In rooms with high solar heat gain or other forms of heat input such as kitchens.

9   To ensure that each heat emitter is fed with sufficient water to enable its full rated heat output.

10  ● Visual check of installation.
    ● Cold flush.
    ● Refill and commission boiler.
    ● Hot flush.
    ● Refill and balance system, set pump operating point.
    ● Instruct user how to operate the system.

## Chapter 9

1   ● Turn off the gas at the emergency control.
    ● Evacuate the building if thought necessary.
    ● Open all doors and windows to allow the gas to disperse.
    ● Remove all possible sources of ignition, do not operate electrical switches.
    ● Locate and repair the escape, leaving the installation safe.

2   Methane, 88 to 95%; ethane, 3 to 8%; propane, 0.7 to 2%; butane, 0.2 to 0.7%; carbon dioxide, 0.6 to 2.0%; nitrogen, 0.3 to 3.0%; and helium, 0.01 to 0.5%.

3   i)   Carbon dioxide and water vapour.
    ii)  Carbon monoxide.

4   ● The type of gas it is designed to burn (usually NG or LPG).
    ● The size and type of injector fitted.
    ● The heat input and output of the appliance (in kW) at the design burner pressure (in mbar).

- A serial number to enable identification of the exact model of appliance so that correct spare parts can be obtained.

5  Procedure for testing natural gas installations with gas meter and appliances fitted;
   - visually inspect the installation for compliance with safety regulations;
   - check that all appliance isolating valves are open and that pilots and burner controls are turned off;
   - connect a u-gauge to the installation using the meter test point, and observe the gauge to see if the water level starts to creep up indicating let-by;
   - gradually raise the pressure to a minimum of 20 mbar by slowly opening the emergency control valve;
   - turn off the valve making sure that the pressure does not exceed 25 mbar;
   - wait one minute for temperature stabilisation and take a reading of the gauge;
   - wait two minutes, then take another reading;
   - if the test is successful: remove gauge, replace test screw, turn gas on slowly and test screw with leak detection fluid;
   - if the test is not successful: trace leaks with leak detection fluid and repair.
   
   Before purging ensure that:
   - there is adequate ventilation by opening windows and doors;
   - inform people that no electrical switches are to be operated and smoking or the use of naked flames is banned;
   - determine the purge volume (not less than 5 times the capacity per revolution of the gas meter mechanism as marked on the meter index;
   - purge pipework and appliances starting from the furthest point away from the meter, allow the air to vent until gas is smelt then close the tap or tighten the union and test the joint with leak detection fluid;
   - check that the correct purge volume has passed through the meter and then light any installed appliances and continue to operate them until the flame picture is normal;
   - fully commission any new appliance(s) in accordance with the manufacturer's instructions and gas safety regulations ensuring that the installation is safe for further use.

6  The purpose of a gas governor is to control the pressure of the gas at a constant value. It operates by using the pressure of the gas on the outlet side acting on a rubber diaphragm to close or open a valve against a spring pressure thus maintaining a constant pressure when the gas is flowing.

7  A labelled diagram similar to Figure 9.27 will suffice.

8  To carry out a spillage test, the appliance should be lit and allowed to operate for 5 minutes. All doors and windows should be closed and if the room contains an extractor fan, it should be running during the test. Next, a lit smoke match should be introduced just inside the draught diverter whilst the appliance is firing. The match should be moved to test all round the diverter; if all the smoke is drawn away the test is passed.

9  i)   $(21-7) \times 4.5 = 63$ cm$^2$ vent required.
   ii)  $1.8 \times 1.3 \times 2.1 = 4.9$ m$^3$ room volume; from Table 9.5 vent size required is 100 cm$^2$ plus an opening window.
   iii) High-level vent size required is $12 \times 9 = 108$ cm$^2$. Low-level vent size required is $12 \times 9 = 108$ cm$^2$.

10 **Primary flue**: creates the initial flue draught and enables the burner to function correctly during short periods of down blow.
   **Draught diverter**: allows air to enter the secondary flue to dilute the products of combustion; it breaks, and so controls, the amount of pull that the secondary flue can exert over the appliance; it allows down blow to escape from the flue into the room.
   **Secondary flue**: is the run of flue pipe between the draught diverter and the terminal; it is a channel for the products of combustion to the terminal.
   **Terminal**: prevents the entry of rain, leaves and debris or birds nests blocking the flue; it assists in the release of flue products from the secondary flue; it minimises down blow effects.

## Chapter 10
1  iv)
2  iii)
3  ii)
4  iii)
5  i)
6  i)  When the water level rises above the level of the siphon, the pressure of water will force some water through the siphon which could then set up full siphonic action creating an automatic flush.
   ii) Water could back-siphon or flow back through the ball-valve and contaminate the water main.
7  When the handle is pulled down, the lever inside the cistern pulls up the plunger which lifts water over the top of the crown of the siphon. As the water flows over the top of the siphon a partial vacuum is created inside the siphon tube, atmospheric pressure acting on the surface of the water in the cistern will now be greater than the pressure inside the siphon tube so siphonic action forces the contents of the cistern through the siphon tube and down the flush pipe (see following diagram).

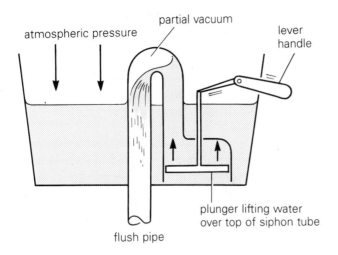

atmospheric pressure    partial vacuum    lever handle

plunger lifting water over top of siphon tube

flush pipe

8  i)    stainless steel
   ii)   vitreous china
   iii)  glazed fireclay
   iv)   vitreous enamelled steel

9  To prevent undue movement of the bath which may be caused by expansion and contraction or simply by the fact that they are lightweight and can move when in use. Any movement may result in water leaking over the sides where they are fixed against a wall.

10 All bidets with submersible sprays should be supplied with water in such a way that it can not back-siphon into the supply pipes and cause contamination of the water mains (see diagram below).

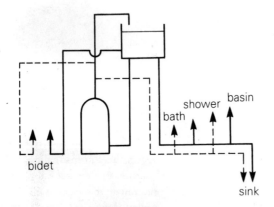

bidet    bath    shower    basin    sink

**Chapter 11**

1  i)

2  i)

3  ii)

4  iii)

5  i)

6  Simple bottle trap showing depth of seal (see diagram below).

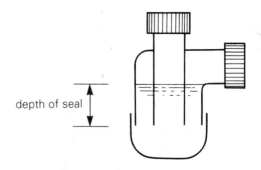

depth of seal

7  Advantages of the two-pipe system:
   ● on low-rise work there is less pipework;
   ● shorter installation time;
   ● appliances can be grouped separately, soil appliances in one place, waste appliances in another place;
   ● if one stack becomes blocked, the appliances connected to the other stack can still be used.
   Disadvantages of the two-pipe system:
   ● on high-rise work there is more pipework;
   ● longer installation time on high-rise work because of additional pipework;
   ● more maintenance;
   ● can be unsightly due to more pipework.

8  Traps connected to stacks at lower levels may loose their seals due to compression because discharge flowing down the stack causes the pressure in the stack beneath the discharge to build up, eventually reaching above atmospheric pressure thereby causing an imbalance and forcing the trap water seal out into the appliance (see diagram below).

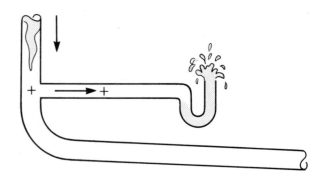

9  In very hot climates, plastic rainwater goods will be subject to problems due to thermal movement which may cause distortion or breakage of pipework, gutters and fixings unless adequate allowances for expansion and contraction are provided. Plastics are also subject to degradation by excessive sunlight.

10 Typical half-round gutter and downpipe details to a pitched roof (see following diagram).

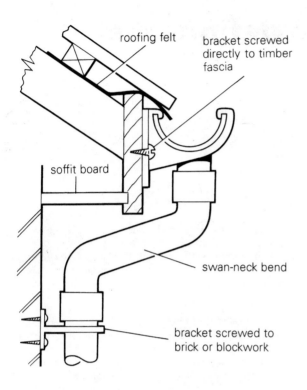

roofing felt

bracket screwed directly to timber fascia

soffit board

swan-neck bend

bracket screwed to brick or blockwork

## Chapter 12

1  Keep the runs of drain straight between access points; lay the drains with a fall that enables self-cleaning velocity; provide access for rodding; and ensure the drain is adequately supported and trenches are carefully backfilled.

2  By leaving a space of at least 50 mm all round and packing with rockwool or facing with sheet metal; or, by using 'rocker pipes' either side of the wall.

3  i)  Ensure that the sides of the trench cannot collapse by boarding and strutting the sides.
   ii)  Allow time for any sewer gases to dissipate before descending into the inspection chamber; station an assistant at ground level to man a safety rope. Prevent contaminated water from entering cuts and body orifices and wash thoroughly after completing the work.

4  To allow sewer gases to escape to atmosphere safely and to prevent loss of trap seals due to siphonage.

5  By using an incidence board and spirit level.

6  1000/40 = 25 mm/m

7  By using the flouroscent dye. Coloured water is poured down the gully; the inspection chamber can then be observed to see which inlet it issues from.

8  Self-cleaning velocity occurs when the drain is laid with a fall that enables the water flow to carry away any solids effectively.

## Chapter 13

1  Because they are easily worked and have the ability to form a self-protecting oxide skin that prevents further corrosion.

2  The timber understructure should be checked to make sure that the surface is reasonably smooth, any nails are punched below the surface, all debris and dirt is swept off and the correct type of underlay is placed.

3  Copper nails with serrated shanks and large heads.

4  To fix the metal to the roof by incorporating cleats and allow expansion to occur.

5  i)  restriction of thermal movement, due to inadequate fixings;
   ii)  installing pieces that are too long;
   iii)  poor fixing into mortar joints.

6  By use of intermediate fixings, such as secret tacks.

## Chapter 14

1  The site plan.

2  In the bill of quantities.

3  On the valve chart.

4
| Measured length | scale multiplier | actual length of tube |
|---|---|---|
| 1 × 0.120 m × | 200 | = 24.0 m |
| 1 × 0.083 m × | 200 | = 16.6 m |
| 1 × 0.049 m × | 200 | = 9.8 m |
| 2 × 0.010 m × | 200 | = 4.0 m |
| | | total 54.4 m |
| | | (say 55 m) |

5  i)  Fire-fighting water.
   ii)  Natural gas.
   iii)  Central heating mains.

6  Materials required: 7 m × 15 mm galvanised steel tube, 6 × 15 mm pipe clips, 2 × 15 mm equal tees, 3 × 15 elbows, 2 × 15 mm union tap connectors, 1 × 15 mm stop-valve, 1 × drain-valve.

7  i)  2
   ii)  Approximately 50%.

8  i)  Brickwork to first floor and first floor joists.
   ii)  Battening and tiling.
   ii)  Four carpenters are required.

9  The valve should be examined and replaced.

## Appendix

1  iii)  2
2  ii)  25.11
3  iv)  95 750
4  ii)  1.54 m
5  iv)  1.33 m
6  795 litres
7  63.77 kN/m$^2$
8  6.98 kW
9  672 metres of pipe needed
10  220 mm

# Key words and definitions

**a.c.**   Alternating electric current.

**Air admittance valve**   A check-valve, fitted at the high point of a pipe system, that is held closed by the system pressure. If this falls to below atmospheric pressure, the valve opens and allows air to enter the system to prevent siphonage.

**Alloy**   An intimate mixture of two or more metals. For example, brass is a mixture of copper and zinc.

**Annealing**   A process using heat to soften certain types of metal, such as copper, to enable easier working. Annealing is also used to relieve internal stresses in welded components.

**Anti-siphon pipe**   A ventilation pipe that connects directly to an appliance branch pipe near the trap at one end and to a ventilation stack at the other.

**Anti-siphon trap**   A trap (usually bottle type) fitted with a small air admittance valve, or with specially designed internal waterways, to prevent siphonage destroying the water seal.

**Atmospheric pressure**   The pressure exerted by the air that surrounds our planet. At sea level this is about 100 kPa, which is equivalent to a pressure of about 10 m head of water.

**Backflow**   The flow of water back along the pipe opposite to the normal direction of flow; this can result in contamination of the water supply.

**Back-siphonage**   Backflow caused by the siphoning of liquid from a cistern or sanitary appliance into the pipe feeding it.

**Ball valve**   A valve to control the water inlet to a cistern. This uses a ball-shaped buoyant float and lever to open and close the valve mechanism in relation to the water level.

**Barrier cream**   A cream rubbed into the hands before starting work that helps protect them from contamination by dirt, grease, etc.

**Brittle**   Liable to break when bent; cast iron is an example of a brittle metal.

**Burrs**   Raised surface of metal or other material, formed on the outside or inside of pipes after being cut with pipe-cutters.

**Calorific value**   The amount of heat energy given off when a unit of fuel is burnt. The c.v. of natural gas is 38.5 MJ/m$^3$.

**Calorifier**   A cylindrical hot water storage vessel containing a tubular heat exchanger which is heated by either water or steam.

**Capillarity**   The phenomenon where liquid will flow between two close surfaces due to surface tension acting between the close surfaces and the surface of the liquid, e.g. molten solder flows between the fitting and the pipe in a capillary fitting.

**Carburising flame**   An oxyacetylene flame containing excess acetylene.

**Circulation pressure**   The force available to cause water flow in a pipe circuit. In a gravity system, the circulation pressure is larger when the temperature difference is great between flow and return. It is also larger when there is more vertical height between the boiler and the storage vessel.

**Cistern**   A fixed container for storing water at atmospheric pressure, usually covered with a close-fitting lid to prevent entry of dirt or insects.

**Closed circuit**   Any system of pipes or water fittings through which water circulates but from which water is not drawn off for use. For example, a heating circuit carrying hot water from the boiler to the radiators and back to the boiler.

**Cock**   The name given to a simple valve (usually $\frac{1}{4}$ turn plug type).

**Coefficient of thermal expansion**   The amount by which an object changes in length for each unit of temperature difference.

**Compression**   The build-up of air pressure inside a sanitary pipe system, usually near the foot of a stack, causing trap seals to be blown and lost.

**Conduction**   The transfer of heat energy through a solid.

**Convection**   The movement of heat energy by moving liquid or gas due to density differences.

**Corrosion**   The deterioration and breakdown of metals subject to chemical or atmospheric action.

**Crown**   The highest point on the inside or outlet side of a trap.

**Current**   The flow of electricity (measured in amperes).

**d.c.**   Direct electric current.

**Dead leg**   A run of hot water pipe through which circulation cannot occur, requiring cold water to be run off before hot water is available at the tap.

**Degradation**   A term used to describe the breakdown and failure of plastics.

**Delivery head**   The height that a pump can effectively lift water.

**Dezincification**   A form of electrolytic corrosion that results in the loss of zinc from certain types of brass pipe fittings, causing them to become brittle and porous.

**Discharge**   Solid or liquid soil or waste matter carried in a sanitary pipework system.

**Distribution pipe**   Any pipe carrying water from a cistern or hot water apparatus supplied from a feed cistern, and under pressure from the cistern.

**Double feed indirect cylinder** An indirect hot water storage vessel that is cylindrical in shape and has separate connections for both the primary and secondary cold feed pipes.

**Double insulation** A method of protection given to portable power tools to ensure that no exposed electrical terminal or wire can come into contact with the casing. The casing itself is non-conductive. No earthing connection is required with double insulated equipment.

**Draught diverter** A fitting in an open flue between the primary and secondary parts of the flue. It breaks the pull of the secondary flue, diverts down-blow and allows the products of combustion to be diluted.

**Ductile** The description of a metal that can be drawn out or stretched into a thinner section.

**Expansion cistern** A cistern fitted to the water heating system to accommodate any increase in volume of water that occurs as the system is heated from cold.

**Feather edge** A fine ground and sloping edge to the end of the wall of a metal pipe.

**Feed cistern** Any storage cistern that supplies cold water to a hot water apparatus, cylinder or tank.

**Filler metal** A metal rod added when welding, brazing or soldering.

**Flashings** Sheet materials, usually non-ferrous metal, formed to prevent rain entering buildings near abutments, such as parapet walls, chimneys, etc., or where pipes pass through roofs. Also known as weatherings.

**Float-operated valve** See ball valve.

**Float switch** An electrical switch which is operated by the movement of a float that rises and falls in sympathy with the water level in a cistern or tank.

**Flood level** The position at which water flowing into a sanitary appliance would spill over or flood if the outlet and overflow were blocked.

**Flushing cistern** A cistern fitted with a device (usually a siphon) that rapidly discharges the cistern water into a watercloset pan or urinal.

**Flux** A paste or powder material used when soldering or brazing to dissolve surface oxides and enable the solder to adhere to the parent metal.

**Foot valve** A non-return valve fitted to the bottom of the suction pipe of a pump. It prevents the water flowing out of the suction pipe so keeping the pump primed.

**Fuse** A component in an electric circuit designed to melt easily and break the circuit when a fault, such as a short-circuit, occurs (fuse: to melt).

**Gas fittings** A general term used to avoid repeating a list of separate items; it includes anything fitted in a system in connection with the supply and use of gas.

**Hard water** Water that contains dissolved calcium or magnesium salts; these make the formation of a soap lather more difficult and can cause pipes to fur and eventually become blocked.

**Heat length** The measured length of tube needed to be heated or annealed to ensure accuracy when forming bends by hand.

**Heat treatment** A process of heating a metal to alter its properties, e.g. annealing a metal to soften it after work hardening.

**High-carbon steel** Steel containing from 0.65 to 1.5% carbon; it is used to make tools.

**High pressure system** This term usually refers to a pipework system subject to the water mains pressure, but can also refer to closed systems that operate at higher than atmospheric pressure.

**Impervious** The property of a material that allows it not to absorb water, or allow water to pass through it: waterproof.

**Indirect cylinder** A hot water storage vessel in which the stored water is heated by passing hot water through a heat exchanger without mixing the primary and secondary water.

**Instantaneous water heater** An appliance in which water is heated immediately to the working temperature as it passes through the heat exchanger.

**Intensity of pressure** The water pressure acting at a particular level subject to the head or height of water above this level.

**Intervertebral discs** Spongy, fibrous cartilage that separates and acts as a bearing between vertebrae in the spine.

**Invert (level)** A term that describes the lowest point on the bore of a pipe. It is used when setting out drainage falls.

**Joule** The SI unit for energy; it is the work done when a force of one newton moves through a distance of one metre.

**Kinetic energy** The energy of a moving body is called kinetic energy; as water flows along a pipe is has kinetic energy.

**Kink** Deformation or collapse of a pipe wall when insufficiently supported either inside or outside during bending.

**Lap weld** A joint between two pieces of metal where one lies on top of the other; the edge of the top piece forms a fillet weld.

**L.E.L** Lower explosive limit: the smallest proportion of fuel gas to air that can be ignited.

**Lockshield valve** A valve that does not have a wheel or handle for operation. The spindle, being enclosed by the shield, cannot be easily tampered with to prevent unauthorised adjustment.

**Low-carbon steel** Steel containing less than 0.3% carbon; used to make steel tube.

**Low pressure system** A water system that is usually open to the atmosphere; a cistern-fed or storage system.

**Malleable** A term to describe the property of a metal that can be easily worked into shape by hammering with tools. Lead is an example of a malleable metal.

**Manometer** An air pressure testing gauge consisting of a U-tube half filled with water. Used to carry out tests on drains and sanitary pipework, or for testing gas pressure in pipelines and appliances.

**Neutral flame** The normal oxyacetylene flame, produced when equal amounts of oxygen and acetylene gas are burnt. This flame is used when welding lead and low-carbon steel.

**Neutral point** The place in a closed circulation system where the pump positive pressure is used up and suction commences.

**Newton** The SI unit for force; one newton is the force that gives a mass of 1 kg an acceleration of 1 metre per second per second. When accounting for the force of gravity, a 1 kg weight has a force of 9.81 newtons.

**Non-ferrous metal** A metal or alloy that does not contain iron; copper, brass and bronze are examples.

**Non-wetted area** The part of a stack above the highest connection, usually acting as a ventilation pipe from that point upwards.

**Open flue**   An open flue is one that has a draft diverter fitted, either as a part of the appliance or close to it. Open flues must be tested to ensure that down-blow does not create danger.

**Over-pumping**   A problem caused by wrong positioning of the pump, between the cold feed and open vent in an open hot water or heating system. The pump pressure causes water to circulate around the vent and feed; this oxygenates the water causing corrosion.

**Oxidation/oxidisation**   Corrosion of metals by the effect of oxygen, either from the atmosphere or a wrongly adjusted flame.

**Oxidising flame**   A flame containing slightly excess oxygen; it is used when brazing copper using a brass filler metal.

**Oxygen**   A colourless odourless gas that is very active. It supports combustion and causes corrosion of metals.

**Pascal**   The SI unit for pressure; one pascal is equal to one newton per metre squared.

**Patina**   A thin surface coating that forms on non-ferrous metals, and which gives them protection against the further effects of oxidation.

**Plumbo-solvent**   The term used to describe water that will dissolve lead.

**Potable**   A term used to describe water that is safe and fit to drink.

**Power**   The rate of doing work is called power; it is work divided by time. A rate of working of one joule per second is called one watt. A larger unit used in water heating is the kilowatt; this is equal to 1000 watts.

**Pressure switch**   An electrical switch that is operated by fluid pressure moving a diaphragm. It is often used to control the pump on a boosted water system.

**Primary circuit**   A pair of pipes (flow and return) connected between the boiler and a hot water storage vessel to enable heat to be carried from the boiler to heat the vessel by water flow.

**Proprietary fitting**   A fitting made by a particular company, often known by that company's name, e.g. 'Yorkshire' fittings.

**Quarter-turn ball valve**   A valve containing a drilled sphere that can be turned by a lever handle. When the hole in the ball aligns with the pipe axis, the water can flow; turning this through 90° stops the flow.

**Radiation**   The movement of heat energy by waves, either through the air or space.

**Regulator**   A device for reducing and controlling the pressure of a gas to a constant pressure.

**Ripple**   Deformation in the form of 'ripples' is caused when insufficient pressure is applied to a pipe in a bending machine.

**Room-sealed appliance**   An appliance supplied and installed with its own flue duct and combustion air inlet; this makes it safer than an open-flued appliance.

**Sacrificial anode**   An aluminium sacrificial anode which can be fitted inside a copper hot water cylinder by the manufacturer to prevent the copper being corroded by aggressive water. The aluminium, being corroded by electrolysis, protects the copper until it is consumed.

**Safe outlet**   A point above and away from any openings into the building, where a ventilation stack can terminate without causing a nuisance due to foul gases entering the building.

**Sanitary appliance**   A fitting that receives and disposes of soil matter (excreta), or is used for personal washing, bathing or preparing food and washing kitchen utensils.

**Sanitary pipework**   A system of above ground pipework that collects soil and waste water discharged from sanitary appliances and conveys it to a drainage system.

**Secondary circuit**   A system of pipes, kept hot by water flow, running from the top of a hot water storage vessel, around the building to positions close to hot water discharge points before returning to connect back into the vessel. Secondary circulation shortens the length of dead legs and saves water by reducing cold run off.

**Secondary system**   The part of the hot water system through which water is drawn off for use.

**Self-cleansing**   A soil appliance, trap or pipe designed with smooth and regular sides to ensure that any soil or waste matter flowing though it will not be left behind.

**Service pipe**   The pipe for supplying water from the main, and subject to the pressure of the main.

**Servicing valve**   A valve that is used for shutting off the flow of water to a water fitting to enable maintenance of the fitting.

**Single feed indirect cylinder**   A hot water storage vessel that has only one cold feed pipe connection and an internal heat exchanger. This is specially designed to form an air seal between the primary and secondary water to allow for the expansion of the primary water.

**Single phase electrical supply**   An a.c. electrical supply carried by two conductors (wires); for safety a third earth wire is used, connected to any metal casings and connecting them to earth.

**Siphon**   The main component of a flushing cistern. When the lever is operated, siphonic action is created in a tube that is in the form of an inverted 'J'. This causes water to flow over and down the tube to clean the WC pan.

**Siphonage**   A method of moving a liquid out of its container, up over the rim and down to a lower level through a tube. Siphonage can be started by suction at the lower end of the tube; atmospheric pressure on the surface of the liquid forces it up and over the rim. It will then continue to flow because there is more weight of liquid in the long length of tube.

**Soft water**   Water that does not contain dissolved limestone or chalk, and so easily forms a soap lather.

**Solenoid valve**   A valve that can be opened and closed by an electromagnet. Solenoid valves are used to enable electrical control of the flow of fuel to a burner.

**Sparge pipe**   Pipe used to deliver water to urinals from a flushing cistern for the purposes of cleansing. It may be perforated or attached to spreader outlets.

**Specific heat capacity**   A term that describes the quantity of energy required to heat (or cool) a substance by each unit of temperature.

**Spring-back**   The retraction or opening up, by a couple of degrees, of machine bends on pipes when the pressure roller is released.

**Stack**   A main vertical pipe in a sanitary pipework system. The term stack can be used to refer to a soil, waste or ventilation pipe.

**Stratification**   A term which describes the effect of hot water layering in a storage vessel. Because it is less dense, the hotter water collects at the top of the vessel.

**Suction lift**   The height that a pump can raise water by. In practice this is limited to a maximum of about 8 metres.

**Swarf**   Small, loose particles or turnings of metal or other material formed by cutting or threading operations.

**Tack weld**   A small weld used to hold work in position before the complete weld run is made.

**Tap**   A valve, usually fitted to an item of sanitaryware, to control the flow of water out of the pipework system. Also used to describe a tool used to form female threads in drilled holes.

**Tank**   A rectangular closed vessel that can contain water under pressure.

**Template**   A model or prototype of, for example, a pipe bend or offset, used as a guide when making several the same.

**Thermo-electric effect**   A term to describe what happens when two different metals are joined and the joint is heated. This results in a small electric current that can be used in conjunction with a weak solenoid valve as a flame failure device, as in the thermo-couple / gas valve found on heating boilers.

**Thermostat**   A device that controls temperature by means of expansion.

**Three phase electric supply**   An a.c. electrical supply of three alternating voltages partially superimposed on one another and carried by three conductors (wires). Usually used to power heavy machinery.

**Throating**   Deformation of a pipe on a bend caused by too much pressure in a bending machine.

**Trap**   A specially shaped pipe fitting, connected to the outlet of a sanitary appliance, designed to hold a small quantity of water that acts as an air seal preventing odours escaping from waste and soil pipes.

**U.E.L.**   Upper explosive limit; the largest proportion of fuel gas to air that can be ignited.

**Unvented primary circuit**   A primary circuit that does not have a vent pipe. In this case, water expansion is allowed for by fitting an expansion vessel.

**Vacuum breaker**   A device to allow air into a pipe system to prevent pressure below atmospheric from creating back-siphonage.

**Ventilation (vent) pipe**   A pipe open to the atmosphere that allows the escape of air or steam from a hot water or heating system, or, on a sanitary pipe system, the vent pipe allows air to enter or escape to prevent loss of trap seals.

**Vertebrae**   A collection of bones that form the 'backbone'. They enclose and protect the spinal chord.

**Voltage**   The pressure of electricity.

**Warning pipe**   A pipe from a cistern or hot water apparatus which is fixed so that its outlet is in a conspicuous position and any discharge of water can be readily seen.

**Washout thread**   That part of a thread that is left incomplete when cutting a taper thread on a pipe. It should remain visible outside the fitting once this has been tightened on to the thread.

**Waste pipe**   A pipe used to carry liquid discharge from waste appliances.

**Water fittings**   A general term used to avoid repeating a list of separate items; it includes anything used in a system connected with the supply and use of water.

**Water hammer**   A loud concussive noise often caused by closing taps too quickly on high pressure mains. Caused by the sudden stopping of the water; this causes the kinetic energy to be transferred to the pipe and be lost as sound waves.

**Water seal**   The depth of water contained in the U-tube of a trap; this forms a barrier between the atmosphere in the room and the gases in the sanitary pipework system and drains.

**Work hardening**   The gradual loss of workability or malleability of a metal as it is formed or worked.

**Working drawing**   A drawing that can be used as a template or guide when measuring or marking out and checking the accuracy of bends and offsets on pipes.

**Zone valve**   A motorised valve that can be opened and closed by a thermostat to control the flow in a section of a (heating) system.

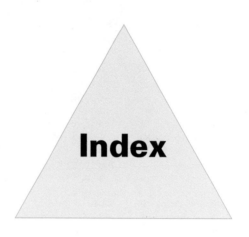

# Index